Essential M
for GCSE

with Exam Practice and Revision

▶ FOUNDATION ◀

MARK BINDLEY
RENIE VERITY

Stanley Thornes (Publishers) Ltd

First published in 1996 by

Stanley Thornes (Publishers) Ltd
Ellenborough House
Wellington Street
CHELTENHAM
GL50 1YW

A catalogue record of this book is available from the British Library.

ISBN 0 7487 2432 X

96 97 98 99 00 / 10 9 8 7 6 5 4 3 2 1

Artwork by Steve Ballinger, Hardlines

Typeset by Wyvern Typesetting, Bristol
Printed and bound in Great Britain at T J Press, Padstow, Cornwall

Contents

Introduction

About Essential Maths for GCSE

This book is designed to help students pass GCSE at Foundation Level.

It can be used:

- as a two year course for students in Years 10 and 11.
- as a one year course for students in Further Education.
- as a course for an Adult Education class.
- as a teaching and revision aid for parents or private tutors helping students to prepare for GCSE mathematics.

It features:

- a contents organisation carefully matched to the new GCSE syllabuses in mathematics.
- very extensive explanations and worked examples.
- PAUSE exercises. These follow explanations and worked examples and are designed to test understanding of key points and provide practice in skills and techniques.
- REWIND exercises. These provide a systematic revision of skills and techniques at the end of major sections of the book.
- FASTFORWARD exercises. These provide a wide range of actual past paper questions to ensure students are familiar with the question format used in examinations.

This book assumes that:

- students will own and use a scientific calculator (unless it is specifically indicated otherwise, all exercises should be completed with a calculator);
- Students will obtain a copy of the individual GCSE syllabus they are studying. This will indicate the exact coverage required and dictate the sections of the book that must be studied.

Some advice to students

There is no 'correct' way to succeed in examinations and everybody has their own special ideas and study methods.

I will however offer the following general advice which I hope you may find helpful in developing your own failsafe route to success.

- As you work through the PAUSE exercises, try to keep your solutions in an organised folder or exercise book. These can form a valuable revision aid during the final weeks, days and hours before the examination.
- Working through the REWIND exercises during the final weeks of your course is a very good way to revise. You can make a note of all the questions that cause difficulty and repeat them after a few days to make certain that you have mastered the necessary techniques.
- Most GCSE examinations include a page giving formulae etc. Make sure you obtain a copy of this so you do not waste time memorising unnecessary information.
- Obtain as many past papers for your particular syllabus as you possibly can and work through them using the teaching notes in this book to help you.
- During the final revision period, try to work through as many of the worked examples in this book as possible. Don't just read the examples, cover the solution with a piece of paper and try to solve the problem. If you cannot solve the problem study the solution and then try again. If you are really serious about passing with a good grade, you need to master every worked example in this book!
- Go into the examination feeling prepared. Make sure you have a calculator, spare calculator, pencils, pens, geometrical instruments, sweets, tissues, mascots, cushions and everything else you need.

Good luck! Remember, everything is possible with enough effort.

Mark Bindley

Number

People in earlier times *needed* mathematics.

- They needed to *count* their possessions.
- They needed to *measure time* and, since the sun and stars were our first clocks, this meant *measuring angles*.
- They needed to *measure* the *length* of the land that they farmed.
- As trade developed, they needed to *measure weight* and *volume*.

At first, people only used whole numbers.

'I own 7 cows, 5 goats and 24 sheep.'

'There are 200 people living in our settlement.'

You cannot, however, solve all problems with whole numbers and so *fractions* and *decimals* were invented and used.

SECTION 1 | Whole Numbers

Place value in whole numbers

Our number system is based on groups of ten.
There are 264 dots in this picture:

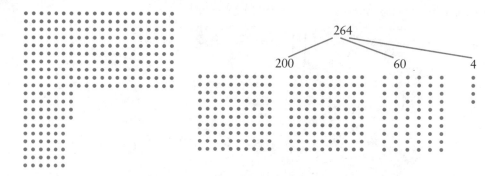

2, 6 and 4 are called the ***digits*** of the number 264.

Examples

2460 teachers awarded bonus for hard work

1. In this newspaper headline, how many teachers does each digit in
   the number represent?

   > The 2 digit represents 2000 teachers.
   > The 4 digit represents 400 teachers.
   > The 6 digit represents 60 teachers.
   > The 0 digit represents zero teachers.

2. a) Write down all the numbers you can make using the digits 2, 6
      and 4.
   b) What is the largest number you can make with the digits 2, 6
      and 4?

   a) 264, 246, 426, 462, 624, 642.
   b) The largest number is 642.

1 For each headline, write down the value that each digit in the number represents.

a) │ 17 Arrested in Dawn Raid │

b) │ New Supermarket creates 226 jobs │

c) │ Children raise £650 for animal charity │

d) │ MP claims £7433 expenses in one month │

e) │ Woman burns husband's collection of 24 979 beer mats │

f) │ Salary increase of £67 900 for Utility Boss │

In questions 2 to 4:
   a) Write down all the numbers you can make using the digits.
   b) What is the largest number you can make with the digits?

2 7, 8 and 0   3 9, 9 and 2   4 2, 3, 4 and 5

Reading and writing whole numbers

Large numbers have their digits grouped in threes.

Examples

7	205		12	714
seven thousand	two hundred and five		twelve thousand	seven hundred and fourteen

450	803		7	900	250
four hundred and fifty thousand	eight hundred and three		seven million	nine hundred thousand	two hundred and fifty

PAUSE

1 Write each number in words.

   a) 2250   c) 20 049   e) 805 700

   b) 75 291   d) 122 717   f) 1 813 446

2 Write these numbers in figures.

   a) six thousand five hundred and nineteen

   b) two thousand seven hundred and eighty six

   c) sixty thousand

   d) seventy three thousand four hundred and ninety six

   e) five hundred and thirty thousand and eighty five

   f) one million six hundred and thirty three thousand one hundred
      and fifty three

Approximating whole numbers

Numbers are often rounded to the nearest 10.

For example, if a dress shop had 18 customers one afternoon the owner might say, 'I had about 20 customers this afternoon'.
Or, if a driver was travelling at 63 mph she might say, 'I was travelling at about 60 mph'.

The special sign ≈ means is *approximately equal to*.
We can write 18 ≈ 20 or 63 ≈ 60.
We can use a number line to help us round numbers.

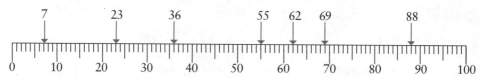

From the diagram we can see:

   7 ≈ 10   23 ≈ 20   36 ≈ 40

   62 ≈ 60   69 ≈ 70   88 ≈ 90

When a number is in the middle we *always round up*. 55 is in the middle of 50 and 60 so we write:

$$55 ≈ 60$$

1 Round these numbers to the nearest 10, using a number line to help you.

a) 8   c) 25   e) 47   g) 64   i) 83
b) 12   d) 36   f) 52   h) 78   j) 94

2 A shopkeeper likes to keep about 100 cans of coke in stock. This is how she works out how many cans she needs to order. She counts the cans left and takes this number away from 100. She then rounds to the nearest 10.

With 47 cans left: $100-47=53$, she orders 50 cans.
With 62 cans left: $100-62=38$, she orders 40 cans.

How many cans will she order if she has:

a) 96 cans left,   c) 46 cans left,   e) 27 cans left,   g) 4 cans left,
b) 19 cans left,   d) 62 cans left,   f) 76 cans left,   h) 51 cans left?

Larger numbers can be rounded to the nearest 10 or the nearest 100. For example, if a farmer plants 376 trees in an orchard, he might say:

'I have planted about 380 trees'

or

'I have planted about 400 trees'.

We can write $376 \approx 380$ or $376 \approx 400$.

You should *never* round to the nearest 10 and then to the nearest 100.
For example, 846 rounded to the nearest 10 is 850.
But, 846 rounded to the nearest 100 is 800, not 900.
You do not round to 850 and then to 900.

We can use a number line to help us round numbers.

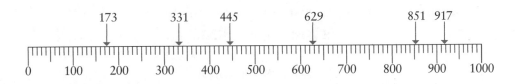

5

From the diagram we can see that, to the nearest 10:

173 ≈ 170	331 ≈ 330	851 ≈ 850
629 ≈ 630	445 ≈ 450	917 ≈ 920

We can also see that, to the nearest 100:

173 ≈ 200	331 ≈ 300	851 ≈ 900
629 ≈ 600	445 ≈ 400	917 ≈ 900

■   ■ ■ ■

PAUSE

Use a number line from 0 to 1000 to:

1 Round these numbers to the nearest 10.

a) 87	c) 250	e) 478	g) 683	i) 849
b) 123	d) 325	f) 549	h) 788	j) 971

2 Round the numbers in question 1 to the nearest 100.

3 This table shows information on complaints about ITV programmes (source: ITC Annual Report 1993).

Category of complaint	Number of complaints	Number of advertisements referred to
Misleading	858	476
Offensive	952	241
Harmful	473	195
Other	298	150
Total	2581	1062

a) Copy the table, showing each number rounded to the nearest 10.
b) Copy the table, showing each number rounded to the nearest 100.

■ ■

Even larger numbers can be rounded to the nearest 10 or the nearest 100 or the nearest 1000.

For example, if a used car costs £8255, we might say:

'it costs about £8260',

or

'it costs about £8300',

or
'it costs about £8000'.

We can write: $42\,783 \approx 42\,780$ or $42\,783 \approx 42\,800$ or $42\,783 \approx 43\,000$.

PAUSE

1 Round these numbers to the nearest 10.
   a) 746   c) 2943   e) 4715   g) 6454   i) 8590
   b) 1567   d) 3166   f) 5884   h) 7444   j) 9599

2 Round the numbers in question 1 to the nearest 100.

3 Round the numbers in question 1 to the nearest 1000.

4 This table shows information about marriages in the United Kingdom (source: Annual Abstract of Statistics 1994).

Status before marriage	Number married in 1994
Bachelor	256 538
Divorced man	83 069
Widower	10 132
Spinster	259 084
Divorced woman	81 224
Widow	9 431
Total number of people married	699 478

Type of marriage	Number of marriages
First marriage for both partners	222 369
First marriage for one partner	70 884
Re-marriage for both partners·	56 486
Total number of marriages	349 739

a) Copy the table, showing each number rounded to the nearest 10.
b) Copy the table, showing each number rounded to the nearest 100.
c) Copy the table, showing each number rounded to the nearest 1000.

Adding and subtracting whole numbers

Many simple calculations can be done 'mentally', that is to say, without a calculator or written calculations.

Suppose we have calculations like $43+27$, $65+37$, $98-23$ or $93-28$. One of the best ways to think the problems through is like this:

Examples

$$43+27 = 40+3+20+7 = 60+10 = 70$$
$$65+37 = 60+5+30+7 = 90+12 = 102$$
$$98-23 = 90+8-20-3 = 70+5 = 75$$
$$93-28 = 90+3-20-8 = 70-5 = 65$$

On this map, the numbers shown beside the roads are the distances in kilometres between each road junction.

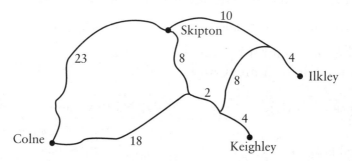

We can make a table like this to show the shortest distance between each pair of places.

	Colne	Skipton	Keighley	Ilkley
Colne		23	24	32
Skipton	23		14	14
Keighley	24	14		16
Ilkley	32	14	16	

The information can be shown more simply in a table like this:

Clone

23	Skipton
24	14	Keighley
32	14	16	Ilkley

PAUSE

In questions 1 to 3 make a simple table to show the shortest distance between each pair of places. Work out all your answers without a calculator or written calculations. Distances are in kilometres.

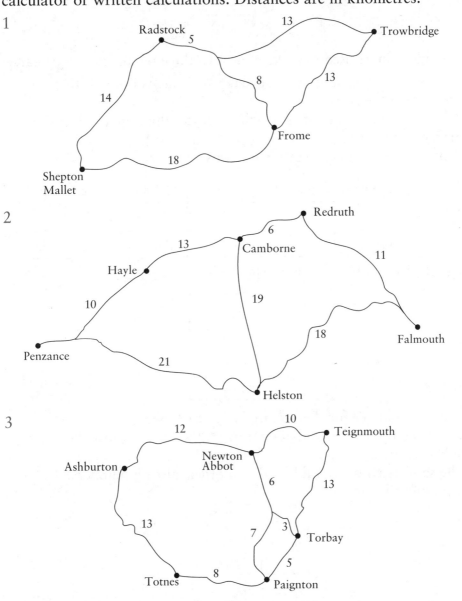

1

Radstock — 5 — 13 — Trowbridge
14
8
13
Frome
18
Shepton Mallet

2

Redruth
6
13 — Camborne — 11
Hayle
19
10
18 — Falmouth
Penzance
21
Helston

3

10
12
Newton Abbot — Teignmouth
Ashburton
6
13
13
7 3 — Torbay
5
Totnes — 8 — Paignton

This square is called a *magic square* because the total along any row, column or diagonal is 18.

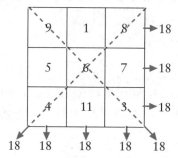

These rules can be used to make your own three by three magic square:

- Choose any two numbers but make sure one is not exactly two times the other.
- Choose any third number which is greater than the total of the first two numbers.
- Construct your magic square like this:

third number+first number		third number+second number
	third number	
third number−second number		third number−first number

If we use these rules with 1, 5, and 7 we get this square:

8		12
	7	
2		6

The magic number for this square is 21 (8+7+6).

Because the top row already contains 8 and 12, we know the missing number must be 1 to make a 'magic' total of 21.

In the same way, we can fill in all the other missing numbers. This is the completed magic square:

8	1	12
11	7	3
2	13	6

In this exercise work out all your answers without a calculator or written calculations.

1 Copy and complete each magic square. Remember the totals along any column row or diagonal must be the same.

a)

6		
7	5	3

c)

15	1	11
7		

b)

9		7
	6	
		3

d)

17		
	13	10
		9

2 Make a magic square with each of these sets of numbers.

   a) 1, 4 and 7   b) 2, 3 and 8   c) 4, 6 and 13   d) 15, 25 and 50

3 a) Somebody using these rules picked 8 as their third number. What will the magic total of their square be?
   b) What is the rule which connects the third number to the magic square total?

4 This is a magic triangle.

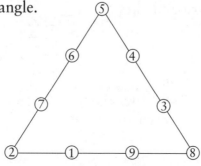

Copy these shapes and fill in numbers to make them 'magic'.

a)   b)

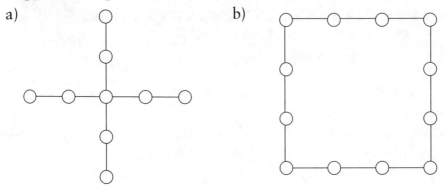

■ ■

Addition sums can be worked out with written calculations.
It is important to practise these methods, even if you prefer to use a
calculator. In exams you may be asked to show all your working out
(including 'carry' figures) to prove you did not use a calculator.
These examples show how the methods are used:

Examples

1. 356 + 125

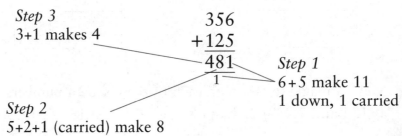

Step 3
3+1 makes 4

356
+125
481
1

Step 1
6+5 make 11
1 down, 1 carried

Step 2
5+2+1 (carried) make 8

2. 475 + 89

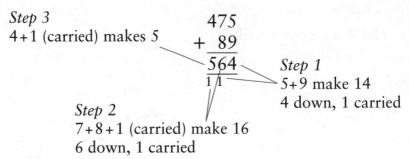

Step 3
4+1 (carried) makes 5

475
+ 89
564
1 1

Step 1
5+9 make 14
4 down, 1 carried

Step 2
7+8+1 (carried) make 16
6 down, 1 carried

Do not use a calculator for this exercise.

1	785+19	5	4253+3682	9	7327+6444
2	574+57	6	456+17	10	6478+23+479
3	678+215	7	397+820		
4	117+986	8	1329+850		

11 Lear is saving for a holiday. These are the amounts she saves each week for twenty weeks.

£23   £19   £35   £42   £11   £26   £51   £19   £5   £19
£22   £38   £45   £46   £33   £18   £18   £40   £27   £73

She starts this record to show how much she has saved each week and the total saved.

Saved this week	Total saved
£23	£23
£19	£42
£35	£77

Copy and complete the savings record.

12 Raj plays cricket for his school. These are his batting scores in his first ten innings of the season.

89   47   67   19   125   68   17   96   9   85

He starts this record to show his score for each innings and his total score for the season.

Score	Total so far
89	89
47	136

Copy and complete Raj's record.

Subtraction sums can be worked out with written calculations.
It is important to practise these methods, even if you prefer to use a
calculator. In exams you may be asked to show all your working out
(including 'borrow' figures) to prove you did not use a calculator.

These examples show how the methods are used:

1. 356–28

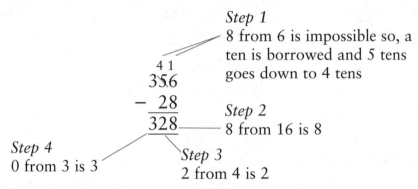

Step 1
8 from 6 is impossible so, a
ten is borrowed and 5 tens
goes down to 4 tens

$$\begin{array}{r} {}^{4\ 1} \\ 3\cancel{5}6 \\ -\ 28 \\ \hline 328 \end{array}$$

Step 2
8 from 16 is 8

Step 4
0 from 3 is 3

Step 3
2 from 4 is 2

2. 475–89

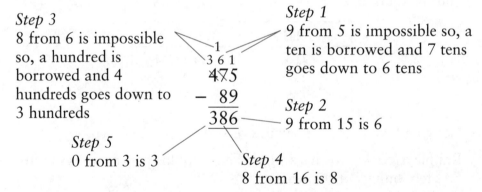

Step 3
8 from 6 is impossible
so, a hundred is
borrowed and 4
hundreds goes down to
3 hundreds

Step 1
9 from 5 is impossible so, a
ten is borrowed and 7 tens
goes down to 6 tens

$$\begin{array}{r} {}^{1} \\ {}_{3\ 6\ 1} \\ 4\cancel{7}5 \\ -\ 89 \\ \hline 386 \end{array}$$

Step 2
9 from 15 is 6

Step 5
0 from 3 is 3

Step 4
8 from 16 is 8

PAUSE

Do not use a calculator for this exercise.

1 45–15	3 473–48	5 822–536	7 296–67	9 333–255
2 84–58	4 521–345	6 63–27	8 473–88	10 544–298

11 In the darts game '501', a player's scores are subtracted from 501 until they reduce their score to exactly zero. Kirsty and Steven play a game of 501. These are their scores:

Kirsty   52   68   47   81   34   51   29   68   53   18

Steven   78   13   49   53   39   72   29   59   9   68

They chalk their score on a board like:

Kirsty		Steven	
	501		501
52	449	78	423
68	381	13	410

a) Copy and complete the table of scores.
b) Who won the game?

12 A caretaker keeps a daily record of the number of litres of heating oil used and the amount left in the storage tank. This is part of his record for November.

Date	Litres used	Litres in tank
1st	247	2321
2nd	189	2132
3rd	207	1925

During the next 7 days he records these quantities of oil used:

175   156   295   188   207   268   199

a) Copy and complete the caretaker's record up to November 10th.
b) How much oil was in the tank on October 31st?
c) The caretaker always orders more oil when the level in the tank drops below 500 litres. After how many days did the caretaker order more oil?

■■

Addition and subtraction sums can be worked out with a calculator. The next exercise is designed to give you practice in using a calculator to solve problems which require a mixture of addition and subtraction.

These are the scoring rules for darts.

a dart in the outer circle scores a 'double' this dart scores 40.

this dart scores 4

a dart in the inner circle scores a 'treble' this dart scores 18

this dart scores 17

In the bull's eye formed by the two small centre circles, the outer circle scores 25 and the inner circle scores 50.

In questions 1 to 8 write down the score made with the three darts.

1 A 9, a treble 5, a 20.

2 A double 20, a 20, an 18.

3 A 16, a 19, a treble 17.

4 A double 19, a 3, a treble 15.

5 A double 5, a treble 18, a double 4.

6 A double 1, a treble 20, a 14.

7 A double 11, a treble 7, a 3.

8 A 7, a 2, a double 2.

9 A player starts with 501 and then subtracts each of the scores in questions 1 to 8. Draw a table to show her score and the total left after each score.

We can make many different totals with a calculator, using a restricted number of keys. For example, to make 466 using only the 3 key and the 4 key we can use the calculation:

■ ■

PAUSE

1 Write down a calculator calculation, using only the 3 key, the 4 key, the + key, the − key and the = key which gives each of these answers.

a) 40   b) 77   c) 787   d) 37   e) 35

2 Write down a calculator calculation, using only the 5 key, the 7 key, the + key, the − key and the = key which gives each of these answers.

a) 24   b) 132   c) 548   d) 79   e) 652

3 Write down a calculator calculation, using only the 6 key, the 9 key, the + key, the − key and the = key which gives each of these answers.

a) 48   b) 84   c)102   d)1887   e)3774

■ ■

12 and 24 hour clocks

This is a 12 hour clock:

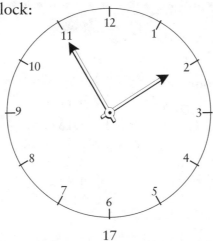

17

The hour hand goes round two times each day. The first time is from Midnight to Noon and second from Noon to Midnight.

Times from Midnight to Noon are followed by a.m. (ante meridiem or before noon).

Times from Noon to Midnight are followed by p.m. (post meridiem or after noon).

8 a.m. means 8 o'clock in the morning.
8 p.m. means 8 o'clock in the evening.

This can lead to confusion so many bus and train timetables use a 24 hour clock.

A 24 hour clock divides the day into hours and minutes passed since Midnight.

So, 13.20 hours (13.20 h) means 13 hours and 20 minutes have passed since Midnight. This is the same as 1.20 p.m. in 12 hour time.

Examples

1. Change into 24 hour time.

   a) 9 a.m   b) 9 p.m   c) 11.30 a.m.   d) 10.45 p.m.

   a) 9 a.m. = 09.00 h   c) 11.30 a.m. = 11.30 h

   b) 9 p.m. = 21.00 h   d) 10.45 p.m. = 22.45 h

2. Change into 12 hour time.

   a) 09.23 h   b) 16.39 h

   a) 09.23 h = 9.23 a.m.   b) 16.39 h = 4.39 p.m.

PAUSE

1 Change into 24 hour time.

a) 3 a.m.	f) 6 p.m.	k) 7.15 a.m.	p) 4.45 p.m.
b) 3 p.m.	g) 11 a.m.	l) 7.15 p.m.	q) 1.55 a.m.
c) 5 a.m.	h) 11 p.m.	m) 2.25 a.m.	r) 1.55 p.m.
d) 5 p.m.	i) 8 a.m.	n) 2.25 p.m.	s) 10.05 a.m.
e) 6 a.m.	j) 8 p.m.	o) 4.45 a.m.	t) 10.05 p.m.

2 Change into 12 hour time.

a) 02.00 h	f) 23.00 h	k) 15.41 h	p) 13.02 h
b) 14.00 h	g) 22.00 h	l) 09.51 h	q) 11.49 h
c) 07.00 h	h) 10.00 h	m) 00.35 h	r) 20.46 h
d) 19.00 h	i) 16.01 h	n) 14.15 h	s) 04.17 h
e) 11.00 h	j) 08.22 h	o) 10.17 h	t) 17.36 h

■■■■■■■■■■■■■■■■■■■■■■■■■■■■■■■■■■■■■

Journey times and timetables

Using the 24 hour clock we can find journey times by subtraction. If we 'borrow' from the hours to the minutes we 'borrow' 60, not 10.

Examples

1. A train leaves Peterborough at 05.24 h and arrives in London at 06.46 h. How long does the journey take?

$$
\begin{array}{r}
06.46 \\
-05.24 \\
\hline
1.22 \\
\hline
\end{array}
$$

The journey takes 1 hour 22 minutes.

2. A bus leaves Ipswich at 06.58 h and arrives in Cambridge at 08.35 h. How long did the journey take?

$$
\begin{array}{r}
{}^{7}{}^{6}\llap{0}8.{}^{2}\llap{3}{}^{1}\llap{5} \\
-06.58 \\
\hline
1.37 \\
\hline
\end{array}
$$

The journey takes 1 hour 37 minutes.

■■■■■■■■■■■■■■■■■■■■■■■■■■■■■■■

PAUSE

Find the time for each journey.

1 Leave 06.56 h, arrive 08.59 h.

2 Leave 10.06 h, arrive 12.39 h.

3 Leave 09.15 h, arrive 15.36 h.

4 Leave 12.17 h, arrive 12.47 h.

5 Leave 06.24 h, arrive 11.48 h.

6 Leave 13.09 h, arrive 17.32 h.

7 Leave 17.23 h, arrive 23.30 h.

8 Leave 16.58 h, arrive 22.06 h.

9 Leave 00.34 h, arrive 21.52 h.

10 Leave 21.32 h, arrive 23.21 h.

11 Paul catches a coach from Woking to London Heathrow.
The coach leaves Woking at 1340 and arrives at London
Heathrow at 1428.

a) What was his arrival time in 12 hour clock time?
b) How many minutes did the journey take?   (SEG)

12 A train from London arrived at Leeds station at 01.24 h.
The Journey had taken 2 hours 37 minutes.
Calculate the time the train left London.   (ULEAC)

13 Here is a timetable for Amina's school bus.

Bus Stop	Time
Bus Station	08:00
Station Road	08:15
Grange Drive	08:20
Hooley Ave.	08:30
Kings Road	08:40
School Road	08:45

Amina catches the bus at Grange Drive.

a) At what time should the bus be at Grange Drive?
b) How long should the bus take to get from Grange Drive to
   School Road?   (ULEAC)

INTERCITY

Peterborough → Newcastle and Edinburgh

Peterborough depart	Newcastle arrive	Edinburgh arrive
06 57	09 27	11 16
08 51	11 08	12 50
09 47	11 59	13 45
11 47	13 52	15 34
12 17	14 37	16 16
13 47	15 52	17 38
14 17	16 37	18 19
15 47	17 59	19 41
19 21	21 50	23 32

a) i) How long, in hours and minutes, does it take the 0657 train to travel from Peterborough to Newcastle?

   ii) The distance from Peterborough to Newcastle is 200 miles. Calculate the average speed for this journey, in miles per hour, of the 0657 train from Peterborough.

b) Wayne has to arrive in Edinburgh before 5 p.m.
Write down the time of the latest train that he can catch from Peterborough. (MEG)

15 | **Belfast–Londonderry** | *Maiden City Flyer* | *Goldline* EXPRESS SERVICE |

		Monday to Saturday								
		MO						FO		FO
LONDONDERRY	dep	0630	0700	0900	1100	1300	1500	1600	1730	1900
Dungiven	dep	0700	0730	0930	1130	1330	1530	1630	1800	1930
Maghera (Glenshane Rd)	dep	0715	0745	0945	1145	1345	1545	1645	1815	1945
Castledawson (Glenshane Rd)	dep	0720	0750	0950	1150	1350	1550	1650	1820	1950
Toomebridge	dep	0730	0800	1000	1200	1400	1600	1700	1830	2000
BELFAST	arr	0810	0840	1040	1240	1440	1640	1740	1910	2040

		Monday to Saturday								
		MO						FO		FO
BELFAST	dep	0830	0930	1130	1330	1530	1730	1630	1830	2000
Toomebridge	dep	0905	1005	1205	1405	1605	1805	1705	1905	2035
Castledawson (Glenshane Rd)	dep	0915	1015	1215	1415	1615	1815	1715	1915	2045
Maghera (Glenshane Rd)	dep	0920	1020	1220	1420	1620	1820	1720	1920	2050
Dungiven	dep	0940	1040	1240	1440	1640	1840	1740	1940	2110
LONDONDERRY	arr	1010	1110	1310	1510	1710	1910	1810	2010	2140

FO Friday only
MO Monday only

Courtesy of Ulsterbus Ltd

Mandy Brown lives in Belfast. She wants to visit her grandmother in Londonderry on Wednesday.

a) What is the earliest time a bus will leave Belfast for Londonderry on Wednesday?

b) How long should the journey take?

c) Mandy leaves on the last bus that day from Londonderry to Belfast. At what time should she arrive back in Belfast?

d) The distance from Londonderry to Dungiven is 20 miles. At what average speed is the bus travelling over this part of the journey if it keeps to the time-table? (NICCEA)

16

NEWCASTLE–CHESTER-LE-STREET–DURHAM–DARLINGTON   BUS TIMETABLE

SUNDAY

	am	am	am	am	am	am	am	am	am					pm
NEWCASTLE Worswick Street	5.15	6.35	7.45	8.25	8.55	9.40	–	10.40	11.10		40	10		9.40
GATESHEAD Metro interchange	5.23	6.43	7.53	8.33	9.03	9.48	–	10.48	11.18		48	18		9.48
Low Fell Lyndhurst	5.33	6.53	8.03	8.43	9.13	9.58	–	10.58	11.28		58	28		9.58
Birtley Station Lane	5.40	7.00	8.10	8.50	9.20	10.05	–	11.05	11.35		05	35		10.05
Barley Mow Inn	5.43	7.03	8.13	8.53	9.23	10.08	–	11.08	11.38		08	38		10.08
CHESTER-LE-STREET Front Street	5.48	7.08	8.18	8.58	9.28	10.13	–	11.13	11.43		13	43		10.13
Plawsworth Red Lion	–	–	–	–	–	10.22	–	11.22	11.52	then	22	52		10.22
Framwellgate Moor Salutation	–	–	–	–	–	10.28	–	11.28	11.58	at	28	58		10.28
Durham County Hall	–	–	–	–	–	10.30	–	11.30	12.00	these	30	00		10.30
DURHAM Bus Station	–	–	–	–	–	10.33	10.37	11.37	12.03	mins.	37	03	until	10.37
Nevilles Cross Church	–	–	–	–	–	–	10.41	11.41	–	past	41	–		10.41
Croxdale Roundabout	–	–	–	–	–	–	10.47	11.47	–	each	47	–		10.47
Thinford	–	–	–	–	–	–	10.51	11.51	–	hour	51	–		10.51
Ferryhill Bus Station	–	–	–	–	–	–	10.54	11.54	–		54	–		10.54
Chilton Wheatsheaf	–	–	–	–	–	–	11.00	12.00	–		00	–		11.00
Rushyford Eden Arms	–	–	–	–	–	–	11.02	12.02	–		02	–		11.02
Newton Aycliffe Vane Road	–	–	–	–	–	–	11.07	12.07	–		07	–		11.07
Newton Aycliffe Town Centre	–	–	–	–	–	–	11.09	12.09	–		09	–		11.09
Aycliffe Village North Briton	–	–	–	–	–	–	11.15	12.15	–		15	–		11.15
DARLINGTON Bus Station	–	–	–	–	–	–	11.32	12.32	–		32	–		11.32

a) Dennis travels on the 8.55 am bus from Newcastle to Chester-le-Street.

  i) What time does the bus arrive in Chester-le-Street?

  ii) How many minutes does the journey take?

b) Anne travels on the 1.30 pm bus from Durham County Hall to Chilton Wheatsheaf. What time does she arrive at Chilton Wheatsheaf?

c) How many buses leave Newcastle for Durham between 11.30 am and 9.30 pm?

d) George catches the 10.37 am bus at Durham Bus Station and travels to Newton Aycliffe Vane Road. The distance by bus is 15 miles.

Calculate the average speed of the bus in miles per hour. (NEAB)

Multiplication of whole numbers by 10, 100 or 1000

Examples

1. $67 \times 10 = 670$

Hundreds	Tens	Units
	6	7
6	7	0

2. $35 \times 100 = 3500$

Thousands	Hundreds	Tens	Units
		3	5
3	5	0	0

3. $24 \times 1000 = 24\,000$

Ten Thousands	Thousands	Hundreds	Tens	Units
			2	4
2	4	0	0	0

PAUSE

Do not use a calculator for this exercise.

1   A supermarket sells bags of ten oranges.

How many oranges are there in:

a) 2 bags,   c) 12 bags,   e) 47 bags,   g) 79 bags,   i) 101 bags,
b) 5 bags,   d) 23 bags,   f) 80 bags,   h) 100 bags,   j) 144 bags?

2 There are 100 centimes in a French franc.

How many centimes are there in:

a) 4 francs, c) 15 francs, e) 42 francs, g) 100 francs, i) 1000 francs,

b) 7 francs, d) 20 francs, f) 90 francs, h) 101 francs, j) 278 francs?

3 This table shows how many people are employed in different types of jobs (source: Employment Gazette 1994).

Type of employment	Thousands employed	
	1981	1994
Agriculture, forestry and fishing	353	246
Coal, oil and natural gas extraction and processing	344	79
Electricity, gas and water supply	356	237
Manufacturing industries	6098	4243
Construction	1100	773
Wholesale distribution and repairs	1112	1077
Retail distribution	2069	2281
Hotels and catering	891	1167
Transport	973	847
Postal services and telecommunications	429	361
Banking, finance and insurance	1706	2671
Public administration	1842	1779
Education	1552	1812
Medical and other health services, veterinary services	1251	1567
Other services	1274	1754
Totals	21350	20894

Each number in the table must be multiplied by 1000 to find the real number of people employed. For example, there were $973 \times 1000 = 973\,000$ people employed in transport in 1981.

a) Write down the actual number of people employed in these industries in 1981 and 1994.

  i) Coal, oil and natural gas extraction and processing.

ii) Construction.

iii) Hotels and catering.

b) How many fewer people were employed in Transport in 1994 than in 1981?

c) How many more people were employed in Banking, finance and insurance in 1994 than in 1981?

■■■■■■■■■■■■■■■■■■■■■■■■■■■■■■■■■■■■

Using multiplication by 10, 100 or 1000 to extend multiplication tables

x	1	2	3	4	5	6	7	8	9	10
1	1	2	3	4	5	6	7	8	9	10
2	2	4	6	8	10	12	14	16	18	20
3	3	6	9	12	15	18	21	24	27	30
4	4	8	12	16	20	24	28	32	36	40
5	5	10	15	20	25	30	35	40	45	50
6	6	12	18	24	30	36	42	48	54	60
7	7	14	21	28	35	42	49	56	63	70
8	8	16	24	32	40	48	56	64	72	80
9	9	18	27	36	45	54	63	72	81	90
10	10	20	30	40	50	60	70	80	90	100

We can extend our use of the multiplication tables.

For example, to multiply by 700:

■ multiply by 7 using the 7 times table,

■ multiply the result by 100 to get the overall answer.

Examples

1. 8×30

$30 = 3 \times 10$

multiply by 3: $8 \times 3 = 24$

multiply by 10: $24 \times 10 = 240$

2. 20×700

$700 = 7 \times 100$

multiply by 7: $20 \times 7 = 140$

multiply by 100: $140 \times 100 = 14\,000$

3. 4×6000

   $6000 = 6 \times 1000$

   multiply by 6: $\qquad 4 \times 6 = 24$

   multiply by 1000: $24 \times 1000 = 24\,000$

PAUSE

Do not use a calculator for this exercise.

1	3×40	7	90×6	13	80×40	19	50×200	25	40×5000
2	50×5	8	3×60	14	6×200	20	500×30	26	500×900
3	2×40	9	70×90	15	8×300	21	3×9000	27	800×200
4	80×9	10	80×80	16	400×4	22	30×900	28	300×700
5	7×60	11	60×60	17	500×8	23	4×7000	29	600×500
6	70×7	12	50×70	18	8×600	24	20×6000	30	200×9000

SECTION 2 Types of Number

12 can be divided exactly by 3: $12 \div 3 = 4$

12 cannot be divided exactly by 5: $12 \div 5 = 2$ remainder 2

This is a list of all the numbers which divide exactly into 12:

1, 2, 3, 4, 6 and 12

Any number which divides exactly into 12 is called a *factor* of 12. So, the factors of 12 are, 1, 2, 3, 4, 6 and 12.

If a number has 2 as one of its factors, it is called an *even* number.

14 is an even number because it divides exactly by 2

0 and numbers ending in 0 like 30 are even.

If a number does not have 2 as one of its factors, it is called an *odd* number.

9 is an odd number because it does not divide exactly by 2

If a number has exactly two factors it is called a *prime* number. A prime number is a number which can only be divided exactly by itself and the number 1.

7 is a prime number because it has only two factors,
the numbers 7 and 1

9 is not a prime number because it has three factors,
the numbers 9, 3 and 1

When we multiply 12 by the numbers 1, 2, 3, 4, and 5, we get 12, 24, 36, 48 and 60. These numbers all divide exactly by 12. Any number which divides exactly by 12 is called a *multiple* of 12.

The first 5 multiples of 12 are, 12, 24, 36, 48 and 60.

PAUSE

1 Write down the factors of 8.

2 Write down the factors of 25.

3 Write down the factors of 13.

4 a) Write down all the factors of these numbers:
   i) 18 ii) 21 iii) 23 iv) 16
   b) i) Write down the condition for a number to be prime.
   ii) Which number in a) is prime?

5 Which of 42, 170, 901, 1325 and 1500 are even numbers?

6 The first 10 prime numbers are 2, 3, 5, 7, 11, ...

7 The first 7 multiples of 6 are, ...

8 The first 6 multiples of 7 are, ...

9 Look at the numbers 11, 12, 13, 14, 15, 16, 17, 18.
   a) Which of the numbers are multiples of 3?
   b) Which of the numbers are factors of 36?

10 Look at the numbers 7, 10, 13, 16, 19, 21, 24.
   a) Which of the numbers are factors of 21?
   b) Which of the numbers are multiples of 7?
   c) Which of the numbers are prime?

Square, rectangular and triangular numbers

Some sets of numbers are given special names because of the patterns into which that number of dots can be arranged.

For example, these are the first five *square numbers*.

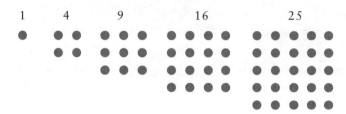

These are the first six *rectangular numbers*.

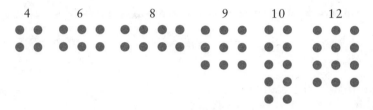

The pattern of dots must have at least two rows and two columns. Squares count as special rectangles.

These are the first five *triangular numbers*.

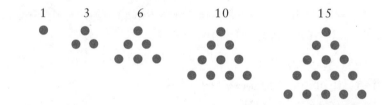

■ ■

PAUSE

1 Write down the first 12 square numbers.

2 Write down the first 20 rectangular numbers.

3 Write down the first 10 triangular numbers.

■ ■

Square roots

The numbers 1, 4, 9, 16, 25, ... are the square numbers.
The numbers 1, 2, 3, 4, 5, ... are the **square roots** of these numbers.
This is the special sign for the square root of a number √   or √, so

$$\sqrt{36} = 6$$

PAUSE

1 Copy and complete.

a) $\sqrt{81}$ =   d) $\sqrt{100}$ =   g) $\sqrt{400}$ =   j) $\sqrt{2500}$ =

b) $\sqrt{49}$ =   e) $\sqrt{144}$ =   h) $\sqrt{900}$ =   k) $\sqrt{6400}$ =

c) $\sqrt{121}$ =   f) $\sqrt{64}$ =   i) $\sqrt{1600}$ =   l) $\sqrt{10\,000}$ =

SECTION 3 Estimation and Calculation

Multiplying whole numbers without a calculator

An estimate is made first by rounding numbers between 10 and 100 to the nearest 10. Numbers between 100 and 1000 are rounded to the nearest 100. The calculations are then worked out like this:

Examples
1. 385×7

Estimate: $400 \times 7 = 2800$

Step 3
7×3 is 21 plus 5 (carried)
makes 26

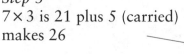

$$\begin{array}{r} 385 \\ \times \quad 7 \\ \hline 2695 \\ {\scriptstyle 5\ 3} \end{array}$$

Step 1
7×5 is 35
5 down, 3 carried

Step 2
7×8 is 56 plus 3 (carried) makes 59
9 down, 5 carried

29

2. 264 × 30

Estimate: 300 × 30 = 9000

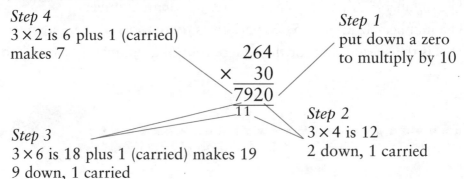

Step 1
put down a zero
to multiply by 10

Step 4
3 × 2 is 6 plus 1 (carried)
makes 7

$$\begin{array}{r} 264 \\ \times\ \ 30 \\ \hline 7920 \\ {\scriptstyle 11} \end{array}$$

Step 2
3 × 4 is 12
2 down, 1 carried

Step 3
3 × 6 is 18 plus 1 (carried) makes 19
9 down, 1 carried

PAUSE

Do not use a calculator in this exercise. Show an estimate and an accurate answer for every calculation.

1 18 × 6	6 573 × 9	11 79 × 800	16 374 × 60
2 34 × 9	7 57 × 90	12 23 × 300	17 990 × 90
3 7 × 59	8 5 × 602	13 450 × 70	18 832 × 400
4 2 × 92	9 63 × 50	14 675 × 3	19 400 × 567
5 8 × 76	10 85 × 400	15 9 × 556	20 2341 × 500

Long multiplication is used with larger numbers. It is a combination of the two techniques you have already used.

Examples

1. 385 × 37

Estimate: 400 × 40 = 16 000

$$\begin{array}{r} 385 \\ \times\ \ 37 \\ \hline 11550 \\ {\scriptstyle 21} \end{array}$$ ——— *Step 1* 385 × 30

$$\begin{array}{r} 2695 \\ {\scriptstyle 53} \end{array}$$ ——— *Step 2* 385 × 7

$$\begin{array}{r} \hline 14245 \\ {\scriptstyle 11} \end{array}$$ ——— *Step 3* 11 550 + 2695

2. 426×258

Estimate: $400 \times 300 = 120\,000$

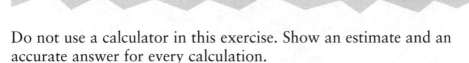

$$
\begin{array}{r}
426 \\
\times\ \ 258 \\
\hline
85200 \\
{\scriptstyle 1} \\
21300 \\
{\scriptstyle 1\ 3} \\
3408 \\
{\scriptstyle 2\ 4} \\
\hline
109908 \\
{\scriptstyle 1}
\end{array}
$$

— Step 1 426×200
— Step 2 426×50
— Step 3 426×8
— Step 4 $85\,200 + 21\,300 + 3408$

PAUSE

Do not use a calculator in this exercise. Show an estimate and an accurate answer for every calculation.

1 234×45	6 762×41	11 367×231	16 361×194
2 571×26	7 208×53	12 333×421	17 282×828
3 672×44	8 1102×22	13 406×203	18 327×109
4 980×53	9 675×25	14 292×315	19 447×774
5 747×29	10 337×89	15 928×273	20 621×234

Division of whole numbers by 10, 100 or 1000

Examples

1. $670 \div 10 = 67$

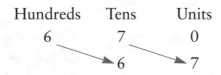

Hundreds	Tens	Units
6	7	0
	6	7

2. $3500 \div 100 = 35$

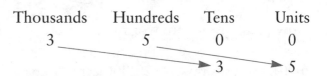

Thousands	Hundreds	Tens	Units
3	5	0	0
		3	5

31

3. $24\,000 \div 1000 = 24$

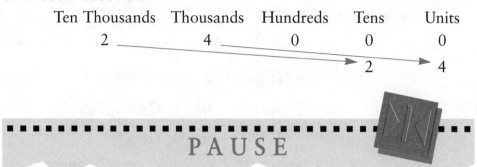

Ten Thousands	Thousands	Hundreds	Tens	Units
2	4	0	0	0
			2	4

PAUSE

1 A supermarket sells bags of ten oranges.

How many bags of oranges could be made with:

a) 60 oranges, b) 230 oranges, c) 790 oranges, d) 100 oranges,
e) 140 oranges?

2 There are 100 centimes in a French franc.

How many francs are worth:

a) 400 centimes, b) 2000 centimes, c) 4200 centimes,
d) 10 100 centimes, e) 27 800 centimes?

3 Angela was doing a project on newspapers. She collected this information about the daily sales of some popular newspapers.

Paper	Circulation
Daily Mail	1 784 000
Guardian	400 000
Daily Mirror	2 484 000
Daily Star	746 000
Independent	284 000
Today	580 000
Sun	4 008 000
Times	472 000
Financial Times	297 000

Angela decided to sort the papers into order of sales. She also decided to write the numbers divided by 1000 to make her table simpler. This is the start of her new table.

Paper	Circulation (thousands)
Sun	4 008

a) How would Angela write the sales for the Guardian?
b) How would Angela write the sales for the Daily Mirror?
c) Which paper has a circulation of 297 thousand?
d) Which paper has a circulation of 1784 thousand?
e) i) Which paper has the smallest circulation?
   ii) How would Angela write this number?

Using division by 10, 100 or 1000 to extend multiplication tables

x	1	2	3	4	5	6	7	8	9	10
1	1	2	3	4	5	6	7	8	9	10
2	2	4	6	8	10	12	14	16	18	20
3	3	6	9	12	15	18	21	24	27	30
4	4	8	12	16	20	24	28	32	36	40
5	5	10	15	20	25	30	35	40	45	50
6	6	12	18	24	30	36	42	48	54	60
7	7	14	21	28	35	42	49	56	63	70
8	8	16	24	32	40	48	56	64	72	80
9	9	18	27	36	45	54	63	72	81	90
10	10	20	30	40	50	60	70	80	90	100

For example, to divide by 900:
- divide by 100,
- divide the result by 9 using the 9 times table to get the overall answer.

Examples

1. $720 \div 80$

$$80 = 10 \times 8$$

divide by 10: $720 \div 10 = 72$

divide by 8: $\quad 72 \div 8 = 9$

2. $45\,000 \div 900$

$$900 = 100 \times 9$$

divide by 100: $45\,000 \div 100 = 450$

divide by 9: $\quad 450 \div 9 = 50$

3. $24\,000 \div 6000$

$$6000 = 1000 \times 6$$

divide by 1000: $24\,000 \div 1000 = 24$

divide by 6: $\quad 24 \div 6 = 4$

PAUSE

Do not use a calculator in this exercise.

1	$120 \div 40$	11	$3600 \div 60$	21	$27\,000 \div 900$
2	$100 \div 20$	12	$6300 \div 70$	22	$27\,000 \div 3000$
3	80×40	13	$3200 \div 80$	23	$28\,000 \div 4000$
4	$720 \div 90$	14	$1200 \div 60$	24	$120\,000 \div 6000$
5	$420 \div 70$	15	$2400 \div 30$	25	$200\,000 \div 5000$
6	$490 \div 70$	16	$1600 \div 400$	26	$450\,000 \div 9000$
7	$540 \div 90$	17	$4000 \div 800$	27	$1\,600\,000 \div 8000$
8	$180 \div 30$	18	$4800 \div 600$	28	$21\,000\,000 \div 7000$
9	$630 \div 90$	19	$2400 \div 300$	29	$3\,000\,000 \div 5000$
10	$640 \div 80$	20	$15\,000 \div 300$	30	$810\,000 \div 9000$

Dividing whole numbers without a calculator

An estimate is made first by rounding numbers between 10 and 100 to the nearest 10 and numbers between 100 and 1000 to the nearest 100. The calculations are then worked out like this:

Examples

1. $216 \div 8$

   Estimate: $200 \div 8 = 25$

   Step 1 8 into 21 goes 2 times

   Step 5 8 into 56 goes 7 times

   Step 2 8×2 is 16

   Step 3 $21 - 16$ is 5

   Step 4 Bring down the 6

   Step 6 8×7 is 56

   Step 7 $56 - 56 = 0$

$$8\overline{)216} \quad 27$$
$$\underline{16}$$
$$56$$
$$\underline{56}$$
$$0$$

   Answer: $216 \div 8 = 27$

35

2. $651 \div 15$ *Step 1* 15 into 65 goes 4 times

   Estimate: $700 \div 20 = 35$

$$15\overline{)651}$$
43

Step 5 15 into 51 goes 3 times

Step 2 15×4 is 60 ——60

Step 3 $65 - 60$ is 5 ——51 —— *Step 4* Bring down the 1

Step 6 15×3 is 45 ——45

                  6 —— *Step 7* $51 - 45 = 6$

Answer: $651 \div 15 = 43$ remainder 6

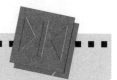

PAUSE

Do not use a calculator in this exercise. Show an estimate and an accurate answer for every calculation.

1 715×13	6 $418 \div 38$	11 $923 \div 34$	16 $99 \div 21$
2 275×25	7 $377 \div 29$	12 $798 \div 37$	17 $302 \div 21$
3 $858 \div 39$	8 $378 \div 42$	13 $721 \div 22$	18 $602 \div 39$
4 $817 \div 19$	9 $416 \div 26$	14 $587 \div 33$	19 $998 \div 46$
5 $528 \div 24$	10 $784 \div 14$	15 $826 \div 13$	20 $957 \div 36$

When we are using a calculator, the answer is usually checked with an *inverse operation*.

Here a calculator is used to find remainders.

Example

A baker starts filling bags of 24 bread rolls from a pile of 453 rolls. How many bags can she fill and how many rolls will she have left over?

        4 5 3 ÷ 2 4 = 18.875

Check **1 8 . 8 7 5 × 2 4 =** 453

So, the baker can fill 18 bags.

1 8 × **2 4** = 432

Check **4 3 2** ÷ **2 4** = 18

4 5 3 − **4 3 2** = 21

Check **4 3 2** + **2 1** = 453

So, the baker has 21 rolls left over.

The next exercise is designed to give you practice in solving problems which require a mixture of calculations.

PAUSE

1 Sally's pen leaked all over her Maths homework. Each ink blot covered a single figure. Write out Sally's homework again, filling in all the missing numbers.

> a) 8 × █ = 8 ✓   f) █6 × 5 = 8█ ✓
>
> b) 4 × █ = █0 ✓   g) 2█ × 4 = 1█8 ✓
>
> c) 6 × █ = █6 ✓   h) 23 × █ = 13█ ✓
>
> d) █ × 3 = █1 ✓   i) 12 × 1█ = 1█4 ✓
>
> e) █ × 9 = 6█ ✓   j) █4 × 9 = 30█ ✓

2 Sam's pen was leaking as well. Each ink blot covered a single figure. Write out Sam's homework again, filling in all the missing numbers.

> a) 3█ ÷ 8 = █ ✓   f) █8 ÷ 7 = █4 ✓
>
> b) █6 ÷ 6 = █1 ✓   g) 8█ ÷ 10 = █ ✓
>
> c) 5█ ÷ █ = 6 ✓   h) █7 ÷ █ = 11 ✓
>
> d) █7 ÷ 9 = █ ✓   i) 5█ ÷ 3 = █7 ✓
>
> e) █8 ÷ 7 = █ ✓   j) 144 ÷ █2 = █2 ✓

3 How many tins or cartons are there in each of these damaged cases?

a)   b)   c)

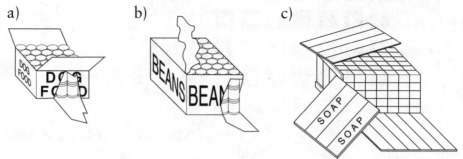

4 The measurement across the top of a can is called its diameter.

In each of these pictures, find the diameter of a single can and the length of the case.

a)   b)   c)

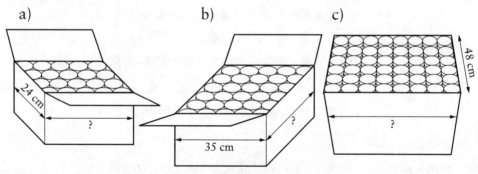

5 In each part, write down how much is received for each equal share and how much is left over.

a) £28 shared by 7 people.
b) 38 sweets shared by 9 children.
c) 6 dozen roses shared by 5 brides.
d) 2 dozen mince pies shared by 10 carol singers.
e) 3000 exercise books shared by 12 school departments.
f) £200 000 shared by 8 lottery winners.
g) 153 marbles shared by 8 children.
h) 327 mice shared into 33 cages.

i) 250 sandwiches shared by two rugby teams and a referee (1 team has 15 members).

j) 280 sandwiches shared by 4 hockey teams and two referees (1 team has 11 members).

■■

Foreign currency and exchange rates

TOURIST RATES – BANK SELLS

Australia 1.97	France 7.50	Italy 2,355	Singapore 2.13
Austria 15.25	Germany 2.1925	Malta 0.5425	South Africa 5.42
Belgium 45.00	Greece 367.00	Netherlands 2.4625	Spain 183.50
Canada 2.04	Hong Kong 11.63	New Zealand 2.23	Sweden 10.49
Cyprus 0.7075	India 56.55	Norway 9.60	Switzerland 1.78
Denmark 8.49	Ireland 0.9550	Portugal 228.00	Turkey 93,812
Finland 6.97	Israel 4.76	Saudi Arabia 5.69	USA 1.4950

Supplied by NatWest Bank (excluding Indian rupee and Israeli shekel).

Example

Angela Seed and David King are going to France.
Angela changes £200 into French Francs and David changes £150 into French Francs. How much do they both receive?

Angela receives $200 \times 7.50 = 1500$ francs.
David receives $150 \times 7.50 = 1125$ francs.

■■■■■■■■■■■■■■■■■■■■■■■■■■■■■■■■■■■■ ■■

PAUSE

Change:

1 £100 into French Francs,

2 £480 into French Francs,

3 £155 into French Francs,

4 £186 into French Francs,

5 £1000 into U.S.A. dollars,

6 £100 into U.S.A. dollars,

7 £350 into U.S.A. dollars,

8 £475 into U.S.A. dollars,

9 £1000 into Canadian dollars,

10 £100 into Canadian dollars,

11 £350 into Canadian dollars,

12 £475 into Canadian dollars,

13 £100 into Belgian Francs,

14 £480 into Belgian Francs,

15 £250 into Belgian Francs,

16 £257 into Belgian Francs,

17 £500 into Spanish Pesetas,

18 £200 into Spanish Pesetas,

19 £180 into Spanish Pesetas,

20 £58 into Spanish Pesetas.

■■

Example

During her French holiday, Angela Seed sees a pair of jeans priced at 247 francs. What is the equivalent price in British money?

$247 \div 7.50 = £32.93$ (to the nearest penny)

PAUSE

Find the equivalent price in British money for each item.

1 A hat priced at 112.50 French Francs.
2 A sandwich priced at 22.00 French Francs.
3 A dress priced at 370.00 French Francs.
4 A bottle of wine priced at 13.00 French Francs.
5 A hire car priced at $22.50 a day (U.S.A. dollars).
6 A CD priced at $7.80 (U.S.A. dollars).
7 A computer priced at $897 (U.S.A. dollars).
8 A car priced at $11,960 (U.S.A. dollars).
9 A carpet priced at 28,275 Indian Rupees.
10 A pair of skis priced at 180 Swiss Francs.
11 A glass of beer priced at 5.00 German Marks.
12 A meal priced at 1280 Greek Drachmas.
13 A disco ticket priced at 2000 Greek Drachmas.
14 A taxi ride priced at 1100 Spanish Pesetas.
15 An ice cream priced at 105 Spanish Pesetas.

SECTION 4 Decimals

Place value in decimals

Remember, whole numbers are written under these column headings:

.....   1000s   100s   10s   1s

So, a whole number like 2743 represents:

.....	1000s	100s	10s	1s
	2	7	4	3

Or, $2000+700+40+3$

Decimals are written under these column headings:

| ..... | 1000s | 100s | 10s | 1s | $\frac{1}{10}$s | $\frac{1}{100}$s | $\frac{1}{1000}$s | ..... |

The *decimal point* is used to separate the whole number columns from the fraction columns.

So, the decimal number 2743.823 represents:

.....	1000s	100s	10s	1s	$\frac{1}{10}$s	$\frac{1}{100}$s	$\frac{1}{1000}$s	.....
	2	7	4	3	8	2	3	

Or, $2000+700+40+3+\frac{8}{10}+\frac{2}{100}+\frac{3}{1000}$

Examples

1. Write 74.13 as an addition of separate column values.

$$74.13 = 70+4+\tfrac{1}{10}+\tfrac{3}{100}$$

2. What decimal number represents $\tfrac{9}{10}+5+70+\tfrac{3}{100}$?

$$\tfrac{9}{10}+5+70+\tfrac{3}{100}=75.93$$

3. What are the largest and the smallest numbers you can make with the digits 0, 3 and 6 and a decimal point?

The largest is 63.0, the smallest is 0.36.

PAUSE

1 Write each number as an addition of separate column values.

a) 2.7   f) 13.8   k) 87.5
b) 3.9   g) 1.38   l) 34.105
c) 75.2   h) 0.138   m) 0.001
d) 7.52   i) 8.75   n) 1.01
e) 138   j) 0.875   o) 101.101

2 What decimal number represents each of these additions?

a) $4+\frac{5}{10}$

b) $10+3+\frac{2}{10}$

c) $300+40+8+\frac{3}{10}$

d) $\frac{9}{10}+1$

e) $7+\frac{6}{10}+10$

f) $3+30+\frac{1}{10}$

g) $6+\frac{1}{10}+\frac{5}{100}$

h) $7+\frac{3}{10}+\frac{7}{100}$

i) $7+\frac{6}{10}+\frac{5}{100}+\frac{3}{1000}$

j) $700+50+\frac{1}{100}$

k) $600+4+\frac{5}{10}$

l) $\frac{3}{10}+30+500+\frac{1}{1000}+\frac{7}{100}$

3 What are the largest and the smallest numbers you can make with each set of digits and a decimal point?

a) 0, 7 and 4

b) 0, 9 and 1

c) 4, 5 and 6

d) 7, 2 and 8

■ ■

Ordering decimals

Example

Ryan works for a vet, one of his jobs is to weigh each dog who comes to the surgery. These are his records for one day.

5.5 kg, 3.6 kg, 6.2 kg, 2.3 kg, 6.9 kg, 8.8 kg, 4.4 kg, 0.7 kg, 7.1 kg

a) Draw a number line from 0 to 10 kg and show these weights.

b) Write a list of the weights sorted into order.

a)

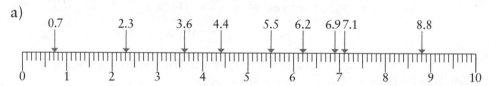

b) This is the ordered list of weights:

0.7 kg, 2.3 kg, 3.6 kg, 4.4 kg, 5.5 kg, 6.2 kg, 6.9 kg, 7.1 kg, 8.8 kg.

■ ■

PAUSE

In questions 1 to 3:

a) Use graph paper to draw a number line from 0 to 10. Show these weights.

b) Write a list of the weights sorted into order.

1 6.1, 2.2, 8.3, 7.4, 3.5, 4.6, 5.7, 1.8, 9.9, 1.3

2 3.1, 5.2, 9.3, 1.4, 4.5, 2.6, 6.7, 7.8, 7.0, 8.9

3 8.1, 1.2, 6.3, 3.4, 7.5, 9.6, 4.7, 5.8, 2.7, 1.9

■■

Example

Mrs Stockley was in charge of the long jump on school sports day. This is her record of the lengths of the last ten jumps.

Length (in m) 3.05, 3.78, 3.55, 3.31, 3.10, 3.01, 3.48, 3.82, 3.66, 3.93

a) Draw a number line from 3.0 to 4.0 and show these lengths.
b) Write a list of the lengths sorted into order.

a)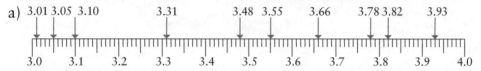

b) This is the ordered list of lengths.

    3.01, 3.05, 3.10, 3.31, 3.48, 3.55, 3.66, 3.78, 3.82, 3.93

PAUSE

Use graph paper to draw the number lines.

1 Paul measured the heights of ten of his relations for a maths project. These are his results.

   Heights (in m) 1.63, 1.97, 1.15, 1.48, 1.70, 1.53, 1.08, 1.32, 1.85, 1.23

   a) Draw a number line from 1 metre to 2 metres and show these heights.
   b) Write a list of the heights sorted into order.

2 a) Draw a number line from 5.0 to 6.0 and show these numbers:
      5.23, 5.57, 5.51, 5.8, 5.06, 5.33, 5.4, 5.61, 5.9, 5.17

   b) Write a list of the numbers sorted into order.

3 a) Draw a number line from 40.0 to 41.0 and show these numbers:
      40.5, 40.07, 40.7, 40.91, 40.19, 40.68, 40.86, 40.23, 40.32, 40.4

   b) Write a list of the numbers sorted into order.

■■

Example

A plant researcher weighs the ten tubers produced by a new variety of potato. These are her results.

Weight (in kg) 0.437, 0.454, 0.489, 0.467, 0.47, 0.405, 0.424,
0.496, 0.443, 0.418

a) Draw a number line from 0.40 to 0.50 and show these weights.
b) Write a list of the weights sorted into order.

a)
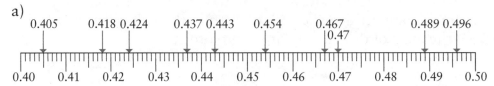

b) This is the ordered list of weights:

0.405, 0.418, 0.424, 0.437, 0.443, 0.454, 0.467, 0.47, 0.489, 0.496

PAUSE

Use graph paper to draw the number lines.

1 A quality control inspector measures the actual volume of liquid inside ten bottles marked 'contents 1 litre'. These are her results.

Volume (in litres) 1.013, 1.07, 1.032, 1.047, 1.052, 1.068, 1.02,
1.009, 1.041, 1.037

a) Draw a number line from 1.0 to 1.1. Label the line 1.00, 1.01,
1.02 ..... 1.10. Show these volumes.
b) Write a list of the volumes sorted into order.

2 A trading standards officer checks the actual weight of ten blocks of cheese, each labelled 'weight 5 kg'. These are his results:

Weight (in kg) 5.007, 4.962, 4.981, 5.027, 5.048, 4.956, 4.972,
4.99, 5.015, 5.03

a) Draw a number line from 4.95 to 5.05 and show these weights.
b) Write a list of the weights sorted into order.

3 a) Draw a number line from 15.30 to 15.40 and show these numbers:

15.392, 15.308, 15.38, 15.319, 15.374, 15.328, 15.363, 15.339, 15.35, 15.340

b) Write a list of the numbers sorted into order.

■■■

Example

Write the numbers 3.71, 3.07, 3.7, 3.17, 3.107 in order of size, smallest first.

We have to draw a number line. To make sure all the numbers fit, the line can go from 3 to 4.

3.107 is hard to place on this line. It lies between 3.10(0) and 3.11(0).

The numbers in order are: 3.07, 3.107, 3.17, 3.7, 3.71.

■■■■■■■■■■■■■■■■■■■■■■■■■■■■ PAUSE ■■■■■■■

Use graph paper to draw your own number lines. List the numbers in order, smallest first.

1 5.84, 5.8, 5.48, 5.408, 5.08

2 2.1, 2.61, 2.16, 2.06, 2.106

3 8.57, 8.517, 8.75, 8.5, 8.705

6 9.165, 9.65, 9.56, 9.5, 9.605

4 10.306, 10.6, 10.613, 10.31, 10.36

7 0.7, 0.3, 0.73, 0.07, 0.873

8 17.503, 17.05, 17.305, 17.5, 17.35

5 7.21, 7.12, 7.2, 7.102, 7.82

■■■

Approximating decimals

Decimals are often rounded.
For example, if a carpenter measured a length as 5.7 cm, he might say, 'it's about 6 cm long.'

Or, if a shopkeeper weighted a piece of cheese as 2.1 kg, she might say, 'it weighs about 2 kg'.

This is called rounding a decimal *to the nearest whole number*.

We can use a number line to help us round decimals to the nearest whole number. This diagram shows how.

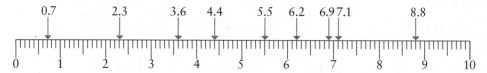

From the diagram we can see:

$$0.7 \approx 1 \qquad 2.3 \approx 2 \qquad 3.6 \approx 4 \qquad 4.4 \approx 4 \qquad 5.5 \approx 6$$
$$6.2 \approx 6 \qquad 6.9 \approx 7 \qquad 7.1 \approx 7 \qquad 8.8 \approx 9$$

PAUSE

In questions 1 to 5 use a number line. Write out each list of numbers rounded to the nearest whole number.

1 6.1, 2.2, 8.3, 7.4, 3.5, 4.6, 5.7, 1.8, 9.9, 1.3

2 3.1, 5.2, 9.3, 1.4, 4.5, 2.6, 6.7, 7.8, 7.0, 8.9

3 8.1, 1.2, 6.3, 3.4, 7.5, 9.6, 4.7, 5.8, 2.7, 1.9

4 1.6, 0.3, 2.3, 3.6, 4.2, 5.9, 6.5, 7.7, 8.4, 9.7

5 1.5, 2.4, 0.5, 3.9, 5.1, 6.4, 7.3, 8.6, 4.9, 9.8

Decimals are often rounded to a set number of decimal places.
For example, if a plan researcher measured the height of a shrub as 1.23 m, she might record the height as 1.2 m.

Or, if she measured the height of another shrub as 2.37 m, she might record the height as 2.4 m.

This is called rounding a decimal *to one decimal place*.

We can use a number line to help us round decimals to one decimal place. This diagram shows how:

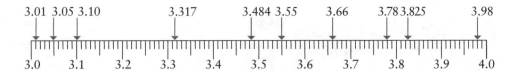

From the picture we can see:

$3.01 \approx 3.0$	$3.05 \approx 3.1$	$3.10 \approx 3.1$
$3.317 \approx 3.3$	$3.484 \approx 3.5$	$3.55 \approx 3.6$
$3.66 \approx 3.7$	$3.78 \approx 3.8$	$3.825 \approx 3.8$	$3.98 \approx 4.0$

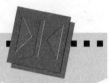

PAUSE

1 Paul measured the heights of ten of his relations for a maths project. These are his results.

Heights (in metres) 1.63, 1.97, 1.15, 1.48, 1.70, 1.53, 1.08, 1.32, 1.85, 1.23

Use a number line to write out a list of these heights rounded to the nearest 10 centimetres (one decimal place).

In questions 2 to 7, use a number line to write each list of numbers correct to one decimal place.

2 5.23, 5.57, 5.51, 5.80, 5.06, 5.33, 5.40, 5.61, 5.9, 5.17

3 5.275, 5.537, 5.598, 5.892, 5.041, 5.373, 5.408, 5.695, 5.98, 5.133

4 8.07, 8.90, 8.73, 8.65, 8.15, 8.20, 8.47, 8.33, 8.50, 8.82

5 8.035, 8.917, 8.771, 8.654, 8.155, 8.296, 8.429, 8.363, 8.547, 8.888

6 15.73, 15.09, 15.42, 15.94, 15.26, 15.18, 15.61, 15.83, 15.35, 15.50

7 15.755, 15.067, 15.489, 15.995, 15.237, 15.132, 15.69, 15.861, 15.347, 15.553

A vet weighs a cat and finds it weighs 1.237 kg. He records this weight as 1.24 kg, this is called rounding a decimal *to two decimal places*.

We can use a number line to help us round decimals to two decimal places. This diagram shows how:

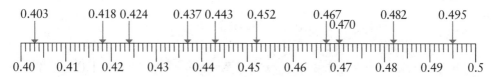

From the diagram we can see:

$0.403 \approx 0.40$ $0.418 \approx 0.42$ $0.424 \approx 0.42$

$0.437 \approx 0.44$ $0.443 \approx 0.44$ $0.452 \approx 0.45$

$0.467 \approx 0.47$ $0.470 \approx 0.47$ $0.482 \approx 0.48$ $0.495 \approx 0.50$

■ ■

PAUSE

Use a number line drawn on graph paper to write each list of numbers correct to two decimal places.

1 5.591, 5.509, 5.582, 5.518, 5.573, 5.527, 5.562, 5.538, 5.551, 5.549

2 15.398, 15.302, 15.387, 15.316, 15.376, 15.322, 15.364, 15.331, 15.358, 15.341

3 A quality control inspector measures the actual volume of liquid inside ten bottles marked 'contents 1 litre'. These are her results.

Volume (in litres) 1.013, 1.073, 1.032, 1.047, 1.052, 1.068, 1.021, 1.009, 1.041, 1.037

Use a number line to write a list of the volumes correct to two decimal places.

4 A trading standards officer checks the actual weight of ten blocks of cheese, each labelled 'weight 5 kg'. These are his results:

Weight (in kg) 5.007, 4.962, 4.981, 5.027, 5.048, 4.956, 4.972, 4.994, 5.015, 5.030

Use a number line to write a list of the weights correct to two decimal places.

5 Use a calculator to work these out. Give each answer correct to two decimal places.

a) $\sqrt{3}$ d) $\sqrt{8.4}$ g) $\sqrt{3.25}$ j) $\sqrt{19.1}$

b) $\sqrt{7.5}$ e) $\sqrt{42}$ h) $\sqrt{90}$ k) $\sqrt{22.7}$

c) $\sqrt{20}$ f) $\sqrt{150}$ i) $\sqrt{18}$ l) $\sqrt{200}$

Adding and subtracting decimals without a calculator

The decimal points go underneath each other. Extra 0s can be added to fill in the gaps.

Examples

1. $3.57 + 18.173$

$$
\begin{array}{r}
3.57 \\
+18.173 \\
\hline
21.743 \\
\hline
_{1}_{1}
\end{array}
$$

2. $17 - 14.84$

$$
\begin{array}{r}
{}^{6}\cancel{17}{}^{9}\cancel{.}{}^{1}00 \\
-14.84 \\
\hline
2.16
\end{array}
$$

PAUSE

Work these out without using a calculator.

1 a) $4.65 + 7.8$ c) $0.968 + 2.17$ e) $19 + 15.7 + 12.35$

   b) $16.705 + 10.53$ d) $0.0432 + 0.608$ f) $18.14 + 12 + 14.9$

49

2 a) 16.73−14.84   d) 10.6−7.135   g) 14−7.4
  b) 11.3−8.14   e) 0.56−0.162   h) 4−3.61
  c) 19.6−15.43   f) 0.07−0.056   i) 10−8.715

■■■■■■■■■■■■■■■■■■■■■■■■■■■■■■■■■■■■■■■

Multiplying and dividing decimals without a calculator

Examples

1. 3.741 × 6

$$\begin{array}{r} 3.741 \\ \times \quad 6 \\ \hline 22.446 \\ \end{array}$$
2 4 2

2. 14.5 ÷ 4

$$\begin{array}{r} 3.625 \\ 4\overline{)14.500} \\ \end{array}$$
2 1 2

■■■■■■■■■■■■■■■■■■■■■■■■■■ P A U S E ■■■

Work these out without using a calculator.

1 a) 12.4 × 4   c) 6.034 × 6   e) 12.506 × 9
  b) 8.24 × 7   d) 10.28 × 5   f) 0.243 × 8

2 a) 14.7 ÷ 2   c) 18.85 ÷ 4   e) 11.73 ÷ 5
  b) 17.4 ÷ 3   d) 0.127 ÷ 4   f) 9.007 ÷ 6

■■■■■■■■■■■■■■■■■■■■■■■■■■■■■■■■■■■■■■■

Multiplication of decimals by 10, 100 and 1000

These are the important metric tables:

■ Length

　　　　　10 millimetres (mm) = 1 centimetre (cm)
　　　　　100 cm = 1 metre (m)
　　　　　1000 m = 1 kilometre (km)

■ Weight

　　　　　1000 grams (g) = 1 kilogram (kg)

■ Volume

$$1000 \text{ cubic centimetres } (cm^3) = 1 \text{ litre } (L)$$
or
$$1000 \text{ millilitres } (ml) = 1 \text{ litre } (L)$$

Note: millilitres and cubic centimetres are different names for the same unit.

Examples

1. Change 8.67 centimetres into millimetres.
   $8.67 \times 10 = 86.7$ millimetres

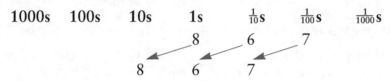

2. Change 2.3 metres into centimetres.
   $2.3 \times 100 = 230$ centimetres

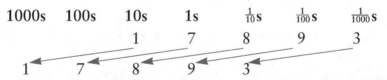

3. Change 17.893 metres into centimetres.
   $17.893 \times 100 = 1789.3$

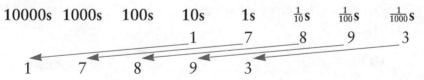

4. Change 17.893 kilograms into grams.
   $17.893 \times 1000 = 17893$

PAUSE

Try to do as many as you can without a calculator. Use your calculator to check your work.

1 Change each of these lengths into millimetres (multiply by 10).

a) 17 cm   d) 8.9 cm   g) 8.93 cm   j) 1.047 cm
b) 1.7 cm   e) 9.32 cm   h) 1.243 cm
c) 0.17 cm   f) 7.85 cm   i) 1.47 cm

2 Change each of these lengths into centimetres (multiply by 100).

a) 2.45 m   d) 12.375 m   g) 1.2 m   j) 0.765 m
b) 2 m   e) 0.895 m   h) 5.7 m
c) 0.45 m   f) 1.557 m   i) 7.3 m

3 Change each of these weights into grams (multiply by 1000).

a) 1.237 kg   d) 8.23 kg   g) 16.6666 kg   j) 7.0314 kg
b) 1.657 kg   e) 7.6 kg   h) 0.1 kg
c) 7.045 kg   f) 7.8923 kg   i) 0.456 kg

4 Change each of these volumes into millilitres (multiply by 1000).

a) 6.4 L   d) 6.4735 L   g) 0.0001 L   j) 0.000 25 L
b) 6.47 L   e) 0.01 L   h) 1.0001 L
c) 6.473 L   f) 0.001 L   i) 0.00 234 L

Division of decimals by 10, 100 and 1000

Examples

1. Change 654 millimetres into centimetres.

$654 \div 10 = 65.4$

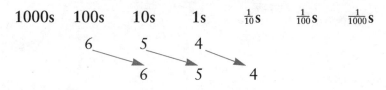

1000s	100s	10s	1s	$\frac{1}{10}$s	$\frac{1}{100}$s	$\frac{1}{1000}$s
	6	5	4			
		6	5	4		

2. Change 45 centimetres into metres.

$45 \div 100 = 0.45$

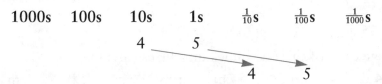

1000s	100s	10s	1s	$\frac{1}{10}$s	$\frac{1}{100}$s	$\frac{1}{1000}$s
		4	5			
				4	5	

3. Change 178.3 centimetres into metres.

$178.3 \div 100 = 1.783$

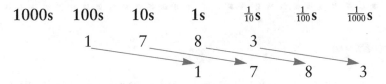

1000s	100s	10s	1s	$\frac{1}{10}$s	$\frac{1}{100}$s	$\frac{1}{1000}$s
	1	7	8	3		
		1	7	8	3	

4. Change 1.4 grams into kilograms.

$1.4 \div 1000 = 0.0014$ kilograms

1000s	100s	10s	1s	$\frac{1}{10}$s	$\frac{1}{100}$s	$\frac{1}{1000}$s	$\frac{1}{10000}$s
			1	4			
						1	4

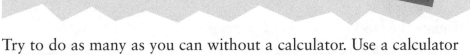

PAUSE

Try to do as many as you can without a calculator. Use a calculator to check your work.

1 Change each of these lengths into centimetres (divide by 10).

a) 17 mm   d) 8.9 mm   g) 78.5 mm   j) 0.6 mm
b) 1.7 mm   e) 93.2 mm   h) 785 mm
c) 0.17 mm   f) 7.85 mm   i) 0.785 mm

2 Change each of these lengths into metres (divide by 100).

a) 245 cm   d) 12.3 cm   g) 1.2 cm   j) 8652 cm
b) 200 cm   e) 8.95 cm   h) 5.7 cm
c) 45 cm   f) 1.557 cm   i) 7355 cm

3 Change each of these weights into kilograms (divide by 1000).

a) 1237 g   d) 823 g   g) 16.6 g   j) 7.3 g

b) 1657 g   e) 76 g   h) 100 g

c) 7045 g   f) 78 923 g   i) 10 g

4 Change each of these volumes into litres (divide by 1000).

a) 6.4 cm^3 d) 6473.5 cm^3 g) 300 cm^3 j) 650 cm^3

b) 6.47 cm^3 e) 0.01 cm^3 h) 70 cm^3

c) 6 cm^3 f) 0.001 cm^3 i) 5000 cm^3

Weekly wages

People who earn a *weekly wage* are paid a fixed rate for each hour they work.

Example

Claire works 34 hours at a rate of £4.20 per hour. Calculate her weekly wage.

$$\text{weekly wage} = 34 \times £4.20 = £142.80$$

PAUSE

Calculate the weekly wage in each case:

1 28 hours at £4.15 per hour   6 36 hours at £2.75 per hour

2 35 hours at £4.80 per hour   7 32 hours at £5.60 per hour

3 16 hours at £3.50 per hour   8 18 hours at £4.50 per hour

4 18 hours at £2.90 per hour   9 22 hours at £7.22 per hour

5 40 hours at £5.31 per hour   10 27 hours at £4.23 per hour

Overtime

Jemma Hill works for a catalogue company and is paid £3.80 per hour. If she works more than 40 hours in a week she is paid for each extra hour at a higher *overtime rate*. This rate is calculated by multiplying her normal hourly rate by 1.5. This is how her wages are calculated in a week when she works 44 hours:

Basic	40 × £3.80 = £152
Overtime	4 × 1.5 × £3.80 = £22.80
Total	weekly wage = £152 + £22.80 = £174.80

An overtime rate like this is often called 'time and a half'. Other overtime rates may be 'time and a quarter' (basic rate × 1.25) or 'double time' (basic rate × 2). People are also paid overtime rates for working at weekends or during public holidays.

Example

Surbajit Singh works as a driver. He is paid £4.50 per hour for each hour he works from Monday to Saturday. If he works more than 40 hours he is paid overtime at a rate of 'time and a half'. If he works on Sunday he is paid overtime at a rate of 'double time'. Calculate his wage in a week when he works 46 hours from Monday to Saturday and 5 hours on Sunday.

Basic	40 × £4.50 = £180
Overtime	6 × 1.5 × £4.50 = £40.50
Sunday	5 × 2 × £4.50 = £45
Total	weekly wage = £180 + £40.50 + £45 = £265.50

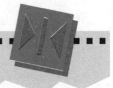

PAUSE

A company pays its workers £4.80 per hour for a basic 40 hour week from Monday to Saturday. Overtime is paid at a rate of 'time and a half'. Any work on Sunday is paid at an overtime rate of 'double time'.

Calculate each persons' wage:

	Name	Hours worked Monday to Saturday	Hours worked Sunday
1	Mr Smith	38	2
2	Ms Brown	40	3
3	Ms Jones	43	0
4	Mr Black	48	1
5	Mr Patel	42	3
6	Ms Hodgson	35	6
7	Ms Dearman	48	4
8	Mr Williams	46	5
9	Ms Toms	51	2
10	Mr Baines	34	10

Mixed problems

PAUSE

1 Megan paints plates in a factory.

She earns 16p each for the first 300 plates she paints in one week.

a) Calculate the total amount she earns for the first 300 plates.

She earns 22p each for every plate more than 300 she paints in the same week One week she earned £74.84.

b) Calculate the total number of plates she painted in that week.

(ULEAC)

2

> **ASSISTANT COOK**
> **£3.22 per hour**
> To work 28 hours per week at the
> Chuter Ede Primary School,
> Wolfit Avenue.

a) Work out the Assistant Cook's full weekly wage.

b) Work out the Assistant Cook's yearly wage if she works
38 weeks each year. (ULEAC)

3 Sally and Charles are asked to work out 2.175^2.
Their calculator display shows:

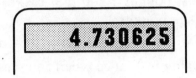

Sally gives the answer as 4.7.

Charles gives the number correct to three decimal places.

Write down his answer. (SEG)

4 During October, a central heating boiler was used, on average, for 4.5 hours per day.

During November, the same boiler was used, on average, for 5.8 hours per day.

a) Calculate the total time for which the boiler was used during October and November.

While it is being used the boiler uses 2.44 litres of oil per hour.

b) Calculate the amount of oil used during the two months, correct to the nearest litre. (NICCEA)

■ ■

Imperial units

Imperial units were used in the UK until the 1970s when the country started to change to metric units. Many people still think and work in imperial units.

These are the main Imperial tables:

	Imperial measures	Approximate metric equivalents
Length	12 inches = 1 foot 3 feet = 1 yard 1760 yards = 1 mile	1 inch = 2.54 centimetres 1 foot = 30.48 centimetres, 1 yard = 0.91 metres 5 miles = 8 kilometres
Weight	16 ounces = 1 pound	2.2 pounds = 1 kilogram
Volume	8 pints = 1 gallon	1.76 pints = 1 litre, 1 gallon = 4.55 litres

Examples

1. Mr Brown has just bought a 10 kg bag of weedkiller for his lawn. How many pounds of weedkiller has he bought?

$$10 \times 2.2 = 22 \text{ pounds of weedkiller}$$

2. Mrs Brown has just bought a 100 pint cask of beer. How many litres of beer has she bought?

$$100 \div 1.76 = 56.82 \text{ litres (correct to two decimal places)}$$

3. Jenny Jones is driving in France when she sees this sign:

PARIS 272 km

How far is she from Paris?

$$272 \div 8 \times 5 = 170 \text{ miles}$$

4. Jack is an old carpenter who prefers to work in feet and inches. He is asked to build a framework 80 cm wide by 150 cm high. What are these measurements in inches?

$$80 \div 2.54 = 31.5 \text{ inches (to one decimal place)}$$
$$150 \div 2.54 = 59.1 \text{ inches (to one decimal place)}$$

PAUSE

1 Mr Smith is buying lawn seed. The type he is interested in comes in 1 kg, 2 kg, 5 kg, 15 kg and 20 kg sizes. Mr Smith can't think in kilograms and wants to know what these weights are in pounds. Convert all these sizes into pounds for Mr Smith.

2 Mrs Baker did a milk round and had always delivered milk in pint bottles. She wanted to check her prices against those in a supermarket which sold milk in litre containers. To help she asked her daughter to complete this table for her.

Pints	1	2	3	4	5	6	7	8	9	10
Litres										

Pints	10	20	30	40	50	60	70	80	90	100
Litres										

Copy and complete the table, giving all your answers correct to two decimal places.

3 Convert all these French road signs into miles.

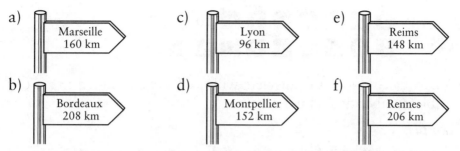

a) Marseille 160 km
b) Bordeaux 208 km
c) Lyon 96 km
d) Montpellier 152 km
e) Reims 148 km
f) Rennes 206 km

4 Jack the carpenter uses these tables to help him convert metric measurements into imperial units but they are covered with grease.

Centimetres	5	10	15	20	25	30
Inches	2.0	3.9				

Centimetres	30.5	61.0				
Feet	1	2	3	4	5	6

Write out some new tables for Jack.

Decimal arithmetic with a calculator

Decimal arithmetic is usually carried out with a calculator. We check our calculator answers with inverse operations.

Examples

1. 3.45 + 12.07

  3 . **4 5** **+** **1 2** . **0 7** **=** 15.52

Check **1 5** . **5 2** **−** **1 2** . **0 7** **=** 3.45

2. 56.9 − 1.99

  5 6 . **9** **−** **1** . **9 9** **=** 54.91

Check **5 4** . **9 1** **+** **1** . **9 9** **=** 56.9

3. 37.8 × 0.27

  3 7 . **8** **×** **0** . **2 7** **=** 10.206

Check **1 0** . **2 0 6** **÷** **0** . **2 7** **=** 37.8

59

4. $27 \div 2.5$

2 7 ÷ 2 . 5 = 10.8

Check   1 0 . 8 × 2 . 5 = 27

In many calculations the answers will need to be rounded to a sensible number of decimal places.

Examples

1. Find the cost of 0.25 kg of cheese if the the cheese costs £4.67 a kilogram.

$$0.25 \times 4.67 = 1.1675$$

But £1.1675 is not a real amount of money so we round the answer to two decimal places.

$$\text{Cost of cheese} = £1.17$$

2. A 2 kilogram cake is shared by 12 people, what weight of cake do they each eat?

$$2 \div 12 = 0.1666667 \text{ (on an eight digit calculator)}$$

An answer like this is called a recurring decimal. The accurate answer is 0.16666666....... with the line of 6 digits going on for ever. This answer can be rounded to 0.2 or 0.17 or 0.167 or 0.1667 depending on the accuracy with which we require the answer.

3. A teacher books a coach for £350 pounds to take a party of 41 students to see a play. How much should each student pay for the coach?

$$350 \div 41 = 8.5365854 \text{ (on a eight digit calculator)}$$

Very long decimal answers like this are common. All decimal divisions must eventually divide out exactly or recur but may only do so after many decimal places. Long decimal answers are rounded to a sensible number of decimal places. In this case, £8.54.

Calculator practice:

1
a) 34.5+23.7+234.6
b) 456.1+678.9+234.9
c) 124.56+456.78+123.89
d) 4590.8+3400.73
e) 1.00234+12.3406
f) 98.456+29.6543
g) 67.048+523.336
h) 34.987+34.67+67.49
i) 23.8+84.9+58.2+41.9+34.8+87.3+78.9+99.9
j) 234.89+555.57+56+68+89.3+0.06+234.567
k) 3456.8−234.9
l) 345.67−234.89
m)78.93−18.564
n) 233.75−231.99
o) 4008.09−3678.54
p) 5916.34−4563.29
q) 98.456−38.439
r) 10 000.67−999.99
s) (23.45+67.89)−23.67
t) (34.5+56.8)−(27.89−16.4)

2
a) 3×0.3 c) 0.4×0.4 e) 0.8×0.1 g) 16×0.2 i) 250×0.4
b) 0.5×5 d) 0.8×7 f) 7×0.2 h) 80×0.5 j) $5 \times 0.2 \times 0.5$

3
a) 34.5×3 d) 34.5×0.3 g) $12.3 \div 5$ j) $459.6 \div 4$
b) 89.4×19 e) 89.4×1.9 h) $45.65 \div 2$ k) $345.98 \div 5$
c) 405.3×47 f) 40.53×4.7 i) $127 \div 8$ l) $1 \div 8$

4 Calculate correct to 1 decimal place.
a) 34.67×23 e) $23.89 \div 7$ i) $1 \div 11$ m)$15 \div 8$
b) 56.7×45 f) $23.78 \div 3.7$ j) $0.56 \div 0.7$ n) $27.3 \div 12.9$
c) 90.98×1.4 g) $78.95 \div 34.7$ k) $12 \div 9$ o) $66.7 \div 6.6$
d) $34.5 \div 3$ h) $13 \div 19$ l) 6.7×9.8 p) 12.58×11

5 Calculate correct to 2 decimal places.
a) 23.45×45.67 c) $0.67 \div 9$ e) $1.5 \times 1.5 \times 1.5$ g) $250 \div 57$
b) $23 \div 7$ d) $1.49 \div 1.7$ f) $3.4 \times 3.4 \times 3.4$ h) $12.31 \div 13.56$

6 Calculate, giving each answer to a sensible number of decimal places.
a) The cost of 3.7 metres of cloth at £5.99 a metre.

b) The amount each person should pay if 7 people are sharing equally a restaurant bill of £94.89.

c) The weight, in grams, of one marble if 25 marbles weigh 580 grams on a scale which is accurate to the nearest gram.

d) The cost of each pencil if a packet of twelve pencils costs £1.85.

e) The volume of wine in each glass if a 700 ml bottle of wine is shared equally between 6 glasses.

■■■

Using the memory and brackets on a calculator

Calculations like:

$$\frac{3.45+6.73}{7.22-3.56}$$

mean you must work out the top value and the bottom value. Then you divide the top value by the bottom value.

Calculations like this can be done on a calculator without writing anything down.

There are two ways to do this:

Method 1: If your calculator has a memory.

If a calculator has a memory there will be at least two keys to use it with.

One of these keys will be used to place the display number in the memory. The key may be marked:

M   **Min**   **STO**   or in some other way.

One of these keys will be used to return the number in the memory to the display. The key may be marked:

MR   **RCL**   or in some other way.

If we assume the keys are marked M and MR, the calculation above would be done like this:

7 **.** **2** **2** **−** **3** **.** **5** **6** **=** **M** **3** **.** **4** **5** **+** **6** **.** **7** **3** **=** **÷** **MR** **=** 2.7814207

Notice that the calculation was started from the *bottom*.

Method 2: If your calculator has brackets.

If a calculator can use brackets there will be two keys marked **(** and **)**

The calculation is equivalent to $(3.45+6.73) \div (7.22-3.56)$ and it is entered in this way.

((3 . 4 5 + 6 . 7 3) ÷ ((7 . 2 2 − 3 . 5 6)) = **2.7814207**

■ ■ ■■ ■ ■ ■■ ■ ■ ■■ ■ ■ ■■ ■ ■ ■■ ■ ■ ■■ ■ ■ ■■ ■ ■■ ■ ■ ■ ■ ■ ■ ■ ■ ■ ■

PAUSE

Use either memory keys or bracket keys to complete these calculations, only writing down your final answer.
Give your answers to 3 decimal places where necessary.

1 $\dfrac{36+74}{23-5}$ 4 $\dfrac{5.6 \div 1.2}{2.7 \times 1.5}$ 7 $\dfrac{3.1 \times 5.5}{6.5 \div 3.7}$ 10 $\dfrac{5.67 \times 1.76}{67.3 \div 1.85}$

2 $\dfrac{56 \times 19}{27+57}$ 5 $\dfrac{3.6+5.4}{2.7-0.4}$ 8 $\dfrac{3.1 \times 2.5}{1.7 \div 0.5}$

3 $\dfrac{4.5 \times 4.5}{1.3-0.9}$ 6 $\dfrac{8.1 \div 0.7}{8.5 \times 2.3}$ 9 $\dfrac{3.67+5.78}{1.34-0.72}$

■ ■

Using the constant function on a calculator

We often need to repeat the same arithmetic with a list of numbers. For example, a plumber may need to complete this table.

Cost of labour + parts	Call out fee (£25)	VAT (17.5%)
£47		
£85		
£59		
£128		
£250		

To complete the middle column, the plumber needs to add £25 to *every* number in the first column, so he uses the *constant function* on his calculator.

Some calculators are different, but on his the plumber enters:

The plumber then enters all the other numbers like this:

4 **7** **=** 72

8 **5** **=** 110

5 **9** **=** 84

1 **2** **8** **=** 153

2 **5** **0** **=** 275

The table now looks like this:

Cost of labour + parts	Call out fee (£25)	VAT (17.5%)
£47	£72	
£85	£110	
£59	£84	
£128	£153	
£250	£275	

The plumber now needs to add the VAT. He knows that to do this he needs to multiply every number in the second column by 1.175. He enters:

1 **.** **1** **7** **5** **×** **=**

He then enters all the other numbers like this:

7 **2** **=** 84.6

1 **1** **0** **=** 129.25

8 **4** **=** 98.7

1 **5** **3** **=** 179.775

2 **7** **5** **=** 323.125

The table now looks like this:

Cost of labour + parts	Call out fee (£25)	VAT (17.5%)
£47	£72	£84.60
£85	£110	£129.25
£59	£84	£98.70
£128	£153	£179.78
£250	£275	£323.13

The plumber sometimes makes special offers. Once, he offered to reduce all bills by £12. To enter a constant subtraction of 12 on his calculator, the plumber enters:

– **–** **1** **2** **=**

Once, the plumber offered to supply all parts at half price. To enter a constant division by 2 on his calculator, the plumber enters:

÷ **÷** **2** **=**

PAUSE

Use the constant function on your calculator in every question.

1 This is a list of prices for 5 bouquets of flowers that a florist is to deliver.

£12.90, £15.34, £13.80, £24.55, £17.58

The florist makes a £3.72 charge for delivery. Write out the list of prices with the delivery charge added.

2 These are the banking charges that a bank asked 5 customers to pay.

£45.27, £8.95, £32.51, £43.99, £89.62

The bank discovered that, due to a computer error, £5.31 too much had been added to these charges. Write out a list of charges reduced by £5.31.

3 These are the bills that a shop has prepared for 5 customers.

£132, £140, £155, £178.60, £198.45

The shop is running a special offer to reduce all bills by 10%. This means each bill must be multiplied by 0.9. Write out a list of bills reduced by 10%.

4 These are a professional gardener's notes of how much fertilizer she usually adds to five different flower beds.

1.5 kg, 1.8 kg, 2.7 kg, 3.9 kg, 2.5 kg

She is using a new concentrated fertilizer which has these instructions:

'To calculate the new amount to use, divide the old amount you used by 3.'

Write out a list of the new amounts of fertilizer she needs to use on the five beds.

5 Copy and complete this table for the plumber.

Parts	Parts ÷ 2	Labour	Labour + parts ÷ 2	Call out fee (£25)	VAT (17.5%)	Special reduction (£12)
£32	£16	£80	£96	£121	£142.18	£130.18
£48		£89				
£64		£32				
£12		£50				
£86		£65				
£25		£37				
£59		£95				
£102		£86				
£155		£43				
£99		£99				
£128		£102				

■■

SECTION 5 Fractions

Fractions (sometimes called common fractions) were once an important method of calculation.

Calculators, computers and metric measurements have made decimal arithmetic so easy that fraction arithmetic is now rarely needed.

It is still important to have a basic understanding of fractions.

> '*Half* our students own a computer.'
>
> '*Nine tenths* of the crowd were well behaved.'
>
> 'She is entitled to *one fifth* of the profits.'

Understanding fractions

A common fraction is written as one number (the numerator) over another number (the denominator). Examples are:

$\frac{1}{2}$ shaded, $\frac{1}{2}$ unshaded

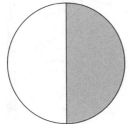

$\frac{3}{4}$ shaded, $\frac{1}{4}$ unshaded

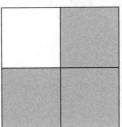

$\frac{5}{6}$ are one type of fish,

$\frac{1}{6}$ is another type of fish

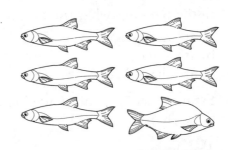

PAUSE

1 Write down the fraction shaded and the fraction unshaded in each of these pictures.

a)   c)   e)   g)   i)

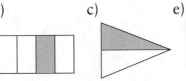

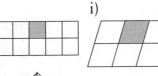

b)   d)   f)   h)   j)

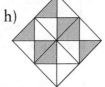

2 This is an abstract painting called 'shapes awake' by the artist Kram Yeldnib.

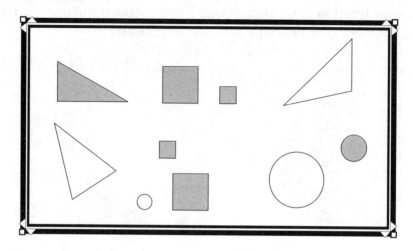

In the painting what fraction of the shapes
a) are triangles
b) are squares
c) are shaded
d) have straight sides
e) are not shaded?

3 Estimate the fraction shaded and the fraction unshaded in each of these shapes.

a)

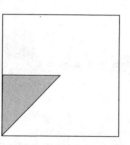

c)

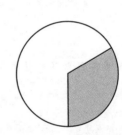

b)

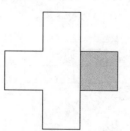

d)

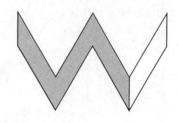

This diagram shows that $\frac{1}{2} = \frac{2}{4}$. Pairs of equal fractions like this are called *equivalent fractions*.

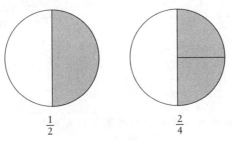

$\frac{1}{2}$ $\frac{2}{4}$

Example

What equivalent fractions are shown in this diagram?

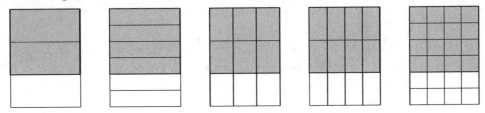

The fractions are $\frac{2}{3}$, $\frac{4}{6}$, $\frac{6}{9}$, $\frac{8}{12}$ and $\frac{16}{24}$.

PAUSE

What equivalent fractions are shown in each of these diagrams?

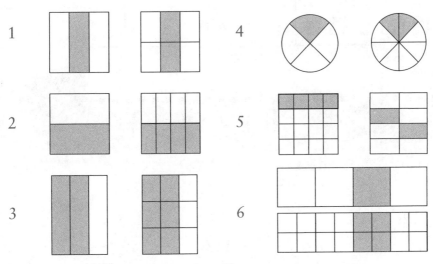

69

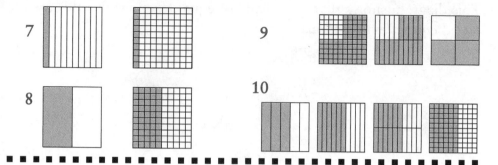

Simplifying fractions

Example

Simplify $\frac{24}{48}$ and $\frac{45}{85}$.

We simplify fractions by spotting common factors of the top and bottom numbers. Dividing by these common factors simplifies the fraction.

$$\frac{24}{48} \overset{\div 24}{\underset{\div 24}{=}} \frac{1}{2} \qquad \frac{45}{85} \overset{\div 5}{\underset{\div 5}{=}} \frac{9}{17}$$

Fractions can also be simplified by using a calculator with a fraction key $a^b/_c$.

Keys to press	Calculator display	Answer
2 **4** $a^b/_c$ **4** **8** **=**	1⌐2	$\frac{1}{2}$
4 **5** $a^b/_c$ **8** **5** **=**	9⌐17	$\frac{9}{17}$

PAUSE

1 Simplify:

a)

$$\frac{50}{70} \overset{\div 10}{\underset{\div 10}{=}} \frac{?}{?}$$

b)

$$\frac{25}{60} \overset{\div 5}{\underset{\div 5}{=}} \frac{?}{?}$$

c)

$$\frac{6}{9} \overset{\div ?}{\underset{\div ?}{=}} \frac{?}{?}$$

d) $\frac{5}{15}$ e) $\frac{4}{8}$ f) $\frac{9}{12}$ g) $\frac{11}{33}$ h) $\frac{30}{40}$ i) $\frac{7}{14}$

j) $\frac{10}{15}$ k) $\frac{100}{200}$ l) $\frac{25}{100}$ m) $\frac{18}{24}$ n) $\frac{25}{30}$ o) $\frac{16}{20}$

■ ■

One quantity as a fraction of another

Examples

1 What fraction of 1 hour is 25 minutes?

   25 minutes is $\frac{25}{60}$ or $\frac{5}{12}$ of one hour

2 What fraction of £1 is 64p?

   64p is $\frac{64}{100}$ or $\frac{16}{25}$ of £1

Keys to press	Calculator display	Answer
[2] [5] [aᵇ/c] [6] [0] [=]	5⌐12	$\frac{5}{12}$
[6] [4] [aᵇ/c] [1] [0] [0] [=]	16⌐25	$\frac{16}{25}$

■ ■

PAUSE

1 Look carefully at this diagram.

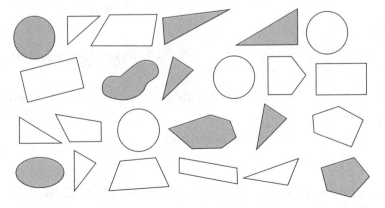

71

What fraction of the shapes are:

a) triangles,
b) quadrilaterals (4 sides),
c) pentagons (5 sides),
d) hexagons (6 sides),
e) circles,

f) drawn with straight lines,
g) either 3 sided or 4 sided,
h) shaded,
i) not shaded,
j) drawn with curved sides?

2 What fraction of 1 minute is:

a) 10 seconds,
b) 25 seconds,
c) 12 seconds,

d) 40 seconds,
e) 30 seconds,
f) 15 seconds?

3 What fraction of 1 hour is:

a) 6 minutes,
b) 50 minutes,
c) 42 minutes,

d) 35 minutes,
e) 45 minutes,
f) 20 minutes?

4 What fraction of a 24 hour day is:

a) 1 hour,
b) 4 hours,
c) 6 hours,
d) 8 hours,
e) 2 hours,

f) 12 hours,
g) 16 hours,
h) 18 hours,
i) 20 hours,
j) 5 hours?

5 What fraction of £1 is:

a) 25p,   c) 10p,   e) 85p,   g) 48p,   i) 2p,
b) 40p,   d) 50p,   f) 75p,   h) 4p,   j) 27p?

■■■■■■■■■■■■■■■■■■■■■■■■■■■■■■■■■■■

Fractions of quantities

Example

If $\frac{3}{5}$ of the 240 apples in a barrel are bad, how many good apples are there?

To calculate $\frac{3}{5}$ of 240, we first divide by 5 to find $\frac{1}{5}$ and then multiply by 3 to find $\frac{3}{5}$.

$$\frac{1}{5} \text{ of } 240 = 240 \div 5 = 48$$
$$\frac{3}{5} \text{ of } 240 = 48 \times 3 = 144$$

So, 144 apples are bad and therefore, 96 are good (240−144).

On a calculator:

 144

144 apples are bad, 96 are good.

PAUSE

1 Find:
   a) $\frac{1}{2}$ of 90
   b) i) $\frac{1}{4}$ of 48
      ii) $\frac{3}{4}$ of 48
   c) i) $\frac{1}{5}$ of 250
      ii) $\frac{2}{5}$ of 250
   d) i) $\frac{1}{7}$ of 91
      ii) $\frac{3}{7}$ of 91
   e) $\frac{4}{5}$ of 100
   f) $\frac{2}{3}$ of 24
   g) $\frac{3}{8}$ of 24
   h) $\frac{7}{9}$ of 81
   i) $\frac{35}{40}$ of 160
   j) $\frac{27}{80}$ of 360

2 There are 25 000 football supporters at a game and the police estimate that $\frac{7}{8}$ of them support the home team. Estimate how many support the away team.

3 Jean-Paul rents 2 videos a week and estimates that $\frac{2}{5}$ of the videos he rents are boring. How many boring videos does he hire in one year?

Adding and subtracting fractions

Examples

1. $\frac{1}{3} + \frac{3}{4}$

We need a number that 3 and 4 both divide into.

Multiples of 3: 3, 6, 9, ⑫ 15 .....
Multiples of 4: 4, 8, ⑫ 16 .....

We need to change both fractions to twelfths:

$$\frac{1}{3} \overset{\times 4}{=} \frac{4}{12} \qquad \frac{3}{4} \overset{\times 3}{=} \frac{9}{12}$$

$$\frac{1}{3} + \frac{3}{4} = \frac{4}{12} + \frac{9}{12} = \frac{13}{12} = 1\frac{1}{12}$$

Calculator sequence	Display	Answer
1 $a^{b/c}$ **3** **+** **3** $a^{b/c}$ **4** **=**	⊔ 1 ⊔12	$1\frac{1}{12}$

2. $\dfrac{7}{8}-\dfrac{5}{6}$

Multiples of 8: 8, 16, ㉔, 32, ...

Multiples of 6: 6, 12, 18, ㉔, 30, ...

We need to change both numbers to 24ths:

$$\overset{\times 3}{\underset{\times 3}{\frac{7}{8}}} = \frac{21}{24} \qquad\qquad \overset{\times 4}{\underset{\times 4}{\frac{5}{6}}} = \frac{20}{24}$$

$$\frac{7}{8}-\frac{5}{6} \quad = \quad \frac{21}{24}-\frac{20}{24} \quad = \quad \frac{1}{24}$$

Calculator sequence	Display	Answer
7 $a^{b/c}$ **8** **–** **5** $a^{b/c}$ **6** **=**	1⊔24	$\dfrac{1}{24}$

3. $1-\dfrac{2}{5}=\dfrac{5}{5}-\dfrac{2}{5}=\dfrac{3}{5}$

Calculator sequence	Display	Answer
	3⊔5	$\dfrac{3}{5}$

▪▪▪▪▪▪▪▪▪▪▪▪▪▪▪▪▪▪▪▪ PAUSE ◁◁ ▪▪▪

1 a) $\frac{2}{5}+\frac{1}{2}$ c) $\frac{1}{4}+\frac{3}{8}$ e) $\frac{1}{2}+\frac{2}{5}$ g) $\frac{1}{6}+\frac{3}{4}$

   b) $\frac{1}{4}+\frac{1}{3}$ d) $\frac{2}{3}+\frac{1}{4}$ f) $\frac{3}{7}+\frac{2}{5}$ h) $\frac{7}{8}+\frac{5}{6}$

2 a) $\frac{1}{2}-\frac{1}{3}$ c) $\frac{3}{4}-\frac{2}{3}$ e) $\frac{3}{8}-\frac{1}{4}$ g) $1-\frac{5}{6}$

   b) $\frac{1}{3}-\frac{1}{4}$ d) $\frac{5}{6}-\frac{1}{3}$ f) $\frac{5}{7}-\frac{3}{5}$ h) $2-\frac{5}{8}$

Multiplying and dividing fractions

Examples

1. $\dfrac{3}{4} \times \dfrac{1}{3} = \dfrac{3}{12} = \dfrac{1}{4}$

Calculator sequence	Display	Answer
3 $a^{b/c}$ **4** **×** **1** $a^{b/c}$ **3** **=**	1⌐4	$\dfrac{1}{4}$

2. $\dfrac{2}{3} \times 1\dfrac{1}{4} = \dfrac{2}{3} \times \dfrac{5}{4} = \dfrac{10}{12} = \dfrac{5}{6}$

Calculator sequence	Display	Answer
2 $a^{b/c}$ **3** **×** **1** $a^{b/c}$ **1** $a^{b/c}$ **4** **=**	5⌐6	$\dfrac{5}{6}$

3. $1\dfrac{2}{3} \div \dfrac{1}{4} = \dfrac{5}{3} \div \dfrac{1}{4} = \dfrac{5}{3} \times \dfrac{4}{1} = \dfrac{20}{3} = 6\dfrac{2}{3}$

*turn the fraction you are dividing
by upside down and multiply*

Calculator sequence	Display	Answer
1 $a^{b/c}$ **2** $a^{b/c}$ **3** **÷** **1** $a^{b/c}$ **4** **=**	6⌐2⌐3	$6\dfrac{2}{3}$

PAUSE

1 a) $\frac{1}{2} \times \frac{1}{3}$ c) $\frac{2}{3} \times \frac{1}{6}$ e) $1\frac{1}{2} \times \frac{1}{3}$ g) $\frac{3}{5} \times \frac{5}{6}$

  b) $\frac{1}{2} \times \frac{3}{4}$ d) $\frac{5}{6} \times \frac{2}{5}$ f) $\frac{1}{4} \times 2\frac{1}{2}$ h) $\frac{7}{8} \times 1\frac{1}{3}$

2 a) $\frac{1}{2} \div \frac{1}{4}$ c) $\frac{2}{3} \div \frac{1}{3}$ e) $\frac{3}{4} \div 4\frac{1}{2}$ g) $2 \div \frac{1}{3}$

  b) $\frac{1}{4} \div \frac{1}{8}$ d) $1\frac{1}{2} \div \frac{1}{2}$ f) $6 \div 1\frac{1}{2}$ h) $7 \div \frac{1}{4}$

Percentages and fractions

Percentages are a special way of writing fractions. Each percentage is a fraction with 100 as the bottom number.

For example:

$$25\% \text{ is the same as } \frac{25}{100} \quad \text{and } 66\% \text{ is the same as } \frac{66}{100}$$

Examples

1. Write 66% and 20% as fractions.

$$66\% = \frac{66}{100} = \frac{33}{50}$$
$$20\% = \frac{20}{100} = \frac{1}{5}$$

2. Write $\frac{4}{5}$ and $\frac{3}{4}$ as percentages.

To do this, we must change the bottom numbers of the fraction to 100.

$$\overset{\times 20}{\frac{4}{5}} = \underset{\times 20}{\frac{80}{100}} \quad \text{and} \quad \overset{\times 25}{\frac{3}{4}} = \underset{\times 25}{\frac{75}{100}}$$

So, $\frac{4}{5} = 80\%$ and $\frac{3}{4} = 75\%$

PAUSE

1 Write each of the following percentages as a fraction in its simplest form.

a) 25%   c) 68%   e) 64%   g) 40%   i) 32%
b) 60%   d) 90%   f) 99%   h) 15%   j) 95%

2 Write each fraction as a percentage.

a) $\frac{1}{2}$ c) $\frac{7}{10}$ e) $\frac{12}{25}$ g) $\frac{6}{25}$ i) $\frac{5}{10}$
b) $\frac{17}{20}$ d) $\frac{11}{20}$ f) $\frac{1}{10}$ h) $\frac{3}{25}$ j) $\frac{11}{25}$

3 By what fraction has the price been reduced in this special offer?

> GIFT SETS
> COTY, YARDLEY, LENTHÉRIC   UP TO 30% OFF
> SELECTED LINES

■■

Calculating a percentage of a quantity

Examples

1. There were 160 questions in a Maths test and Mary Jones obtained a mark of 45%. How many questions did she get right?

   We must calculate 45% of 160, to do this, we remember that 45% is the same as $\frac{45}{100}$.

   $$45\% \text{ of } 160 = \frac{45}{100} \text{ of } 160$$

   $$45\% \text{ of } 160 = 160 \div 100 \times 45 = 72$$

   Step 1: 160 ÷ 100   *Step 2*: × 45
   This finds $\frac{1}{100}$ or   This finds $\frac{45}{100}$ or
   1% of 160.   45% of 160.

   So, Mary got 72 answers correct out of 160.

2. A garage adds 17.5% VAT to the marked price on all the tyres that it sells. How much will a tyre marked with a price of £25.70 actually cost?

   $$17.5\% \text{ of } 25.7 = \frac{17.5}{100} \text{ of } 25.7$$

   $$17.5\% \text{ of } 25.7 = 25.7 \div 100 \times 17.5 = £4.4975$$

   £4.4975 to the nearest penny is £4.50, so the tyre costs
   £25.70 + £4.50 = £30.20

■■■■■■■■■■■■■■■■■■■■■■■■■■■■■■■■■■
PAUSE

1 Calculate:
a) 25% of 156   d) 90% of 855   g) 40% of £56.80
b) 60% of 145   e) 64% of 64   h) 15% of £45
c) 68% of 275   f) 99% of 2500   i) 32% of 45 kg

2 28% of Ms Mutton's monthly income of £1240 goes on mortgage repayments. How much does she pay each month?

3 Mr Asquith, the Labour candidate received 44% of the 28 000 votes cast. How many people voted for Mr Asquith?

4 A year ago, Ms Fox's house was worth £85 500. During the last year house prices have fallen by an average of 12%. Estimate the decrease in the value of Ms Fox's house.

5 Find the amount of VAT (at 17.5%) which will be added to the cost of the replacement window in this advertisement.

REPLACEMENT WINDOWS

EXAMPLE:

4ft x 3ft 6in Double Glazed Window with single top

opening in attractive maintenance-free uPVC.

FULLY FITTED (including sill)

ONLY £184 PLUS VAT

★ With Full 10 Year Guarantee.

■■■■■■■■■■■■■■■■■■■■■■■■■■■■■■■■■■■■

Writing one number as a percentage of another

Rule: To write one number as a percentage of another:
- form a fraction with the two numbers,
- divide the top number by the bottom number,
- multiply by 100.

Examples

1. Kim Ashton scored 72 correct marks out of a possible 80 in a Science test. What was Kim's percentage score?

As a fraction, Kim's score $= \dfrac{72}{80}$.

As a percentage, Kim's score $= 72 \div 80 \times 100 = 90\%$.

2. Write 45 as a percentage of 190.

Percentage $= 45 \div 190 \times 100 = 23.7\%$ (correct to one decimal place).

3. In one box of 240 apples, 36 are bad. In another box of 200 apples, 26 are bad. Which box has the better apples?

In the first box, the percentage of bad apples $=$
$$36 \div 240 \times 100 = 15\%.$$

78

In the second box the percentage of bad apples =
26 ÷ 200 × 100 = 13%.

The second box has the better apples.

4. What is the percentage reduction in price on this toolbox?

BLACK & DECKER
BDK202 Workshop Kit.
Cat. No. 710/4215.

£87.95
Sale Price

£77.95

The box originally cost £87.95 and has been reduced to £77.95, a cash reduction of £10. The percentage reduction is found by writing £10 as a percentage of £87.95.

Percentage reduction = 10 ÷ 87.95 × 100 = 11.4%
(correct to one decimal place).

PAUSE

1 Write:
   a) 8 as a percentage of 25,
   b) 34 as a percentage of 85,
   c) £1.25 as a percentage of £50,
   d) 42 as a percentage of 120,
   e) £5.25 as a percentage of £35,
   f) 48p as a percentage of 64p,
   g) £8.50 as a percentage of £25,
   h) 45 minutes as a percentage of 1 hour,
   i) 36p as a percentage of 45p,
   j) 14 grams as a percentage of 35 grams,
   k) 12 minutes as a percentage of 1 hour 36 minutes,
   l) 5.1 cm as a percentage of 6.8 cm.

2 These are the marks that a group of 20 pupils scored in a test with a maximum mark of 120.

| 43 | 56 | 78 | 89 | 94 | 96 | 102 | 112 | 65 | 105 |
| 84 | 22 | 17 | 68 | 72 | 118 | 88 | 71 | 59 | 60 |

Convert them to percentage marks, correct to the nearest 1%.

3 In one bag of potatoes, 3 out of 20 are rotten, in a second bag 5 out of 30 potatoes are rotten and in a third bag 7 out of 40 potatoes are rotten.

a) What is the percentage of rotten potatoes in each bag?
b) Which is the best bag?

4 In one school, 6 out of 10 teachers are female, in a second school 14 out of 25 teachers are female and in a third school 22 out of 50 teachers are male. Which school has the largest percentage of female staff?

5 Calculate the percentage reductions in price on each of these items:

a)

SWAN
Compact
Microwave Oven.
Cat. No. 420/8341.
£144.95
Sale Price
£134.95

c)

OLYMPUS
Supertrip Compact.
35 mm Camera.
Cat. No. 560/6100.
£54.95
Sale Price
£44.95

b)

BRITAX
"Babysure" Car Seat.
Cat. No. 375/2582.
£27.99
Sale Price
£22.99

6 A personal stereo was priced at £48. In a sale it was reduced to £42.

SALE
Was £48
Now £42

a) By what fraction was the original price reduced?
b) Write your fraction as a percentage.

(ULEAC)

7 When 15 oranges are bought individually the total cost is £1.20.
When 15 oranges are bought in a pack the cost is £1.14.
a) What is the percentage saving by buying the pack?

b) A special offer pack of these oranges has 20% extra free. How many extra oranges are in the special offer pack?

c) What fraction of the oranges in the special offer pack are free?

(SEG)

8

> ### Super Ace Games System
> Normal Price   £120
>
> Sale Price $\dfrac{1}{3}$ off

a) Work out the sale price of the Super Ace Games System.

> ### Mega Ace Games System
> Normal Price   £320
>
> Sale Price   £272

b) Find the percentage reduction on the Mega Ace Games System in the sale. (ULEAC)

9 Jimmy paid £120 for a CD player.

He sold it for £105.

What was his loss as a percentage of the price he paid?

(SEG)

Fractions, percentages and decimals

Fractions, percentages and decimals are all systems to represent part of a quantity.

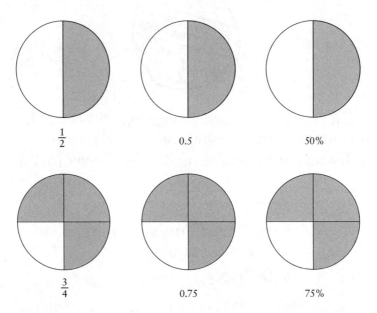

$\frac{1}{2}$ 0.5   50%

$\frac{3}{4}$ 0.75   75%

Rule: To change a fraction to a decimal, divide the top number by the bottom number.

Example

Change $\frac{2}{5}$ to a decimal:

$$2 \div 5 = 0.4$$

Rule: To change a decimal to a percentage, multiply by 100.

Example

Change 0.333 to a percentage:

$$0.333 = 33.3\%$$

Rule: To change a percentage to a fraction, write the percentage over 100 and simplify if possible.

Example

Change 65% to a fraction:

$$65\% = \frac{65}{100} = \frac{13}{20}$$

with $\div 5$ applied to top and bottom.

Any given fraction, percentage or decimal can always be converted to each of the other systems.

Examples

1. Starting with a fraction.

    Change $\frac{5}{8}$ to a decimal and a percentage.
    $$\frac{5}{8} = 5 \div 8 = 0.635$$
    $$0.625 = 62.5\%$$

2. Starting with a decimal.

    Change 0.85 to a percentage and a fraction.
    $$0.85 = 85\%$$

    $$85\% = \frac{85}{100} \overset{\div 5}{\underset{\div 5}{=}} \frac{17}{20}$$

3. Starting with a percentage.

    Change 68% to a fraction and a decimal.

    $$68\% = \frac{68}{100} \overset{\div 4}{\underset{\div 4}{=}} \frac{17}{25}$$

    $$68\% = 0.68$$

PAUSE

1 Change each of these fractions into decimals.

   a) $\frac{3}{4}$ c) $\frac{7}{8}$ e) $\frac{1}{2}$ g) $\frac{1}{4}$ i) $\frac{2}{3}$

   b) $\frac{4}{5}$ d) $\frac{9}{10}$ f) $\frac{1}{5}$ h) $\frac{3}{16}$ j) $\frac{1}{12}$

2 Convert each of the decimals obtained in question 1 into percentages.

3 Change each of these decimals into percentages.

   a) 0.1   c) 0.3   e) 0.64   g) 0.005   i) 0.5

   b) 0.8   d) 0.35   f) 0.08   h) 0.05   j) 0.375

4 Convert each of the percentages obtained in question 3 into fractions.

5 Change each of these percentages into fractions and decimals.
   a) 80%   c) 25%   e) 98%   g) 40%   i) 65%
   b) 32%   d) 70%   f) 55%   h) 48%   j) 50%

6 Convert these fractions to decimals. Use your answers to decide
   which is the bigger fraction in each pair.

   a) $\frac{1}{3}$ and $\frac{1}{4}$ b) $\frac{3}{4}$ and $\frac{4}{5}$ c) $\frac{3}{5}$ and $\frac{5}{6}$ d) $\frac{3}{7}$ and $\frac{5}{9}$ e) $\frac{2}{3}$ and $\frac{5}{7}$

7 In a nine carat gold ring $\frac{9}{24}$ of the weight is pure gold.
   What percentage of the weight of the ring is pure gold?   (SEG)

8 A cockroach has a reaction time of 54 thousandths of a second.
   a) Write the cockroach's reaction time as a fraction in figures.
      Give your answer in its lowest terms.
   b) Give your answer to part a) as a decimal fraction.   (ULEAC)

9 A college is offered a discount of $\frac{1}{8}$ if it pays within 1 week of
   receiving an invoice.
   a) Write $\frac{1}{8}$ as:
      i) a decimal,
      ii) a percentage.
   b) Calculate the amount to be paid by the college if an invoice for
      £4324.35 is paid within one week.
      Give your answer to the nearest penny.   (NEAB)

Simple interest

Banks and Building Societies pay *interest* on any money you save
with them.

The interest is paid each year as a percentage of the money you have
saved.

Example

The Mudshire Building Society pays 5% interest.

How much interest will Hannah Reeve earn if she saves £350 for one
year with the Society?

$$5\% \text{ of } 350 = \tfrac{5}{100} \text{ of } 350$$
$$5\% \text{ of } 350 = 350 \div 100 \times 5 = £17.50$$

Find the interest earned in each case.

1 £500 for one year at 3% interest.

2 £650 for one year at 4% interest.

3 £2000 for one year at 6% interest.

4 £140 for one year at 8% interest.

5 £900 for one year at 2.5% interest.

6 £2500 for one year at 4.8% interest.

7 £750 for one year at 3.2% interest.

8 £895 for one year at 2.9% interest.

9 £1280 for one year at 6.1% interest.

10 £1980 for one year at 5.25% interest.

Hire purchase

If you buy something on hire purchase you do not pay the full price immediately. You pay a *deposit*, usually based on a percentage of the full price. You then pay a number of weekly or monthly instalments. This is often more expensive than paying the full price immediately.

Example

A compact disc player can be bought for £299.99 cash or on hire puchase with a 10% deposit and 100 weekly payments of £2.90. Find the difference between the cash and hire purchase prices.

$$10\% \text{ of } £299.99 = 299.99 \div 100 \times 10 = £30.00$$

(to the nearest penny)

$$100 \times £2.90 = £290.00$$

$$\text{Hire purchase price} = £290.00 + £30.00 = £320.00$$

$$\text{Difference} = £320.00 - £299.99 = £20.01$$

PAUSE

Calculate in each question:

a) the hire purchase price,

b) the difference between the cash and hire purchase price.

	Item	Cash price	Deposit	Repayments
1	Cooker	£280	20%	50 of £5.70 each
2	Camera	£190	10%	24 of £8.45 each
3	Fridge	£350	10%	12 of £28 each
4	T.V.	£420	15%	24 of £15.20 each
5	Car	£3500	20%	36 of £81.25 each
6	Motor Bike	£1250	25%	24 of £44.21 each
7	Video Recorder	£399	10%	100 of £3.80 each
8	Chair	£180	20%	12 of £13.50 each
9	Computer	£1249	15%	36 of £32.44 each

SECTION 7 Ratio

Establishing and simplifying a ratio

A *ratio* is used to compare two or more numbers. For example, we may say

'the ratio of girls to boys in the class is 15 to 12 or 5 to 4'.

By this we mean that for every 5 girls in the group there are 4 boys. This is the same as to saying that the *fraction* of girls in the class is $\frac{5}{9}$. Fractions compare the separate parts into which an object is divided with the *whole object*. Ratios compare the separate parts into which an object is divided *with each other*. Ratios are often written with the word 'to' replaced by the symbol ' : '

The ratio of girls to boys in the class can be written as 5 : 4.

Ratios can be simplified in the same way as fractions.

Examples

1. Simplify the ratio 24 : 90.

   24 and 90 both divide by 6, so we can write:

$$24 : 90 = 4 : 15$$

2. Simplify the ratio 10 mm to 2 cm.

$$10\text{mm to } 2\text{cm} = 10 : 20$$
$$= 1 : 2$$

PAUSE

1 Simplify each of the following ratios

a) 4:6	g) 6:9	l) £2.50:£3.00
b) 12:16	h) 22:33	m) £2.50:£3.50
c) 6:30	i) 20:200	n) 20p:£1
d) 15:18	j) 15:30	o) 45 minutes:1 hour
e) 30:35	k) 1 cm to 1 metre	p) 60°:300°
f) 5:15		

2 Harry Loosealot likes to bet on horses. Last year, out of 250 bets, Harry won 50 times. What is the ratio of Harry's winning bets to his losing bets?

3 Out of 96 students in a school taking GCSE Mathematics, 12 fail. What is the ratio of passes to fails?

Dividing a quantity in a ratio

Ratios are often used to divide a quantity into parts.

Example

Divide 24 sweets between Bill and Belinda in the ratio 5 : 7.

We require 5+7 or 12 'shares':

$$24 \div 12 = 2$$
$$5 \times 2 = 10 \text{ sweets}$$
$$7 \times 2 = 14 \text{ sweets}$$

Bill gets 14 sweets and Belinda gets 14 sweets.

PAUSE

1 Divide 36 kg in the ratios:
   a) 1 : 2   d) 5 : 4   g) 1 : 11   j) 5 : 13
   b) 3 : 1   e) 2 : 7   h) 5 : 7   k) 1 : 2 : 3
   c) 5 : 1   f) 8 : 1   i) 17 : 1   l) 2 : 3 : 4

2 Divide £100 in the ratios:
   a) 3 : 1   d) 5 : 3   g) 1 : 9   j) 3 : 17
   b) 2 : 3   e) 7 : 1   h) 7 : 3   k) 3 : 3 : 4
   c) 1 : 4   f) 1 : 1   i) 19 : 1   l) 2 : 5 : 13

3 Mr Bilson has £300 worth of premium bonds and Mrs Bilson has
   £500 worth of premium bonds. They agree to share any winnings
   in the same ratio as the number of bonds they hold. How do they
   share a win of £25 000?

4 One sunny day, Jane and Jessica decide to sell squash from a stall.
   Jane buys £1.20 worth of ingredients and Jessica buys £1.80 worth
   of ingredients. They agree to share the takings in the same ratio as
   their contributions to the costs. How do they share total takings of
   £15.50? Do you think this is a fair way to share the takings?

Example

A stack of exercise books 20 cm high contains 24 books.

a) How many exercise books are there in a pile 30 cm high?
b) How high is a pile of 48 books?

a) A 20cm pile contains 24 books.
   A 10cm pile contains 12 books.
   A 30cm pile contains 24+12=36 books.

b) 24 books make a 20cm pile.
   48 books make a 20×2=40cm pile.

PAUSE

1 An orange drink has the instructions 'one part orange to six parts water'.

   a) How much water should be added to 50 ml of orange?
   b) What fraction of the dilute drink is water?

2 Here is a recipe for pastry:

   200 g flour
   100 g fat

   a) What fraction of the pastry is fat?
   b) If 300 g of fat is used, how much flour is needed?
   c) If 1000 g of flour is used, how much fat is needed?

3 This is a basic recipe for making an apple pie for 4 people.

   200 grams of flour
   50 grams of lard
   50 grams of butter
   500 grams of apples

   Change this recipe into one to make an apple pie for:

   a) 8 people,   c) 16 people,   e) 10 people,   g) 3 people,
   b) 12 people,   d) 6 people,   f) 2 people,   h) 1 person.

4 A stack of paper is 5 cm high and contains 250 sheets. How high will a stack be that contains:

   a) 500 sheets,   b) 750 sheets,   c) 1000 sheets?

5 To make a party fruit drink, Sally mixes 2 litres of apple juice with 3 litres of ginger ale. How much ginger ale would she mix with these quantities of apple juice:

   a) 4 litres   b) 6 litres   c) 8 litres   d) 3 litres   e) 1 litre?

Understanding negative numbers

On the centigrade temperature scale, the freezing point of water is 0° C. Temperatures on the earth's surface can range from 50° C below freezing to 40° C above freezing.

PAUSE

1 What temperatures are represented by each arrow on this scale?

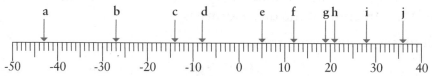

Changes in temperature

Examples

1. What is the change in temperature from arrow **c** to arrow **d** on the temperature scale?

   The temperature goes up 8°C between the arrows, so the change is +8°C.

   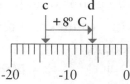

2. What is the change in temperature from arrow **d** to arrow **c** on the temperature scale?

   The temperature goes down 8°C between the arrows, so the change is –8°C.

   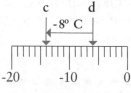

90

Ordering temperatures

The temperature scale can also be used to order temperatures.

Example

Write these temperatures in order, coldest first.

−15°C, 25°C, −20°C, 0°C, 8°C

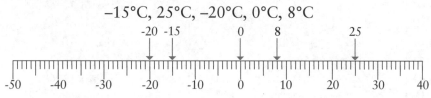

Answer: −20°C, −15°C, 0°C, 8°C, 25°C

PAUSE

What is the change in temperature between arrows:

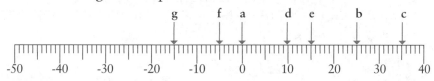

1 a and b   3 b and c   5 d and c   7 g and d
2 a and c   4 b and d   6 d and e   8 g and f

9 Write the temperatures in order, coldest first.
   a) 14°C, −4°C, −30°C, 25°C, −2°C
   b) −1°C, 18°C, −10°C, 16°C, 7°C
   c) 9°C, −5°C, −12°C, 8°C, 0°C
   d) 4°C, −14°C, 7°C, −8°C, −5°C
   e) −6°C, −13°C, −10°C, −20°C, 0°C

10 The table gives the temperature one night and also the temperature
   the next day. Find the rise in temperature in each case.

	Temperature at night	Temperature the next day
a)	2°C	14°C
b)	−1°C	7°C
c)	−15°C	−3°C
d)	−5°C	9°C
e)	−3°C	22°C
f)	−18°C	−6°C

11 The table gives the temperature one morning. It also gives the rise or fall in temperature later that day. Find the new temperature in each case.

	Temperature one morning	Rise or fall in temperature
a)	6°C	rise of 12°C
b)	−2°C	rise of 8°C
c)	−13°C	rise of 10°C
d)	5°C	fall of 9°C
e)	0°C	fall of 12°C
f)	−1°C	fall of 6°C

■ ■

Addition and subtraction of directed numbers

Remember the number line.

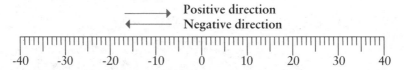

When adding or subtracting negative numbers:

start with a *position* on the number line,

make a *change in position* to obtain your answer.

$18+7=25$ (start at 18, make a change of 7 in the positive direction)

$18+-7=11$ (start at 18, make a change of 7 in the negative direction)

$-18+7=-11$ (start at −18, make a change of 7 in the positive direction)

$-18+-7=-25$ (start at −18, make a change of 7 in the negative direction)

$18-7=11$ (start at 18, make a change of 7 in the negative direction)

$-18-7=-25$ (start at −18, make a change of 7 in the negative direction)

When subtracting a negative number, change this double negative sign to a positive sign:

$$18--7=18+7=25$$
$$-18--7=-18+7=-11$$

1 Copy and complete:

$8+5=$	$-8+5=$	$8-5=$	$8--5=$
$8+-5=$	$-8+-5=$	$-8-5=$	$-8--5=$

2 Copy and complete:

$3+7=$	$-3+7=$	$3-7=$	$-3-7=$
$3+-7=$	$-3+-7=$	$3--7=$	$-3--7=$

When adding or subtracting negative numbers we can make use of the calculator key ⊬, which is used to enter negative numbers.

Examples

1. $18+-7=?$

   【1】【8】【+】【7】【⊬】【=】   11

   this is how –7 is entered

2. $-18+7=?$

   【1】【8】【⊬】【+】【7】【=】   –11

   this is how –18 is entered

3. $18--7=?$

   【1】【8】【–】【7】【⊬】【=】   25

   this is how –7 is entered

Use the ⊬ key or a number line to answer these.

1 Copy and complete:

$13+9=$	$-13+9=$	$13-9=$	$-13-9=$
$13+-9=$	$-13+-9=$	$13--9=$	$-13--9=$

2 Copy and complete:

$5+23=$	$-5+23=$	$5-23=$	$-5-23=$
$5+-23=$	$-5+-23=$	$5--23=$	$-5--23=$

■■■■■■■■■■■■■■■■■■■■■■■■■■■■■■■■■■■■■■

Multiplication and division of directed numbers

There is just one golden rule when multiplying or dividing directed numbers:

If the signs of the two numbers are the same, your answer will be positive, if the signs of the two numbers are different your answer will be negative.

Remember this and you can't go wrong but *don't* try to apply the rule to addition and subtraction!

Examples

Calculator sequences

$18 \times 6 = 108$	`1` `8` `×` `6` `=` 108
$18 \div 6 = 3$	`1` `8` `÷` `6` `=` 3
$-18 \times 6 = -108$	`1` `8` `+/-` `×` `6` `=` −108
$-18 \div 6 = -3$	`1` `8` `+/-` `÷` `6` `=` −3
$18 \times -6 = -108$	`1` `8` `×` `6` `+/-` `=` −108
$18 \div -6 = -3$	`1` `8` `÷` `6` `+/-` `=` −3
$-18 \times -6 = 108$	`1` `8` `+/-` `×` `6` `+/-` `=` 108
$-18 \div -6 = 3$	`1` `8` `+/-` `÷` `6` `+/-` `=` 3

■■■■■■■■■■■■■■■■■■■■■■■■■■■■■■ ■■■

PAUSE

1 Copy and complete:

$10 \times 5=$	$-10 \times 5=$	$10 \times -5=$	$-10 \times -5=$
$10 \div 5=$	$-10 \div 5=$	$10 \div -5=$	$-10 \div -5=$

2 Copy and complete:

$12 \times 8=$	$-12 \times 8=$	$12 \times -8=$	$-12 \times -8=$
$12 \div 8=$	$-12 \div 8=$	$12 \div -8=$	$-12 \div -8=$

3 Copy and complete:

$6.5 \times 5 =$ $-6.5 \times 5 =$ $6.5 \times -5 =$ $-6.5 \times -5 =$
$6.5 \div 5 =$ $-6.5 \div 5 =$ $6.5 \div -5 =$ $-6.5 \div -5 =$

4 Copy and complete:

$1.2 \times 0.4 =$ $-1.2 \times 0.4 =$ $1.2 \times -0.4 =$ $-1.2 \times -0.4 =$
$1.2 \div 0.4 =$ $-1.2 \div 0.4 =$ $1.2 \div -0.4 =$ $-1.2 \div -0.4 =$

■■■■■■■■■■■■■■■■■■■■■■■■■■■■■■■■■■■■

SECTION 9 Powers

Powers of numbers

There is a special way to write chain multiplications of the same number.

3×3 can be written as 3^2

3^2 is read as '3 squared'

$2 \times 2 \times 2$ can be written as 2^3

2^3 is read as '2 to the power 3'
or as '2 cubed'

$4 \times 4 \times 4 \times 4 \times 4 \times 4$ can be written as 4^6

4^6 is read as '4 to the power 6'

Examples

$$3^4 = 3 \times 3 \times 3 \times 3 = 81$$
$$2^5 = 2 \times 2 \times 2 \times 2 \times 2 = 32$$
$$5^2 = 5 \times 5 = 25$$

■■■■■■■■■■■■■■■■■■■■■■■■■■■■■ PAUSE ■■■

Calculate the value of:

1 3^5 3 8^2 5 7^4 7 9^3 9 0.9^2

2 5^3 4 2^8 6 4^7 8 2.5^3 10 1.1^5

■■■■■■■■■■■■■■■■■■■■■■■■■■■■■■■■■■■■

95

Example

Write as a single power of three, $3^3 \times 3^2$,
The calculation $3^3 \times 3^2$ means $(3 \times 3 \times 3) \times (3 \times 3)$,
this can be written as the single power 3^5.

PAUSE

1. Write each of these as a single power of the number.
  a) $2^2 \times 2^3$ b) $3^5 \times 3^4$ c) $4^7 \times 4^3$ d) $2^9 \times 2^2$

The  key on a calculator is useful for finding squares.

Examples

	Calculator sequence	Answer
5^2	**5** x^2	25
2.4^2	**2** **.** **4** x^2	5.76

PAUSE

1 Use x^2 to answer these.
  a) 9^2 c) 18^2 e) 20^2 g) 7.5^2 i) 0.6^2
  b) 12^2 d) 11^2 f) 15^2 h) 8.3^2 j) 0.25^2

Large numbers on a calculator

Calculator displays can be too small to show the answers to some calculations.

Example

$$4\,000\,000 \times 3\,000\,000 = 12\,000\,000\,000\,000$$

The calculator display shows 1.2 13 (Very basic calculators may show error).

This is the way the calculator shows 1.2×10^{13} or 1.2 times 10 thirteen times!

Examples

Write the numbers shown on these calculator displays as normal numbers.

1. 4.2 03   2. 2.7 06   3. 5.6 11

1. $4.2 \; 03 = 4.2 \times 10^3 = 4200$

2. $7 \; 06 = 7 \times 10^6 = 7\,000\,000$ 3. $5.6 \; 11 = 5.6 \times 10^{11} = 560\,000\,000\,000$

■ ◄

PAUSE

1 Write the numbers shown on these calculator displays as normal numbers.

a) 4 02   c) 8.4 06   e) 1.2 04   g) 6.4 06   i) 1.9 02   k) 6.7 04

b) 7 05   d) 9 11   f 3 10   h) 7.2 05   j) 5.6 03   l) 3 12

REWIND

1 One way to find all the prime numbers less than 100 was invented by the Ancient Greek mathematician Eratosthenes. His method is called 'The sieve of Eratosthenes'. Follow these steps which show how his method works.

a) Make a copy of this diagram.

```
 1  2  3  4  5  6  7  8  9 10
11 12 13 14 15 16 17 18 19 20
21 22 23 24 25 26 27 28 28 30
31 32 33 34 35 36 37 38 38 40
41 42 43 44 45 46 47 48 49 50
51 52 53 54 55 56 57 58 59 60
61 62 63 64 65 66 67 68 69 70
71 72 73 74 75 76 77 78 79 80
81 82 83 84 85 86 87 88 89 90
91 92 93 94 95 96 97 98 99 100
```

b) Cross out the number 1, which is not prime because it has only one factor.

c) Cross out all the multiples of 2, except 2 itself. i.e. 4, 6, 8, 10 ...

d) Cross out all the multiples of 3, except 3 itself.

e) Cross out all the multiples of 5, except 5 itself.

f) Cross out all the multiples of 7, except 7 itself.

g) Make a list of the remaining numbers. These are all the prime numbers less than 100.

2 List all the factors of:

a) 24   b) 51   c) 200

3 List all the factors of these numbers that are also prime numbers.

a) 30   b) 84   c) 105

4 Write down the first 12 square numbers.

5 Write down the first 12 rectangular numbers.

6 Write down the first 12 triangular numbers.

7 What is the value of:

a) $\sqrt{81}$ b) $\sqrt{49}$ c) $\sqrt{121}$?

8 Write this list of numbers

75, 134, 267, 348, 482, 591, 608, 771, 836, 945

a) correct to the nearest 10,   b) correct to the nearest 100.

9 Write this list of numbers

897, 1256, 2500, 3789, 4523, 5628, 6171, 7384, 8909, 9173

a) correct to the nearest 10,   c) correct to the nearest 1000.
b) correct to the nearest 100,

10 Estimate the answers to these, then work them out without a calculator.

a) 234+345   c) 345−268   e) 23×56   g) 1458÷27
b) 689+271   d) 451−99   f) 327×87   h) 678÷13

11 Write these lists of numbers in order.

a) 3.4, 6.7, 2.6, 5.4, 7.8, 9.1, 3.7, 2.6, 5.5, 4.0

b) 3.21, 3.25, 2.2, 3.3, 3.27, 3.26, 3.25, 2.28, 3.22, 3.29

c) 1.567, 1.562, 1.567, 1.569, 1.568, 1.563, 1.564, 1.5, 1.56, 1.57

12 Calculate without using a calculator:

a) $89 + 3.0$ c) $8.9 + 0.3$ e) $7.5 - 4.2$ g) $11.5 - 0.6$

b) $8.9 + 3$ d) $8.9 + 30$ f) $7.9 - 1.4$ h) $20 - 17.5$

13 Calculate:

a) $44.67 + 73.86$ c) $114.7 + 75.93$ e) $1376 - 754.56$

b) $523 + 97.9$ d) $33.89 - 13.4$ f) $5431.45 - 476.56$

14 Calculate:

a) $77.5 + 25.9 + 703.6$ c) $(13.956 + 7834.78) - 561.67$

b) $300.1 + 296.9 + 456.9$ d) $(19.65 + 45.78) - (25.65 - 11.97)$

15 Calculate:

a) 3×0.7 e) 0.5×0.2 i) $1000 - 34.7$

b) 0.8×4 f) 10×0.2 j) $10 - 0.96$

c) 0.6×0.6 g) 100×0.2 k) $1000 - 803$

d) 0.9×2 h) 1000×0.5 l) $100 - 0.012$

16 Calculate:

a) 55.5×3 c) 300.5×4.7 e) $17.5 - 8$

b) 23.4×19 d) 36.7×0.34 f) $5 - 0.347$

17 Calculate:

a) 34.67×23 c) 90.98×1.04 e) $23.89 - 7.1$

b) 56.7×45 d) $34.5 - 3$ f) $23.78 - 3.7$

18 Calculate correct to 1 decimal place:

a) $232 \div 7$ b) 3.4×5.7 c) $21.5 \div 6$ d) $18.9 \div 10.4$

19 Calculate correct to 2 decimal places:

a) 67.67×23.07 c) $0.127 \div 0.12$

b) $232 \div 7$ d) $2.34 \div 3.2$

20 Simplify:

a) $\dfrac{50}{60}$ b) $\dfrac{25}{70}$ c) $\dfrac{6}{15}$ d) $\dfrac{12}{18}$ e) $\dfrac{24}{36}$ f) $\dfrac{35}{75}$ g) $\dfrac{65}{75}$

21 Which is the larger of each of the following pairs of fractions:

a) $\dfrac{2}{7}$ and $\dfrac{3}{8}$,   b) $\dfrac{3}{5}$ and $\dfrac{4}{7}$,   c) $\dfrac{3}{50}$ and $\dfrac{5}{60}$?

22 Jane scored 93 out of 120 in an Art exam and 39 out of 50 in a Biology exam. In which exam did she do best?

Write the answers to questions 23 and 24 as fractions in their lowest terms.

23 What fraction of a 24 hour day is:

a) 3 hours, d) 9 hours, g) 14 hours,
b) 5 hours, e) 10 hours, h) 2 hours,
c) 6 hours, f) 12 hours, i) half an hour?

24 What fraction of £1 is:

a) 25p, b) 50p, c) 95p, d) 75p, e) 84p, f) 8p?

25 Calculate:

a) $\frac{3}{5}$ of 250 c) $\frac{3}{4}$ of 144 e) $\frac{4}{5}$ of 250 g) $\frac{3}{8}$ of 96
b) $\frac{1}{2}$ of 70 d) $\frac{3}{7}$ of 21 f) $\frac{2}{3}$ of 48 h) $\frac{7}{9}$ of 108

26 Write each of the following percentages as a fraction in its simplest form.

a) 25% b) 50% c) 56% d) 94% e) 32%

27 Write each fraction as a percentage:

a) $\frac{1}{2}$ b) $\frac{3}{4}$ c) $\frac{3}{10}$ d) $\frac{17}{20}$ e) $\frac{18}{25}$

28 Calculate:

a) 25% of 144 c) 68% of 325 e) 72% of 72
b) 60% of 230 d) 90% of 600 f) 99% of 10 000

29 Increase:

a) 300 by 20% c) £297 by 15% e) £18 493 by 8%
b) £80 by 15% d) £25 000 by 5% f) £1500 by 30%

30 Decrease:

a) 380 by 20% c) £310 by 20% e) £47 000 by 8%
b) £95 by 15% d) £39 000 by 5% f) 1100 by 12%

31 Write:

a) 16 as a percentage of 25
b) 51 as a percentage of 85
c) £12.25 as a percentage of £50
d) 36 as a percentage of 120
e) £5.25 as a percentage of £75
f) 60p as a percentage of 64p
g) £11.30 as a percentage of £25
h) 15 minutes as a percentage of 1 hour
i) 18p as a percentage of 45p
j) 21 grams as a percentage of 35 grams

32 Copy and complete this table.

Fraction	Percentage	Decimal
$\frac{1}{2}$	50%	0.5
		0.25
	75%	
$\frac{1}{5}$		
		0.1
	15%	
$\frac{3}{5}$		
		0.52
	4%	
$\frac{1}{20}$		

33 Simplify each of the following ratios:

a) 4 : 10   b) 12 : 18   c) 6 : 36   d) 15 : 21   e) 20 : 35

34 Divide 40 kg in the ratios:

a) 1 : 3   b) 4 : 1   c) 5 : 3   d) 7 : 1   e) 7 : 3

35 Divide £120 in the ratios:

a) 3 : 1   b) 2 : 3   c) 1 : 4   d) 15 : 9   e) 5 : 2 : 1

36 A pile of text books 40 cm high contains 25 books.

a) How many books are there in a pile 120 cm high?

b) How high is a pile containing 50 books?

37 Copy and complete.

$8+15=$ $8+-15=$ $7+12=$ $7+-12=$
$-8+15=$ $-8+-15=$ $-7+12=$ $-7+-12=$
$8-15=$ $8--15=$ $7-12=$ $7--12=$
$-8-15=$ $-8--15=$ $-7-12=$ $-7--12=$

38 Copy and complete.

$2 \times 5=$ $2 \div 5=$ $2.5 \times 10=$ $2.5 \div 10=$
$-2 \times 5=$ $-2 \div 5=$ $-2.5 \times 10=$ $-2.5 \div 10=$
$2 \times -5=$ $2 \div -5=$ $2.5 \times -10=$ $2.5 \div -10=$
$-2 \times -5=$ $-2 \div -5=$ $-2.5 \times -10=$ $-2.5 \div -10=$

39 Find the value of:

a) 4^6 b) 2^5 c) 10^5 d) 10^4

40 Write each of the following calculations as a single power of the number.

a) $2^4 \times 2^3$ b) $3^7 \times 3^2$ c) $10^5 \times 10^4$

41 Write the numbers shown on these calculator displays as normal numbers.

a) 5 03   b) 7.2 04   c) 9 08   d) 1.6 11

■ ■

FASTFORWARD

1   8   9   10   11   12

a) Which of the five numbers is a square number?
b) Which of the five numbers is a factor of 27?
c) Which of the five numbers is a multiple of six?
d) Which of the five numbers is a prime number?   (ULEAC)

2   8,   12,   15,   16,   18,   19,   20,   21,   24,   32

From the ten numbers listed above select:

a) a prime number,
b) a perfect square,
c) a multiple of 7,
d) the square root of 64,
e) a factor of 30,
f) the next term in the sequence 3, 4, 6, 9, 13, ...   (MEG)

3 To build an extension to a house, Brickie Builders charge a price of £350 per square metre of floor space plus £1000.

Calculate the cost of an extension of 40 square metres of floor space.   (MEG)

4 A school is planning a disco for 936 pupils.
Each pupil will be given 1 can of drink.
Cans of drink are sold in trays of 24.

Work out how many trays of drinks will be needed. Do not use a calculator, show all your working.   (ULEAC)

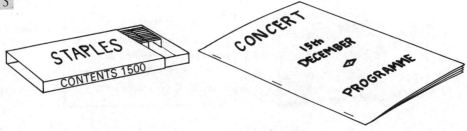

5

David stapled programmes for the school concert. He needed 3 staples for each programme.

He wasted 2 staples (which got bent) for every 35 programmes he stapled.

How many programmes did he staple from a box containing 1,500 staples? (NICCEA)

6 Flour costs 48p per kilogram. Brett bought 205 kg and shared it equally among 14 people. He calculated that each person should pay £0.72.

Without using a calculator, use a rough estimate to check whether this answer is about the right size. *You must show all your working.* (SEG)

7 a) Copy the diagram which shows a mineral water bottle.
Draw the approximate water level on the bottle, if it is three-quarters full.

b) Bottles of mineral water cost 39p each.
Estimate the cost of 142 bottles.
Show how you obtained your estimate.

c) Without using a calculator, work out the *exact* cost of 142 bottles of mineral water at 39p each.
(You must write down enough working to show that you did not use a calculator). (MEG)

CASH PRICE £275
or Hire Purchase 20% deposit of
cash price followed by 24 equal
monthly instalments of £13
or £7.50 per month rental.

22 inch colour T.V.
Full guarantee on parts
and labour for 4 years.

a) How much deposit is required for the Hire Purchase agreement?

b) What is the total cost of buying the television on Hire Purchase?

c) How much is required for 6 months rental?

d) What is the total cost of renting the television for 4 complete years? (SEG)

9 a) Use your calculator to find the value of

$$\frac{730 \times 8.45 \times 7}{83 \times 9}$$

and write down the full calculator display.

b) Express your answer correct to one place of decimals.

(NEAB)

10 a) A girl earns £3.16 an hour as a part-time waitress. If she works for 5 hours, how much does she earn?

b) A boy works in a shop on one day from 9.30 a.m. to 12.30 p.m. and from 1.15 p.m. to 4.45 p.m. He is paid £18.98.
   i) How long does he work?
   ii) How much is he paid per hour? (MEG)

11 In a factory, 214 of the workers all earn the same weekly wage. If their total weekly wage bill is £63 065.80, how much does each worker earn? (MEG)

12 John, Mary and Majid charge for baby-sitting. Their charges are given in the table.

For each hour (or part of an hour) before midnight	For each hour (or part of an hour) after midnight
£1.50	£2.10

Work out the amount earned when:

a) John sat for 3 hours before midnight.

b) Mary sat from 9 o'clock at night until 1 o'clock the following morning.

c) Majid sat from 18.00 to 21.20.   (ULEAC)

13 Packing cases weigh 28 kg each. 25 of the cases are loaded on to a lift. The weight limit for the lift is 750 kg. How much short of the limit is the load on the lift?   (ULEAC)

14

FLOWER'S GARAGE

Phone Carmouth 2345   Main Rd.
                                                  Carmouth
                                                       £

		£
Parts	4 spark plugs at 79p each	a) ....
	b) .... brake pads at £4.52 each	9.04
	4 tyres at c) .... each	98.00
	1 only exhaust system	41.30
	Total cost of parts	d) ....
Labour	4½ hours at £11.00 per hour	e) ....
	Total cost of parts and labour	f) ....
VAT at 17½%		35.18
TOTAL TO PAY		g) ....

A customer received a bill from Flower's Garage. Some of the figures could not be read.

Fill in the spaces marked a) to g) with the correct figures.

(ULEAC)

15 The picture shows a 5 litre can of oil. 1 litre is about $1\frac{3}{4}$ pints.

   a) Write $1\frac{3}{4}$ as a decimal.
   b) Find the number of pints
      of oil in the 5 litre can.

(MEG)

16 $\frac{7}{8}$ of an iceberg is under water.

   a) What is this as a decimal?
   b) What percentage of an
      iceberg can be seen?

(MEG)

17 A school has 840 pupils. $\frac{3}{10}$ of them live less than 1 mile from school. 45% of them live between 1 mile and 3 miles from school. The rest live more than 3 miles from school.

   a) How many pupils live less than 1 mile from school?
   b) What percentage of the pupils live more than 3 miles from
      school?   (ULEAC)

18 Copy and complete the following weekly wage slip.

Name: M. J. Thomas	Date: 6/5/88
Wages	£
40 hours at £4.60 per hour	....
Overtime 6 hours at £6.90 per hour	....
Total Wage (gross)	....
Deductions	
National Insurance	16.56
Superannuation	11.04
Income Tax	48.76
Total Deductions	....
Wage (net amount) Take-home pay	....

(WJEC)

19

The sweets in a box are classed as creams, caramels or toffees. In a box of Keely's Choice, $\frac{3}{8}$ of the contents are creams, $\frac{1}{4}$ of them are caramels and the remainder are toffees.

a) Work out the fraction of the sweets in the box that are either creams or caramels.
b) What fraction of the sweets in the box are toffees?
c) There are 24 sweets in the box. Work out the number of caramels in the box. (ULEAC)

20

A saline drip in a hospital releases 0.1 ml every 3 seconds. How long does it take to empty a 500ml bag? (WJEC)

21 Margaret and David want to find out how much petrol their car uses in miles per gallon. They fill the car with petrol when the reading on the milometer is:

0	2	8	3	4	0

After a few days they stop at a garage selling petrol at £1.70 per gallon. They fill the car up again and the cost of the petrol is £13.60.

By this time the milometer reading is:

0	2	8	6	2	0

How many miles per gallon does the car do over this period?

(WJEC)

22 Taking 8 kilometres per hour to be 5 miles per hour, find
   a) the speed in kilometres per hour equivalent to the British speed limit of 30 miles per hour,
   b) the speed in miles per hour equivalent to the French speed limit of 60 kilometres per hour. (MEG)

23 A machine always works at the same rate. It produces 150 rods in 5 minutes. How long will it take to produce 375 rods? (SEG)

24 'Alpha Cars' offers a Sierra for hire at £15 a day plus 5p per kilometre. How much would it cost Mr Jones to hire the Sierra for a day and drive 240 kilometres? (SEG)

25 Zenka wants to buy her father a packet of electric drill bits for his birthday. In the first packet that she looks at, there are four different drills and their sizes are marked in inches.

The sizes are $\frac{3}{8}$, $\frac{1}{4}$, $\frac{1}{2}$ and $\frac{1}{8}$

a) Which is the larger size drill bit, $\frac{3}{8}$ or $\frac{1}{4}$?
b) Write the four sizes in order, starting with the smallest.

(NEAB)

26 Joan divides her pocket money into three parts. She spends one third of it on makeup. She spends three-fifths of it on magazines. The rest is saved.

a) What fraction of her pocket money is saved?

b) If she saves 6p each week, how much pocket money does she receive? (SEG)

27 Peter earns £5 per week by working on Saturday mornings. He saves 60% of his wage.

a) How much does he save each week?

b) Given that he spends $\frac{1}{4}$ of the rest on a weekly magazine, how much does this magazine cost him? (SEG)

28 Bill Jones's salary was £950 per month. His boss gave him a salary increase of 8%.

a) Calculate 8% of £950.

b) What was his new salary per month? (SEG)

29 Use your calculator to complete the following calculations:

a) $\dfrac{7.2 \times 2.9}{14.4} = \dfrac{\rule{2cm}{0.4pt}}{14.4} = \ldots\ldots$

b) $(8.1)^2 \div 24 = \ldots\ldots \div 24 = \ldots\ldots$ (SEG)

30 The rate of exchange is 2.95 German Marks to £1 sterling.

a) A tourist changes £25 into Marks. How many Marks would she receive?

b) She pays 42 Marks for a gift to bring home. What is the cost of the gift in pounds and pence to the nearest penny? (SEG)

31 The basic price of a camera is £35. VAT is added at the rate of 17.5%. Calculate the amount to be paid for the camera. (MEG)

32

a) Calculate the reduction in the price of the camera.

b) What is this reduction as a percentage of the normal price?

SALE
35mm Camera
was £39.95
Now £31.96

(NEAB)

33 At the beginning of 1987 a house was valued at £49 500. During 1987 the prices of houses in the area went up by 13%. What was the house worth at the end of 1987? (NEAB)

34 Sarah Jones earns £720 per month.

a) Calculate how much Sarah earns in a year.

b) Her tax allowances for the year are £3400. Calculate her taxable income for the year.

c) The rate of tax is 27% of her taxable income. Calculate the amount of income tax Sarah pays in a year. (WJEC)

35 David wants to buy a television. He can buy a Beovision (the best set there is) for £345 with 12 months free credit or a basic Flan for £295. SUPPOSE he pays £59 deposit on the Beovision and then 11 equal monthly instalments.

a) How much is left to pay after the deposit?

b) How much is each of the 11 instalments?

IF he wants to buy the Flan, he has to pay 20% deposit.

c) What is 20% of £295?

d) How much is left to pay?

Interest is charged on the balance at $16\frac{1}{2}$%.

e) How much is left to pay including the interest?

This has to be paid in 11 instalments.

f) How much is each instalment?

g) Which television would you advise David to buy, and why?

(MEG)

36 John has a full-time job and lives with his parents. He pays them one-fifth of his wages for housekeeping.

a) How much does he pay his parents if he earns £80 a week?

b) John receives a 7% pay rise.

  i) How much extra will he earn each week?

  ii) What is the total weekly amount that he will now pay to his parents? (MEG)

37 Rachel is to buy a new stereo system, costing £240, on an interest free credit scheme.

a) She must pay a 25% deposit. How much is this?

b) How much is left to pay after she has paid the deposit?

c) How much are her monthly payments, if she pays the remainder in six equal monthly payments? (ULEAC)

38 'Electric Kettle: Special Offer 15% off marked price.' The marked price is £27.95. How much would you pay, to the nearest penny, at the 'special offer' price? (ULEAC)

39 Of the total land area of Belgium, 1.4 million hectares is cultivated and six hundred thousand hectares is forest.

a) Write both these numbers in figures.

b) The total land area of Belgium is 3 million hectares. What area of land is neither cultivated nor forest? (MEG)

40 **PARKES TYRES**

Tyres	Cost
145×12	£19.85 each
155×13	£16.50 each
185/60	£37.50 each

Work out the cost of four 155×13 tyres. (ULEAC)

41 In 1972 India had 100 251 000 houses and a population of 638 389 000. How many people were there to each house? Give your answer to the nearest whole number. (MEG)

42 Three friends are using their calculators.

a) Mari multiplies two numbers. The answer is 3.6. Write down *two* numbers she could have multiplied together.

b) John subtracts one number from another. The answer is 4.2. Write down *two* numbers he could have used.

c) Lena divides £14.30 by 3. The answer appears as:

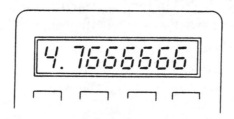

Write down the answer correct to the nearest penny. (WJEC)

43 Each member of Melchester Diners' Club has to pay an annual subscription of £45 and a fee of £5.50 at each meeting attended. The Club has 42 meetings each year.

a) Find the total cost of a year's membership for a member who attends all 42 meetings.

b) To retain membership, a member must attend at least 60% of the year's meetings. Find the minimum number of meetings that a member can attend in a year and still retain membership.

c) Calculate to the nearest penny, the average cost per meeting for a member who attends 32 meetings in the year. (MEG)

44 A recipe for blackcurrant ice cream to serve 4 people is

> 400 g blackcurrants
> 160 g sugar
> 140 ml cream
> 90 ml water

Write down the amounts that you would require to make a similar ice cream to serve 6 people. (MEG)

45

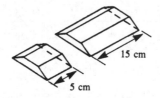

A 20 cm ruler is cut into two pieces 5 cm and 15 cm long. The piece 5 cm long weighs 3 grams. What is the weight of the 15 cm piece? (SEG)

46

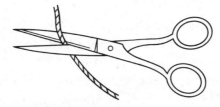

A piece of string is 36 cm long. John cuts it into two pieces, making one piece twice as long as the other. What are the lengths of the two pieces? (SEG)

47 Don has 120 records. The ratio of the number of Don's records to the number of Phil's record is 3:5. How many records does Phil have? (ULEAC)

48 There are 180 pupils in the first year at Bronglais Comprehensive School. The ratio of the number of boys to the number of girls in the first year is 5:4. How many girls are in the first year? (WJEC)

49 To make a shade of orange paint, a decorator mixes yellow and red paint in the ratio of 1 to 3.

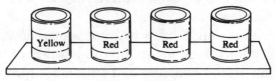

How many tins of yellow paint are needed to mix with 12 tins of red paint? (MEG)

50 Ms Woosnam is planning her GCSE Social Studies course. The marks for the course are divided in the ratio 3:2 between coursework and the written examination. She has 65 lessons to teach and decides to allocate them in the same ratio as the marks. Find the number of lessons that she should devote to coursework and to preparing for the written examination. (MEG)

51 A gang of workers is digging a trench. When there are six workers they manage to dig a trench 18 m long in one day. All the workers dig at the same rate.
   a) Work out the length of trench that one worker could dig in one day.
   b) A group of workers digs 12 m in one day. How many workers are there in the group? (ULEAC)

52 In Wiltshire during one day in February the lowest temperature recorded was – 7°C and the highest temperature was 8°C. What was the temperature difference? (SEG)

53 At 2 a.m., the temperature was – 10°C Celsius. At 5 a.m., the temperature was – 3° Celsius.
   a) At which time was the temperature higher?
   b) What is the difference between the two temperatures? (MEG)

54 a) At noon on a January day the temperature was 3°C. By 6 p.m. it had fallen by 5°C. What was the temperature at 6 p.m.?
   b) At midnight the temperature was – 7°C. By how many degrees had the temperature fallen between noon and midnight? (MEG)

55

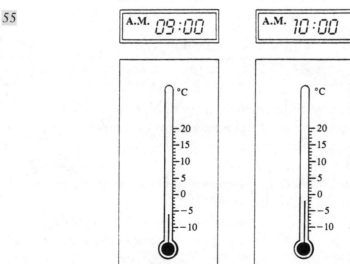

A freezer is switched off at 0900 in order to defrost it. The diagrams show the temperatures in the freezer at 0900 and one hour later at 1000.

a) What is the temperature in the freezer when it is switched off?
b) By how much does the temperature rise in the hour between 0900 and 1000?
c) The temperature rises by the same amount in the next hour. What is the temperature at 1100? (WJEC)

The weather map shows that the temperature in England is –2°C.

a) Calculate the temperature in Scotland if it is 5°C colder than in England.
b) Calculate the temperature in Ireland if it is 6°C warmer than in England. (ULEAC)

57 This table gives the temperature in Sheffield during one week in January 1987.

Day	Sun	Mon	Tues	Wed	Thurs	Fri	Sat
Noon	– 3°C	– 2°C	1°C	– 3°C	2°C	3°C	– 2°C
Midnight	– 8°C	– 8°C	– 6°C	– 10°C	– 6°C	– 3°C	– 5°C

a) What is the lowest temperature in the table?
b) On which day was there the biggest drop in temperature between noon and midnight?
c) How much was this drop?
d) What was the least rise in temperature between midnight one day and noon the following day?
e) On the next Sunday the temperature was 8° higher at noon than at midnight the previous night. What was the temperature at noon? (MEG)

Algebra

Algebra is a branch of mathematics developed by Hindu and Moslem mathematicians.

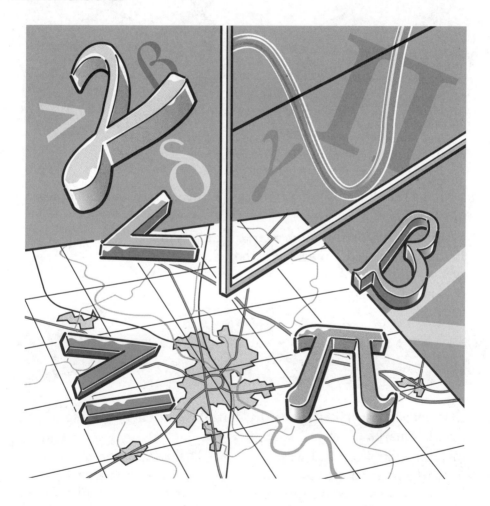

The word algebra was first used by the Arab mathematician Alkarismi in the ninth century.

Using letters to represent numbers

John is playing marbles with Vali, Ben and Hitesh. This picture shows the number of marbles in each person's bag.

We can write this information more simply if we let the letter *m* stand for the number of marbles in John's bag.

Example

In a Maths test, Susan scored *p* marks. Write each of these people's marks using *p*.

a) Wendy, who scored 6 more marks than Susan.

b) Errol, who scored 5 marks less than Susan.

a) Wendy scored $p+6$ marks.

b) Errol scored $p-5$ marks.

PAUSE

1 In a Science test, Hitesh scored *y* marks. Write each of these people's marks using *y*.

   a) John, who scored 21 less marks than Hitesh.

   b) Tom, who scored 11 more marks than Hitesh.

   c) Dick, who scored 1 less marks than Hitesh.

   d) Harry, who scored 5 less marks than Hitesh.

2 Sharon has *x* plants in her garden. Write each of these people's number of plants using *x*.

a) Wendy, who has 7 more
   plants than Sharon.
b) Kimberly, who has 13 more
   plants than Sharon.
c) Nadia, who has 7 less
   plants than Sharon.
d) Shelly, who has 13 less
   plants than Sharon.

After playing a game, the number of marbles owned by each person changes:

We can write this information more simply if we let the letter r stand for the number of marbles in John's bag.

In algebra we usually do not use the multiplication sign.

$2 \times r$ is written as $2r$ (never as $r2$).

In algebra divisions are usually shown by putting one number over another.

$r \div 2$ is written as $\frac{r}{2}$

Examples

1. Sheila, Alan, Sally and Jonathan all collect stamps. Sheila has k stamps. Write each of these people's marks using k.

   a) Alan, who has 2 times as many stamps as Sheila.

   b) Sally, who has Sheila's number of stamps divided by 5.

   c) Jonathan, who has 20 less stamps than Alan.

   a) Alan has $2k$ stamps.

   b) Sally has $\frac{k}{5}$ stamps.

   c) Jonathan has $2k-20$ stamps.

2. Write as simply as possible:

   a) 4 times s

   b) t divided by 7

   c) 6 more than b

   d) 12 less than z

   e) 20 divided by h

   f) v less than 8

117

a) $4s$

b) $\frac{t}{7}$

c) $b+6$

d) $z-12$

e) $\frac{20}{b}$

f) $8-v$

PAUSE

1 Mr Brown's car is worth c pounds. Write the price of each person's car using c.

a) Ms White's car is worth 3 times as much as Mr Brown's car.
b) Ms Green's car is worth Mr Brown's car's value divided by 3.
c) Mr Violet's car is worth 200 pounds less than Ms Green's car.
d) Ms Black's car is worth 250 pounds more than Ms White's car.

2 Greg Allen earns n pounds each week. Write what each of these people earn each week using n.

a) Janice Beesley who earns 3 times as much as Greg.
b) Ruth Nicholl who earns Greg's wage divided by 2.
c) Daphne Hicks who earns 25 pounds a week more than Janice.
d) Jo Seddon who earns 15 pounds less a week than Ruth.
e) Kathy Hobday who earns 30 pounds less a week than Janice.
f) Chris Whitney who earns 12 pounds more each week than Ruth.
g) Ian Goodall who earns 20 pounds less each week than Chris.
h) David Sheppard who earns 45 pounds more a week than Kathy.

3 Write as simply as possible:

a) 3 more than e
b) 18 less than v
c) 5 times w
d) w divided by 5
e) 5 divided by w
f) v less than 18
g) 12 times d
h) 13 more than y
i) t divided by 2
j) 2 divided by t
k) 2 less than m
l) m less than 2

Writing rules (simple formulae)

There are 12 pencils in a box.

118

How many pencils are there in:

a) 2 boxes   b) 5 boxes   c) b boxes

a) number of pencils = $12 \times 2 = 24$ c) number of pencils = $12 \times b = 12b$
b) number of pencils = $12 \times 5 = 60$

In words we can write the rule:

the number of pencils = $12 \times$ the number of boxes.

This is called a *formula* for working out the number of pencils in any number of boxes.

Let n represent the number of pencils and b represent the number of boxes. We can write the formula *in symbol form* like this:

$$n = 12b$$

Examples

1. A plumber is called out for a lot of emergencies. He charges a call out fee of £20 which he adds to the cost of any repairs he does.
   A formula for working out the plumber's total charge is:

   total charge(t) = cost of repairs(r) + £20

   a) Work out the total charge if the cost of repairs is:
      i) £50   ii) £135
   b) Write this formula in symbol form, using the letters in the brackets.

   a) i) total charge = 50 + 20 = £70   ii) total charge = 135 + 20 = £155
   b) $t = r + 20$

2. Jane works in a supermarket. To work out her weekly wage she uses the formula:

$$\text{wages}(w) = \text{number}(n) \text{ of hours worked} \times £5$$

a) Work out her weekly wage if she works:

   i) 20 hours   ii) 35 hours

b) Write this formula in symbol form, using the letters in the brackets.

a) i) wage = $20 \times 5 = £100$ ii) wage = $35 \times 5 = £175$

b) $w = 5n$

PAUSE

1 When making a pot of tea for a group of people, Mr Mitchell uses the formula:

number of tea bags(b) = number of people$(p) + 1$

a) Work out the number of tea bags used for:

   i) 2 people   ii) 3 people   iii) 4 people   iv) 5 people

b) Write this formula in symbol form, using the letters in the brackets.

2 A baker works out the number of rolls needed to fill bags of two dozen rolls. He uses the formula:

number of rolls(r) needed = number of bags$(b) \times 24$

a) Work out the number of rolls needed to fill:

   i) 2 bags   ii) 5 bags   iii) 10 bags   iv) 24 bags

b) Write this formula in symbol form, using the letters in the brackets.

3 A theatre has 500 seats. The manager works out the number of tickets left to sell using this formula:

number(n) of tickets left to sell = $500 -$ number of tickets sold(s)

a) Work out the number of tickets left to sell if the manager has sold:

   i) 40 tickets   ii) 100 tickets   iii) 231 tickets   iv) 449 tickets

b) Write this formula in symbol form, using the letters in the brackets.

4 A lottery syndicate of 12 people agree to share any winnings using the formula:

each person's share(s) = amount won(w) ÷ 12

a) Work out each person's share if the amount won is:

    i) £144   ii) £6000   iii) £8858.40   iv) £125 783

b) Write this formula in symbol form, using the letters in the brackets.

5 Mrs Bellamy is looking at chilled meals in a supermarket. She uses this formula to work out the cost of buying a particular chilled meal for her family.

      cost(c) of meal for family = cost of single meal(m) × 5

a) Work out the cost of a family meal if a single meal costs:

    i) £3.00   ii) £2.50   iii) £1.78   iv) £1.99

b) Write this formula in symbol form, using the letters in the brackets.

6 A restaurant adds a £3 service charge onto the cost of meals. The total bill is worked out with the formula:

      total(t) bill = cost of the meals(m) + £3

a) Work out the total bill if the cost of the meals is:

    i) £24   ii) £60   iii) £38.50   iv) £47.78

b) Write this formula in symbol form, using the letters in the brackets.

7 A football club pays £60 to hire a mini-bus each time they play an away game. Some players travel in their own cars. The treasurer works out what each player must pay to use the bus using the formula:

cost(c) of using bus = £60 ÷ number(n) travelling on the bus

a) Work out what each player must pay if:

    i) 12 use the bus   iii) 8 use the bus
    ii) 10 use the bus   iv) 11 use the bus

b) Write this formula in symbol form, using the letters in the brackets.

8 Sam Brown works in a factory. Each week she gives her mother £40 out of her wages towards the housekeeping. She uses this formula to work out how much she has left.

amount left(l) = wages(w) − £40

a) Work out how much Sam has left in a week when she earns:

    i) £280   ii) £230   iii) £229.50   iv) £267.86

b) Write this formula in symbol form, using the letters in the brackets.

Extending the use of letters to represent numbers

Examples

1. A factory supervisor uses this formula to work out each person's wage.

    wage(w) = number of hours(h) worked × rate(r) per hour

   a) Work out the wage of somebody who:

      i) works for 35 hours at £4.50 per hour,   ii) works for 40 hours at £3.80 per hour.

   b) Write this formula in symbol form, using the letters in the brackets.

   a) i) wage = 35 × £4.50 = £157.50   ii) wage = 40 × £3.80 = £152.00

   b) $w = hr$

2. A shop stocks two brands of crisps, Walker's and Smith's. The shopkeeper makes a profit of 2p for each bag of Walker's crisps sold and a 3p profit for each bag of Smith's crisps sold. The shopkeeper uses this formula to work out the total profit on crisps.

    total profit(p) = 2 × number of bags of Walker's(w) sold + 3 × number of bags of Smiths's(s) sold

   a) Work out the total profit if the shopkeeper sells:

      i) 200 bags of Walker's and 300 bags of Smith's,

      ii) 300 bags of Walker's and 200 bags of Smith's.

   b) Write this formula in symbol form, using the letters in the brackets.

   a) i) total profit = 2 × 200 + 3 × 300 = 1300p = £13.00

      ii) total profit = 2 × 300 + 3 × 200 = 1200p = £12.00

   b) $p = 2w + 3s$

3. A student works out the volume of a cube using this formula:

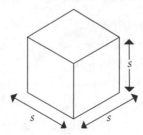

Volume(V) = side length (s) × side length (s) × side length (s)

122

a) Work out the volume of a cube with a side length of:
   i) 2 cm   ii) 5 cm
b) Write this formula in symbol form, using the letters in the brackets.
a) i) Volume $= 2 \times 2 \times 2 = 8$ cubic centimetres
   ii) Volume $= 5 \times 5 \times 5 = 125$ cubic centimetres
b) $V = s \times s \times s$, which is written as $V = s^3$

PAUSE

1 A student works out the perimeter of a rectangle using this formula:

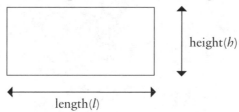

$$\text{Perimeter}(p) = 2 \times \text{length}(l) + 2 \times \text{height}(h)$$

a) Work out the perimeter of a rectangle with:
   i) length $= 5$ cm, height $= 2$ cm
   ii) length $= 14$ cm, height $= 4$ cm
   iii) length $= 8$ cm, height $= 2.5$ cm
   iv) length $= 22.8$ cm, height $= 8.4$ cm
b) Write this formula in symbol form, using the letters in the brackets.

2 A teacher is organising a trip to the theatre. A 53 seater coach will cost £225 and each ticket will cost £12. She uses this formula to work out the total cost of the trip.

total cost$(t) = 12 \times$ number going$(n) + 225$

a) Work out the total cost of the trip if:
   i) 30 pupils go   ii) 40 pupils go   iii) 45 pupils go.
b) Write this formula in symbol form, using the letters in the brackets.

3 To work out the cost per pupil for a theatre trip a teacher uses the formula:

cost per person$(p) = 225 \div$ number going$(n) + 12$

a) Work out the cost per person of the trip if:
   i) 30 pupils go   ii) 40 pupils go   iii) 45 pupils go.

b) Write this formula in symbol form, using the letters in the brackets.

4 Shelly is doing a sponsored swim. She uses this formula to work out how much each sponsor might owe her.

amount(*a*) owed = number(*n*) of lengths swum ×
amount sponsored(*s*) per length

a) Work out how much is owed if:
   i) She swims 100 lengths sponsored at £1.50 per length.
   ii) She swims 50 lengths sponsored at £2.50 per length.
b) Write this formula in symbol form, using the letters in the brackets.

5 A market gardener sells plants in trays of various sizes.

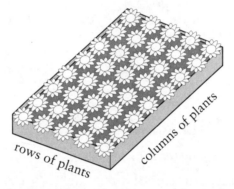

She uses this formula to work out how many plants there are in a tray.
number of plants(*p*) = number in each row(*r*) ×
number in each column (*c*)

a) Work out how many plants there are in a tray with:
   i) 3 rows and 4 columns   iii) 5 rows and 8 columns
   ii) 6 rows and 6 columns   iv) 8 columns and 5 rows
b) Write this formula in symbol form, using the letters in the brackets.

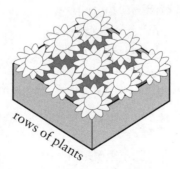

6 Another market gardener always sells plants in square trays of various sizes.

He uses this formula to work out how many plants there are in a tray.

number of plants(p) = number in each row$(r) \times$ number in each row (r)

a) Work out how many plants there are in a tray with:

    i) 3 rows   ii) 5 rows   iii) 8 rows   iv) 4 rows

b) Write this formula in symbol form, using the letters in the brackets.

7 A toy manufacturer sells wooden bricks in packs of various sizes like this:

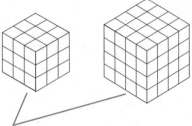

Number of bricks in a row

This is the formula used to work out how many bricks there are in each pack:

number of bricks(b) = number in a row$(r) \times$
number in a row$(r) \times$ number in a row(r)

a) Work out how many bricks there are in a pack with this number of bricks in each row:

    i) 3 bricks   ii) 4 bricks   iii) 5 bricks   iv) 8 bricks

b) Write this formula in symbol form, using the letters in the brackets.

■ ■

Substituting values for letters

Example

If $p = 15$, find the value of:

a) $p + 7$ b) $p - 12$ c) $20 - p$

a) $p + 7 = 15 + 7 = 22$ b) $p - 12 = 15 - 12 = 3$ c) $20 - p = 20 - 15 = 5$

■ ■ ■

PAUSE

1 If $p = 25$ find the value of:

    a) $p + 8$ b) $p - 12$ c) $p + 50$ d) $50 - p$ e) $25 - p$

2 If $x = 3$ find the value of:

   a) $x + 10$ b) $10 - x$ c) $x - 2$ d) $x + 2$ e) $x + x$

3 If $y = 19$ find the value of:

   a) $y + 11$ b) $y - 11$ c) $y + 31$ d) $31 - y$ e) $y + y + y$

4 If $n = 30$ find the value of:

   a) $n - 25$ b) $n + 25$ c) $n - 13$ d) $n + 13$ e) $47 - n$

5 If $q = 7$ find the value of:

   a) $q + 7$ b) $q + q$ c) $q + 14$ d) $q + q + q$ e) $28 - q$

■■■■■■■■■■■■■■■■■■■■■■■■■■■■■■■■■■■■■

Example

   If $z = 20$, find the value of:

   a) $2z$ b) $2z + 5$ c) $\frac{z}{10}$ d) $\frac{z}{5} - 2$

   a) $2z = 2 \times 20 = 40$ c) $\frac{z}{10} = \frac{20}{10} = 2$

   b) $2z + 5 = 2 \times 20 + 5$ d) $\frac{z}{5} - 2 = \frac{20}{5} - 2$

   $\qquad\qquad = 40 + 5$ $\qquad\qquad = 4 - 2$

   $\qquad\qquad = 45$ $\qquad\qquad = 2$

■■■■■■■■■■■■■■■■■■■■■■■■■■■■■■■ ■■■

PAUSE

1 If $y = 4$ find the value of:

   a) $3y$ d) $\frac{y}{2} + 7$

   b) $3y - 6$ e) $\frac{5y}{10}$

   c) $\frac{y}{2}$

2 If $m = 12$ find the value of:

   a) $5m$ d) $\frac{m}{3} - 3$

   b) $2m + 1$ e) $\frac{5m}{6}$

   c) $\frac{m}{4}$

3 If $t = 20$ find the value of:

   a) $\frac{t}{5}$ d) $\frac{7t}{10}$

   b) $3t$ e) $\frac{t}{4} + 22$

   c) $50 - 2t$

4 If $p = 10$ find the value of:

   a) $5p - 1$ d) $\frac{5}{p}$

   b) $5p + 1$ e) $\frac{p}{2} + 7$

   c) $\frac{p}{5}$

■■■■■■■■■■■■■■■■■■■■■■■■■■■■■■■■■■■■■

Examples

If $m=5$ and $n=8$, find the value of:

a) $3m$ b) mn c) m^3 d) $3m^2n$ e) $3m+2n$

a) $3m=3\times5$
   $=15$

b) $mn=5\times8$
   $=40$

c) $m^3=5\times5\times5$
   $=125$

d) $3m^2n=3\times5\times5\times8$
   $=600$

e) $3m+2n=3\times5+2\times8$
   $=15+16$
   $=31$

PAUSE

1 If $x=5$, $y=6$ and $z=3$ find the value of:

a) $3x+2y$ g) yz m) x^2

b) $2x+3y$ h) $2xy$ n) $3x^2$

c) $5x+17$ i) $3xz$ o) y^3

d) $6x$ j) $4yz$ p) z^4

e) xy k) $\dfrac{10}{x}$ q) x^2y

f) xz l) $\dfrac{y}{z}$

2 If $a=4$, $b=5$ and $c=2$, find the value of:

a) $a+b$ h) $2ac$

b) $b-c$ i) ab^2

c) $a+b+c$ j) a^2+c^2

d) $2a+3b$ k) $ab+c$

e) $5c-2b$ l) $ab+ac$

f) ab m) $2ac+b$

g) abc n) $ac+2b$

Substitution which involves adding and subtracting negative numbers

Remember the number line.

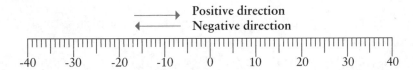

When adding or subtracting negative numbers:
- Start with *a position* on the number line.
- Make a *change in position* to obtain your answer.

$18+7 \ =25$ (start at 18, make a change of 7 in the positive direction)

$18+-7 \ =11$ (start at 18, make a change of 7 in the negative direction)

$-18+7 = -11$ (start at -18, make a change of 7 in the positive direction)

$-18+-7 = -25$ (start at -18, make a change of 7 in the negative direction)

$18-7 = 11$ (start at 18, make a change of 7 in the negative direction)

$-18-7 = -25$ (start at -18, make a change of 7 in the negative direction)

Example

If $p=-5$, find the value of:

a) $p+7$ b) $p-12$

a) $p+7=-5+7=2$ b) $p-12=-5-12=-17$

PAUSE

1 If $p=-25$ find the value of:
   a) $p+8$ d) $50+p$
   b) $p-12$ e) $25+p$
   c) $p+50$

2 If $x=-3$ find the value of:
   a) $x+10$ d) $x+2$
   b) $10+x$ e) $x+x$
   c) $x-2$

3 If $y=-19$ find the value of:
   a) $y+11$ d) $31+y$
   b) $y-11$ e) $y+y+y$
   c) $y+31$

4 If $t=-40$ find the value of:
   a) $t+40$ d) $30+t$
   b) $t-40$ e) $t+t+40$
   c) $t+t$

Substitution which involves multiplying and dividing negative numbers

Remember, there is just one golden rule when multiplying or dividing directed numbers.

If the signs of the two numbers are the same, your answer will be positive, if the signs of the two numbers are different your answer will be negative.

Remember this and you can't go wrong but *don't* try to apply the rule to addition and subtraction! We can apply these rules to the following examples:

$$18\times6=108 \qquad\qquad 18\times-6=-108$$
$$18\div6=3 \qquad\qquad 18\div-6=-3$$

$$-18\times6=-108$$
$$-18\div6=-3$$

$$-18\times-6=108$$
$$-18\div-6=3$$

Example

If $z=-20$, find the value of:

a) $2z$

b) $2z+5$

c) $\frac{z}{10}$

d) $\frac{z}{5}-2$

a) $2z = 2\times-20 = -40$

b) $2z+5 = 2\times-20 + 5$
$\qquad = -40+5$
$\qquad = -35$

c) $\frac{z}{10} = \frac{-20}{10} = -2$

d) $\frac{z}{5}-2 = \frac{-20}{5}-2$
$\qquad = -4-2$
$\qquad = -6$

PAUSE

1 If $y=-4$ find the value of:
   a) $3y$ c) $\frac{y}{2}$
   b) $3y-6$ d) $\frac{y}{2}+7$

2 If $m=-12$ find the value of:
   a) $5m$ c) $\frac{m}{4}$
   b) $2m+1$ d) $\frac{m}{3}-3$

3 If $x=-8$ find the value of:
   a) $3x+4$ c) $\frac{40}{x}$
   b) $4x+3$ d) $\frac{x}{4}$

4 If $a=-25$ find the value of:
   a) $4a-100$ c) $\frac{a}{5}-3$
   b) $100-2a$ d) $\frac{2a}{10}$

Example

If $m=-5$ and $n=8$, find the values of:

a) $3m$

b) $3m+2n$

c) mn

d) m^2

a) $3m=3\times-5=-15$

b) $3m+2n=3\times-5+2\times8=-15+16=1$

c) $mn=-5\times8=-40$

d) $m^2=-5\times-5=-25$

PAUSE

1 If $x=5$, $y=-6$ and $z=-3$ find the value of:

   a) $3x+2y$ h) $3xz$
   b) $2x+3y$ i) $\dfrac{10}{x}$
   c) $5x+17$ j) x^2
   d) $6x$ k) $2x^2$
   e) xy l) $3x^2$
   f) xz m) y^2
   g) $2xy$ n) z^2

2 If $a=-4$, $b=5$ and $c=-2$, find the value of:

   a) $a+b$ h) b^2
   b) $b+c$ i) $3b^2$
   c) $a+b+c$ j) $2b^2$
   d) $2a+3b$ k) a^2
   e) $5c-2b$ l) c^2
   f) ab m) $3c^2$
   g) bc

Substitution in formulae

Formulae can be used to solve problems.

Example

A formula used to calculate the correct dose of medicine for a child older than 12 months is:

$$C=\frac{An}{n+12},$$

where, A is the adult dose, n is the child's age in years and C is the child's dose.

What is the correct dose of a medicine for a child aged 8 years if the adult's dose is 50 ml?

Substituting these values in the formula, we have:

$$C=\frac{50\times8}{8+12} \quad =\frac{400}{20} \quad =20 \text{ ml}$$

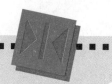

PAUSE

1 A formula to calculate an infant's (less than twelve months old) dose of a medicine is:

$$I = \frac{Am}{150},$$

where I is the infant's dose, A is the adult's dose and m is the infant's age in months.

Copy and complete this table up to 12 months to find an infant's dose when the adult dose is 75 ml:

m	Am	$I = \frac{Am}{150}$
1	75	0.5
2	150	1
3		

2 When an object is dropped from a height, the distance it has fallen and its velocity are given by the formulae:

$$s = 5t^2 \text{ and } v = 10t$$

s is the distance dropped (in metres), v is the velocity (in metres per second) and t is the time (in seconds).

a) The depth of a well can be found by dropping a stone and timing how long it takes to hit the water.
   Copy and complete this table.   .

Time taken for stone to drop(t seconds)	Depth of well ($5t^2$ metres)
1	5 metres
2	
3	
4	
5	

b) Copy and complete this table, showing the velocity with which the dropped stone will hit the water in the well.

Time taken for stone to drop(t seconds)	Velocity of stone ($10t$ metres per second)
1	10 metres per second
2	
3	
4	
5	

Simplification

A piece of mathematical shorthand like $3x+4y$, or $7m^2+9m$, is called an **expression**. The separate parts of an expression, like, $3x$ or $4y$, are called the **terms** of the expression.

So, $5y+7x+5$ is an *expression* with three *terms*.

Example

The perimeter of a shape is the distance round the outside of the shape. Write down an expression for the perimeter of this shape.

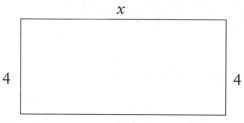

The perimeter is $x+4+x+4=2x+8$.

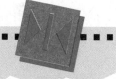

PAUSE

Write down an expression for the perimeter of each shape.

1

3

5

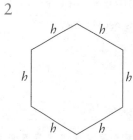

2

4

6

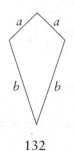

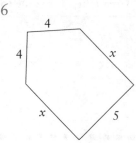

132

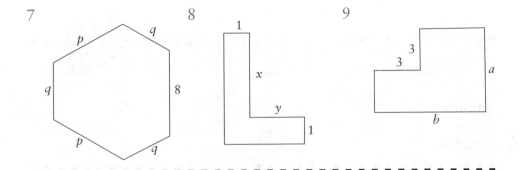

7   8   9

Some expressions can be simplified. For example $7x+3x$ can be written as $10x$. In the same way:

$$3p+2p=5p$$
$$12a-3a=9a$$
$$5p+7q-2p+8q=5p-2p+7q+8q=3p+15q$$

PAUSE

Simplify each expression.

1 $4m+3m$	7 $8a-4a+2a$	13 $3x+2y+2x+3y$
2 $5t-t$	8 $2w-5w+8w$	14 $2e-5f+7e+6f$
3 $e+8e$	9 $-5x+7x$	15 $6m+n+4m+2n$
4 $8x-6x$	10 $-3m+9m$	16 $3s+2r+s+5r$
5 $2z+6z+3z$	11 $-4d+2d$	17 $5r+2q-3r+2q$
6 $7r+2r-3r$	12 $-3k-2k$	18 $7x+5y+2x-3y$

Multiplying terms

Multiplying terms together is done by writing out in full exactly what each term means.

Examples

$$3\times2e=3\times2\times e=6\times e=6e$$
$$6\times3y^2=6\times3\times y\times y=18y^2$$

133

■ ■

PAUSE

Multiply:

1 $3 \times 4v$ 3 $8 \times 5t$ 5 $4c \times 4$ 7 $12 \times z^3$ 9 $4r^2 \times 6$
2 $7 \times 2m$ 4 $7u \times 5$ 6 $2 \times 9z^2$ 8 $3 \times 5m^4$ 10 $7n^3 \times 3$

Multiplying more complicated terms together is still easily done by writing out in full exactly what each term means.

Examples

$$3c \times 5d = 3 \times c \times 5 \times d = 3 \times 5 \times c \times d = 15cd$$
$$3c \times 4c^2 = 3 \times c \times 4 \times c \times c = 3 \times 4 \times c \times c \times c = 12c^3$$

■ ■

PAUSE

Multiply:

1 $3e \times 2f$ 4 $b \times 5a$ 7 $m \times 8m$ 10 $3b^2 \times b$ 13 $2c \times 3c^2$
2 $5r \times 6t$ 5 $2q \times 3r$ 8 $9n \times 2n$ 11 $4y \times y^3$ 14 $3e^2 \times 3e^2$
3 $7m \times n$ 6 $3m \times 5m$ 9 $2a^2 \times a^2$ 12 $5t^2 \times t^3$ 15 $3m^2 \times 2m^3$

Expanding brackets

Brackets are expanded by multiplying all the terms inside the bracket by the term outside the bracket.

Examples

$$4(2m + 6) = 4 \times 2m + 4 \times 6 = 8m + 24$$
$$3(5 - 2x) = 3 \times 5 - 3 \times 2x = 15 - 6x$$

Expand each bracket.

1 $3(2w+7)$ 4 $9(3+s)$ 7 $5(3r-4)$ 10 $4(x^2+1)$ 13 $5(3e+2f)$
2 $5(4m+2)$ 5 $6(2-m)$ 8 $6(2x-1)$ 11 $6(w^3+5)$ 14 $7(3u-2v)$
3 $6(3+2v)$ 6 $3(p+7)$ 9 $4(4-2y)$ 12 $3(5+2m^2)$ 15 $3(2s-3t)$

■ ■

Factorising brackets

To **factorise** an expression we must spot a common factor and then extract this factor outside a bracket.
For example, when we look at the expression:

$$3x+12,$$

we see that each term has 3 as a factor.
Therefore, we can extract 3 outside a bracket and write:

$$3x+12 = 3(x+4)$$

Examples

$$2x+8 = 2(x+4)$$
$$14e-21 = 7(2e-3)$$
$$12w-18 = 6(2w-3)$$

Factorise:

1 $5x+10$	6 $5x-15$	11 $10m+15$	16 $20x+10$
2 $3y+9$	7 $3g-21$	12 $6w+9$	17 $12y+18$
3 $2t+14$	8 $14-7x$	13 $8y+10$	18 $12t+24$
4 $7t+14$	9 $16-2z$	14 $15r-25$	19 $42t+14$
5 $6x+15$	10 $11w-22$	15 $12x-21$	20 $36x+12$

■ ■

Equations

This piece of rope has a length of 120 cm.

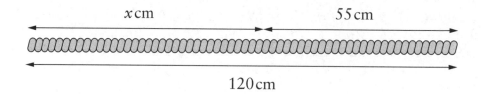

We can write:

$$x + 55 = 120$$

A mathematical statement like this is called an *equation*.

Solving an equation means working out the actual value of the letter. The left hand side and right hand side of an equation are equal. The left hand and right hand sides will therefore still be equal if we choose to *subtract any number from both sides of the equation.*

Subtract 55 from both sides:

$$x + 55 - 55 = 120 - 55$$
$$x = 65$$

Examples

1. Solve the equation:

$$y + 12 = 34$$

   Subtract 12 from both sides:

$$y + 12 - 12 = 34 - 12$$
$$y = 22$$

2. Solve the equation:

$$x + 5 = 2$$

   Subtract 5 from both sides:

$$x + 5 - 5 = 2 - 5$$
$$x = -3$$

Solve:

1 $d+10=11$	6 $13+m=20$	11 $d+11=5$	16 $13+m=12$
2 $e+4=8$	7 $2+g=2$	12 $e+8=2$	17 $2+g=0$
3 $x+7=9$	8 $s+25=27$	13 $x+9=2$	18 $s+25=20$
4 $x+6=13$	9 $s+2=27$	14 $x+13=3$	19 $s+2=-4$
5 $y+7=14$	10 $x+5=15$	15 $y+3=1$	20 $s+5=-2$

■ ■

The left hand side and right hand side of an equation are equal. The left hand side and the right hand side will therefore still be equal if we choose to add *any number to both sides of the equation.*

Examples

1. Solve the equation: $\qquad x-22=5$

   Add 22 to both sides: $\quad x-22+22=5+22$
   $$x=27$$

2. Solve the equation: $\qquad x-5=-2$

   Add 5 to both sides: $\quad x-5+5=-2+5$
   $$x=3$$

Solve:

1 $d-10=11$	6 $m-13=20$	11 $d-11=5$	16 $m-13=-12$
2 $e-4=8$	7 $g-2=0$	12 $e-8=2$	17 $g-2=-2$
3 $x-7=9$	8 $s-25=27$	13 $x-9=2$	18 $s-25=-20$
4 $x-6=13$	9 $s-2=27$	14 $x-13=3$	19 $s-2=-4$
5 $y-7=14$	10 $x-5=15$	15 $y-3=1$	20 $s-5=-2$

■ ■

The left hand side and right hand side of an equation are equal. The left hand and right hand sides will therefore still be equal if we chose to *divide both sides of the equation by any number*.

Examples

1. Solve the equation:

$$2w=10$$

Divide both sides by 2:

$$\frac{2w}{2}=\frac{10}{2}$$

$$w=5$$

2. Solve the equation:

$$3e=-15$$

Divide both sides by −3:

$$\frac{3e}{3}=\frac{-15}{3}$$

$$e=-5$$

PAUSE

Solve:

1 $2x=12$	6 $5x=10$	11 $2s=22$	16 $2x=-4$
2 $4m=16$	7 $6m=24$	12 $3c=12$	17 $8u=40$
3 $5t=25$	8 $9x=90$	13 $4m=40$	18 $5t=-50$
4 $7u=49$	9 $5r=40$	14 $4m=-40$	19 $4x=56$
5 $8e=16$	10 $11z=22$	15 $5z=-55$	20 $2x=-100$

The left hand side and right hand side of an equation are equal. The left hand and right hand sides will therefore still be equal if we choose to *multiply both sides of the equation by any number*.

Examples

1. Solve the equation:

$$\frac{x}{2}=5$$

Multiply both sides by 2:

$$2 \times \frac{x}{2} = 2 \times 5$$

$$x = 10$$

2. Solve the equation:

$$\frac{x}{4} = -7$$

Multiply both sides by 4:

$$4 \times \frac{x}{4} = 4 \times -7$$

$$x = -28$$

PAUSE

Solve:

1 $\dfrac{x}{5} = 2$

2 $\dfrac{z}{3} = 4$

3 $\dfrac{m}{10} = 10$

4 $\dfrac{m}{10} = 1$

5 $\dfrac{w}{6} = 2$

6 $\dfrac{f}{5} = 5$

7 $\dfrac{y}{3} = 21$

8 $\dfrac{x}{7} = 7$

9 $\dfrac{z}{6} = 5$

10 $\dfrac{z}{5} = 6$

11 $\dfrac{y}{3} = -4$

12 $\dfrac{i}{6} = -2$

13 $\dfrac{y}{2} = -9$

14 $\dfrac{y}{9} = -2$

15 $\dfrac{y}{-2} = 9$

16 $\dfrac{y}{-9} = 2$

17 $\dfrac{y}{-9} = -2$

18 $\dfrac{x}{5} = -10$

19 $\dfrac{x}{-5} = -10$

20 $\dfrac{m}{-3} = 50$

Remember, we can:

- add any number to both sides of an equation,
- subtract any number from both sides of an equation,
- multiply both sides of an equation by any number,
- divide both sides of an equation by any number.

Examples

1. Solve the equation $3e - 7 = 11$

$$3e - 7 = 11$$

add 7 to both sides:
$$3e-7+7=11+7$$
$$3e=18$$

divide both sides by 3:
$$\frac{3e}{3}=\frac{18}{3}$$
$$e=6$$

2. Sally gives half her mints to Siloben and then gives 3 mints to Afzal. She has 7 mints left. How many did she start with?

If we let s represent the number of sweets, we can write this equation:
$$\frac{s}{2}-3=7$$

add 3 to both sides:
$$\frac{s}{2}-3+3=7+3$$
$$\frac{s}{2}=10$$

multiplying both sides by 2:
$$2\times s=2\times10$$
$$s=20$$

■ ■

PAUSE

1 $2x+3=7$	6 $3x-4=2$	11 $\frac{z}{2}+1=4$	16 $\frac{t}{3}-1=4$
2 $3x+1=16$	7 $2x-1=9$	12 $\frac{x}{4}+3=5$	17 $\frac{y}{2}-3=-1$
3 $2x+6=20$	8 $3x-10=2$	13 $\frac{x}{3}+4=7$	18 $\frac{y}{3}+2=-1$
4 $5x+8=18$	9 $2x+5=1$	14 $\frac{x}{10}+1=2$	19 $\frac{r}{2}-6=0$
5 $5m+3=8$	10 $4x+14=2$	15 $\frac{y}{4}+5=7$	20 $\frac{x}{2}-7=3$

21 Write down the equation which represents each picture and find the value of the letter.

a) The perimeter is 18 cm.

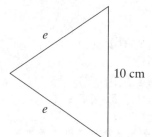

c) The perimeter is 84 cm.

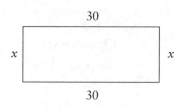

e) The perimeter is 32 cm.

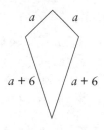

b) The perimeter is is 64 cm.

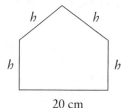

d) The perimeter is is 90 cm.

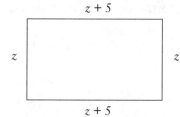

f) The perimeter is 32 cm.

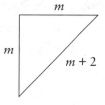

■ ■

Equations with brackets

Example

Solve $3(x+5)=12$

expand the bracket:

$$3x+15=12$$

subtract 15 from both sides:

$$3x+15-15=12-15$$
$$3x=-3$$

divide both sides by 3:

$$\frac{3x}{3}=-\frac{3}{3}$$
$$x=-1$$

141

Solve:

1 $3(2w+7)=45$	5 $5(3r-4)=10$	9 $3(4r+1)=15$
2 $5(4m+2)=50$	6 $6(2x-1)=54$	10 $7(2p-3)=35$
3 $6(3+2v)=54$	7 $4(4+2y)=0$	11 $5(6t-7)=25$
4 $9(3+s)=36$	8 $6(2+m)=36$	12 $2(7+4s)=30$

Equations with letter terms on both sides

Some equations have letter terms on both sides of the equals sign.
In this case, we must first simplify to a single letter term.

Example

$4t-5=3t+12$

subtract $3t$ from both sides:

$$4t-5-3t=3t+12-3t$$
$$t-5=12$$

add 5 to both sides:

$$t-5+5=12+5$$
$$t=17$$

Solve:

1 $8p+4=7p-3$	8 $5s-6=4+3s$
2 $x-15=9-2x$	9 $3w+7=19-w$
3 $4-p=15-2p$	10 $2-p=17-4p$
4 $3e=18-6e$	11 $11-d=19-5d$
5 $5w-17=7-3w$	12 $6g+7=3g-11$
6 $3m+3-m=3m-8$	13 $5h-1=h-21$
7 $\dfrac{x}{2}+3=x+5$	14 $7q+2=q-16$

Number Patterns and Number Sequences

A sequence is a set of numbers which follow a pattern. The simplest example is the set of positive whole numbers.

$$1, 2, 3, 4, 5, 6, 7, 8 \ldots$$

Because this sequence is the most simple and basic of all, these numbers are given a special name. They are called the set of **Natural Numbers**.

Each number in a sequence is called a **term** of the sequence.

The pattern for the whole numbers is that each term is one more than the term before it.

Other sequences have more complicated patterns.

Examples

1. What are the next 2 terms in the sequence: 1, 4, 7, 10, 13, 16 … ?

   Each term is produced by adding 3 to the one before it so the next two terms are 19 and 22.

2. What are the next 2 terms in the sequence: 1, 2, 4, 8, 16… ?

   Each term is produced by multiplying the one before it by 2 so the next two terms are 32 and 64.

3. What are the next 2 terms in the sequence: 100, 90, 80, 70, … ?

   Each term is produced by subtracting 10 from the one before it so the next two terms are 60 and 50.

PAUSE

Give the next two terms in each sequence. Write down the pattern for each sequence.

1 1, 5, 9, 13, 17 .....

2 23, 21, 19, 17 .....

3 1, 3, 9, 27, 81 .....

4 400, 200, 100, 50 .....

5 2, 5, 10, 17, 26 .....

6 1, 2, 4, 7, 11 .....

7 1, 6, 11, 16, 21 .....
8 3, 5, 8, 12, 17 .....
9 6, 15, 24, 33, 42 .....

10 50, 43, 36, 29, 22 .....
11 2, 10, 18, 26, 34 .....
12 2, 4, 8, 16, 32 .....

13 This sequence is called the Fibonacci sequence after Leonardo
Fibonacci who lived in Italy in the twelfth century. Each term is
made by adding the previous two terms:

$$1, 1, 2, 3, 5 \dots$$

Give the next two terms in this sequence.

■ ■

Other sequences can be developed from the set of natural numbers.
For example, if we multiply all the natural numbers by 2, we produce
the set of *even numbers*.

$$2, 4, 6, 8, 10, 12, 14, 16, \dots$$

We use the basic sequence of natural numbers to number the terms in
other sequences.

The first 8 terms in the sequence of odd numbers are numbered like
this:

Term number	1st	2nd	3rd	4th	5th	6th	7th	8th
Term	1	3	5	7	9	11	13	15

Using this notation, we can write:

9 is the 5th term in the sequence of odd numbers

PAUSE

1 Copy and complete:
   a) The 10th term of the sequence of even numbers is .....
   b) The 50th term of the sequence of even numbers is .....
   c) The 50th term of the sequence of odd numbers is .....
   d) The 7th term of the sequence of prime numbers is .....
   e) The 5th term in the sequence of square numbers is .....

■ ■

Describing sequences

We can use mathematical shorthand to describe sequences. If you wanted to know what the 200th even number is, you could write down the first 200 terms of the sequence: 2, 4, 6, 8, 10, 12 ..... You would however probably spot that since the 1st term is 2, the 2nd term is 4 and the 3rd term is 6, it follows that the 200th term must be 400.

If you want to know the nth term, you multiply n by 2.
We can summarise this rule for working out even numbers with a formula like this:

for the even numbers, the nth term $= 2n$.

Example
Find a formula for the nth term of the sequence: 3, 7, 11, 15, 19 .....
It is best to start by constructing a table like this:

T_1	T_2	T_3	T_4	T_5
3	7	11	15	19

(where T_1 is the first term etc)

4   4   4   4

The terms of the sequence go up in 4s. Compare the sequence with the $4 \times$ table.

	T_1	T_2	T_3	T_4	T_5	T_n
Sequence	3	7	11	15	19	$4n-1$
$4 \times$ Table	4	8	12	16	20	$4n$

We can see that each term in our sequence is 1 less than the corresponding term of the $4 \times$ table.
The formula for the nth term is $4n-1$.

■ ■
PAUSE

In questions 1 to 8, find a formula for the nth term of each of the following sequences:

1 1, 3, 5, 7, 9 .....
2 5, 17, 29, 41, 53 .....
3 6, 11, 16, 21, 26 .....
4 4, 7, 10, 13, 16, 19 .....

5 4, 11, 18, 25, 32 .....
6 3, 8, 13, 18, 23 .....
7 1, 9, 17, 25, 33 .....
8 11, 13, 15, 17, 19 .....

9 A gardener always plants flower beds with geraniums, and
   marigolds. Her planting plans for 1, 2 and 3 geraniums are:

M M M	M M M M	M M M M M
M G M	M G G M	M G G G M
M M M	M M M M	M M M M M
1 geranium	2 geraniums	3 geraniums

Find a formula for the number of marigolds needed if n geraniums
are planted.

Square and triangular numbers

Two sequences that are neither arithmetic or geometric are the **square
numbers** and the **triangular numbers**.

The sequence of square numbers is 1, 4, 9, 16, 25 .... They are called
square numbers because the terms of the sequence can be represented
by square patterns of dots like this:

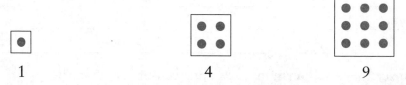

1   4   9

The sequence of triangular numbers is 1, 3, 6, 10, 16 .... They are
called triangular numbers because the terms of the sequence can be
represented by triangular patterns of dots like this:

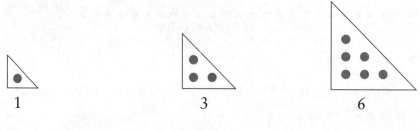

1   3   6

146

1 a) Draw the patterns for the 4th and 5th square numbers.
   b) Continue the sequence of square numbers: 1, 4, 9, 16, 25 ..... up
      to the 10th term.

2 a) Draw the patterns for the 4th and 5th triangular numbers.
   b) Continue the sequence of triangular numbers: 1, 3, 6, 10, 15 .....
      up to the 10th term.

Number machines

This is a **number machine**:

$$x\,2 + 1$$

The number machine shows that we feed in numbers they are first
multiplied by 2 and then added to 1.

If we feed in the numbers 1, 2, 3, 4, 5, we transform these numbers
into 3, 5, 7, 9, 11.

This transformation can be illustrated with a diagram like this:

$$1 \rightarrow 3$$
$$2 \rightarrow 5$$
$$3 \rightarrow 7$$
$$4 \rightarrow 9$$
$$5 \rightarrow 11$$

A diagram like this is called a **mapping diagram** or **arrow diagram**.
To describe the mapping, we write:

$$x \rightarrow 2x + 1$$

This is read as 'x becomes $2x + 1$'.

Example

Draw a mapping diagram to illustrate the mapping $x \rightarrow x + 1$ applied to the set of numbers -3, -2, -1, 0, 1, 2, 3.

This is the required diagram:

$$-3 \rightarrow -2$$
$$-2 \rightarrow -1$$
$$-1 \rightarrow 0$$
$$0 \rightarrow 1$$
$$1 \rightarrow 2$$
$$2 \rightarrow 3$$
$$3 \rightarrow 4$$
$$x \rightarrow x+1$$

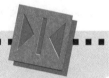

PAUSE

Draw diagrams to show each of the following mappings applied to the numbers $-3, -2, -1, 0, 1, 2, 3$.

1 $x \rightarrow x+4$
2 $x \rightarrow x-1$
3 $x \rightarrow x+3$
4 $x \rightarrow x+2$
5 $x \rightarrow \dfrac{x}{2}$

6 $x \rightarrow 2x$
7 $x \rightarrow 2x+2$
8 $x \rightarrow 2x-1$
9 $x \rightarrow 2x+3$
10 $x \rightarrow x^2$

SECTION 4 Graphs

In the sixteenth century, the French mathematician Rene Descartes developed a new form of mathematics in which algebra was applied to geometry. This branch of mathematics has been named in his honour and is called *Cartesian Geometry*.

Descartes developed a grid of numbers on which pictures of mathematical functions could be plotted. This is an example of the basic cartesian graph.

Example

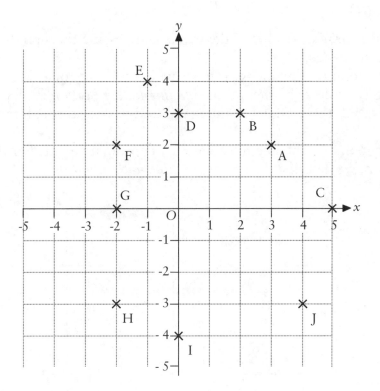

A is the point (3,2)   F is the point (−2,2)
B is the point (2,3)   G is the point (−2,0)
C is the point (5,0)   H is the point (−2,−3)
D is the point (0,3)   I is the point (0,−4)
E is the point (−1,4)   J is the point (4,−3)

PAUSE

1 Draw an *x*-axis and a *y*-axis from −5 to 5. Plot each of the following set of points on your graph, joining them in the order they are plotted.
   a) (0,4), (2,1), (3,−3), (−1,−2), (−4,0), (−1,−1), (−3,3), (1,1), (0,4)
   b) (0,4), (4,0), (4,−4), (0,−4), (−4,0), (−4,1), (−3,1), (−5,2), (−5,0), (0.−5), (5,−5), (5,0), (0,5), (−2,5), (−1,3), (−1,4), (0,4)

Equations for lines parallel with the axes

A line is drawn parallel to the y-axis and passing through the number 4 on the x-axis.

Every point on the line must have an x coordinate of 4. For this reason, we describe the line as, *the line with equation $x=4$*.

A line is drawn parallel to the x-axis and passing through the number -1 on the y-axis.

Every point on the line must have a y coordinate of -1. For this reason, we describe the line as, *the line with equation $y=-1$*.

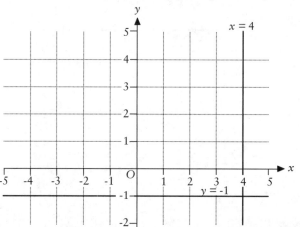

PAUSE

1 Draw a pair of axes from -5 to $+5$. Draw and label the lines with equations:
   a) $x=3$ d) $x=4.5$
   b) $x=-2$ e) $x=-3.5$
   c) $x=0$

2 On the same diagram draw and label these lines.
   a) $y=4$ d) $y=-2.5$
   b) $y=-3$ e) $y=-5$
   c) $y=0$

Equations for lines

Cartesian graphs can be used to show mathematical relationships. For example, the equation $y=2x+1$ is a rule for changing the number x into the number y.

If we take a sequence of values for x, the equation produces a sequence of values for y. These values are usually shown in a table. For example, if we start with a sequence of x values from −3 to 3, we get a table like this:

x	−3	−2	−1	0	1	2	3
y	−5	−3	−1	1	3	5	7

Each pair of x and y values can be shown as coordinates on a graph.

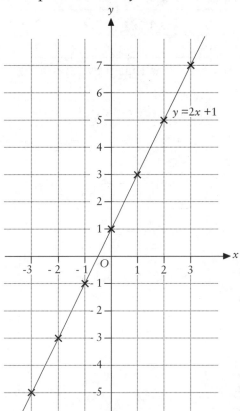

A line has been drawn through the points. This line represents *all* the pairs of values connected by the equation $y=2x+1$.

1 Draw up a table of values for each of the following equations, using all the whole number x values from −3 to 3. Draw an x-axis from −3 to 3 and a y-axis from −7 to 10. Plot the pairs

of values you obtain as coordinates on a graph and, if it seems sensible, connect the points with a straight line.

a) $y=x+4$ b) $y=x-4$ c) $y=2x$ d) $y=\dfrac{x}{2}$ e) $y=2x+4$

■ ■

Graphs of quadratics

This is a table of values for the equation $y=x^2$:

x	−3	−2	−1	0	1	2	3
y	9	4	1	0	1	4	9

If these points are plotted on graph, it is obvious that they do not lie on the same straight line.

This table shows more x and y values which fit the equation $y=x^2$.

x	−3	−2.5	−2	−1.5	−1	−0.55
y	9	6.25	−4	2.25	1	0.25

x	0	0.5	1	1.5	2	2.5	3
y	0	0.25	1	2.25	4	6.25.	9

This is the graph of $y = x^2$.

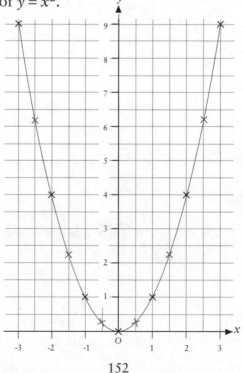

152

The points should be connected with a smooth curve, *not with a series of straight lines*. Values of x which are not whole numbers can be included to help draw the curve.

1 Draw an x-axis from -3 to 3 and a y-axis from -5 to 14. It is easier to draw smooth curves if you make the scale on the x-axis 2 cm to 1 unit and the scale on the y-axis 1 cm to 1 unit.
   Use the same pair of axes for all the graphs in question 1 and question 2.
   a) Use this table to plot a graph of $y=x^2$

x	-3	-2	-1	0	1	2	3
y	9	4	-1	0	1	4	9

   Join the points with a smooth curve and label the graph $y=x^2$

   b) Copy and complete this table for $y=x^2+1$

x	-3	-2	-1	0	1	2	3
y	10					5	

   Plot the points and join them with a smooth curve. Label the graph $y=x^2+1$

   c) Make a table like the one in part b) for each of these:

   i) $y=x^2+2$ ii) $y=x^2+3$ iii) $y=x^2+4$

   Plot each set of points and join them with a smooth curve. Label each curve with its equation.

2 Use the same pair of axes as question 1.
   a) Copy and complete this table for $y=x^2-1$

x	-3	-2	-1	0	1	2	3
y		3				8	

   Plot the points and join them with a smooth curve. Label the graph $y=x^2-1$

   b) Make a table like the one in part a) for each of these:

   i) $y=x^2-2$ ii) $y=x^2-3$ iii) $y=x^2-4$

153

Plot each set of points and join them with a smooth curve. Label each curve with its equation.

3 a) Look carefully at the graphs you have drawn in questions 1 and 2. What do you notice about them?

b) Describe the appearance of these graphs:

i) $y=x^2+10$ ii) $y=x^2-15$

■■

Distance and time graphs

Here is a description of a 12 km journey from home to work lasting 40 minutes.

- The journey started with a 5 minute walk to a bus stop 600 metres from the house.
- There was a 10 minute wait for a bus.
- The bus then travelled 8 km in 10 minutes.
- The was a 5 minute wait for a second bus.
- The second bus completed the journey in the remaining 10 minutes.

From this information, we can draw up this table of times and distances.

Time	5	15	25	30	40
Distance	0.6	0.6	8.6	8.6	12

And draw this graph:

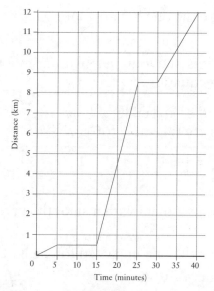

154

To calculate the average speed for a journey we use the formula:

$$\text{average speed} = \frac{\text{distance}}{\text{time}}$$

The journey to work was 12 km in 40 minutes.

The average speed was $\frac{12}{40} = 0.3$ km per minute.

PAUSE

1 A walker, a bicycle, a bus and a car set off in the same direction at the same time. They all travelled for three hours.

a) On graph paper, draw a pair of axes like those shown in the diagram. Use these axes for all parts of this question.

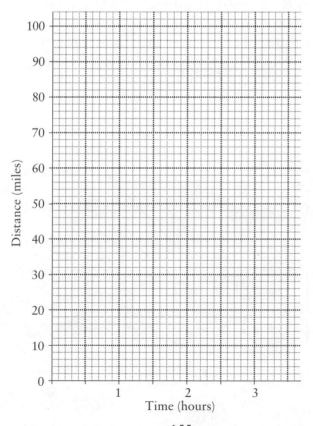

b) The walker travelled at a steady 4 mph.
   Copy and complete this table for the walker.

Time (hours)	1	2	3
Distance (miles)	4		

Plot the points in your table on the graph and join them to get a straight line. Label your line 'walker'.
c) The cyclist travelled at a steady 10 mph.
   Copy and complete this table for the cyclist.

Time (hours)	1	2	3
Distance (miles)	10		

Plot the points and join them to get a straight graph. Label your line 'bicycle'.
d) The bus travelled at a steady 20 mph. Make a table like those in parts b) and c).
   Plot the points and join them to get a straight line.
e) The car travelled at a steady 30 mph. Make a table and draw a graph to show the car journey.
f) Use your four graphs to describe the effect that travelling faster has on a graph of a journey.

2   The graph shows lines representing five different journeys.

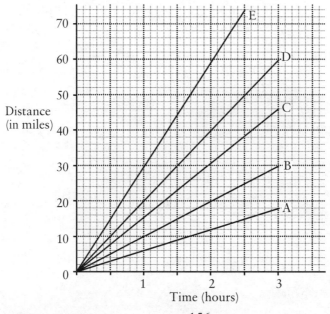

a) Which journey is the slowest?
b) Which journey is the fastest?
c) Use the graph to find the speed in miles per hour for each of the journeys.

3 Mary Walker cycles to school each day. Leaving home she rides to the Co-op where she waits for her friend Benny Shaw. They then ride on together to the end of Pascal Drive, where they wait for their friend Lac Tran. The three then cycle together to school. This graph illustrates Mary's journey one day last week.

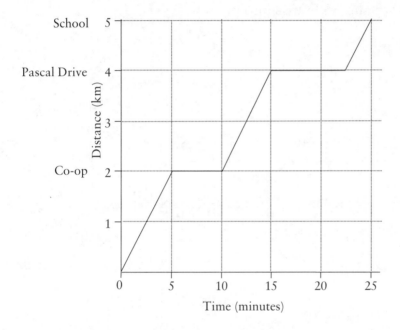

a) How far is the Co-op from Mary's house?
b) How long does Mary wait for Benny?
c) How far is the end of Pascal Drive from the Co-op?
d) How long do Mary and Benny wait for Lac Tran?
e) How far is it from Mary's house to her school?
f) What is Mary's average speed in kilometres per minute for the journey from:
    i) home to the Co-op?
    ii) the Co-op to the end of Pascal Drive?
    iii) home to school?

Conversion graphs

1. The Andrews family are going on holiday to France. They know that £1 is worth 7.50 Francs. Mr Andrews made this table of values.

Pounds	2	4	6	8
Francs	15	30	45	60

Mrs Andrews draws a graph from the table to help the family understand French prices.
This diagram shows how the graph can be used to change £5 into French Francs and 55 Francs into pounds.

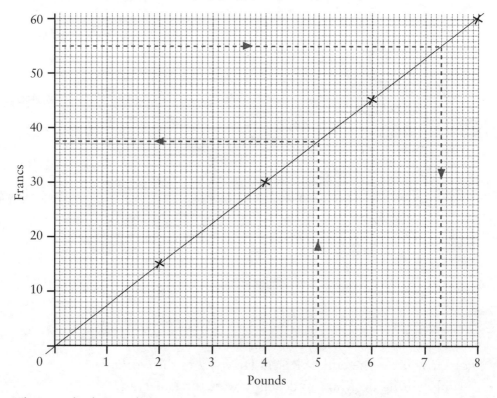

The graph shows that:

$$£5 = 37.5 \text{ Francs}$$

$$55 \text{ Francs} = £7.30 \text{ (approximately)}$$

2. An electrician has a fixed charge of £10 to call at a house plus a charge of £12 for each hour of work done.

We can use this formula to calculate the electrician's charges:

$$c = 12h + 10$$

where c is the charge in pounds and h is the number of hours worked.

We can make this table of values to show the cost of up to 6 hours worked.

Hours worked (h)	1	2	3	4	5	6
Charge (c)	22	34	46	58	70	82

We can then draw this graph:

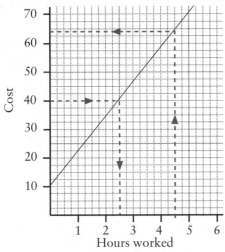

The arrows show how the graph can be used to show that:

■ a £40 charge is made for 2 and a half hours work,
■ 4 and a half hours work costs £64.

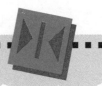

PAUSE

1 A family plan a holiday in Spain
   They know that £1 is worth 175 pesetas.

   a) Complete this table:

Pounds	1	2	5
Pesetas	175		

b) Draw axes which start like this:

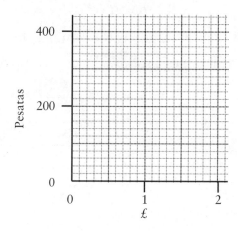

Draw a graph to convert £ into pesetas.

c) Use your graph to find the value of:
   i) £3.20 in pesetas,   ii) 1500 pesetas in £.   (NEAB)

2 This graph shows the cost of using various amounts of electricity:

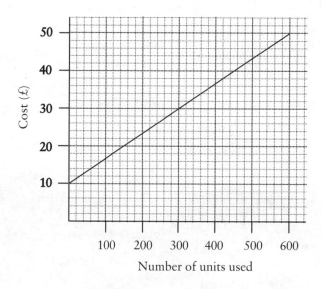

Number of units used

a) What is the cost of using:
   i) 500 units of electricity,   ii) 340 units of electricity?
b) How many units have you used if:
   i) your bill is £30,   ii) your bill is £42?
c) Why do you think the graph starts at £10 on the cost axis?

3 The cost of building a stretch of motorway is estimated at £5 million per kilometre, plus a fixed cost of £15 million.

We can use this formula to calculate the cost of building a motorway:

$$C = 5N + 15$$

Where C is the cost in millions of pounds, and N is the number of kilometres to be built.

a) Copy and complete this table showing the cost of building up to 15 kilometres of motorway.

Number of kilometres (N)	0	5	10	15
Cost (C millions of pounds)	15		65	

b) Plot these points and draw a graph to illustrate the cost of building a motorway. Use axes which start like this and go up to 15km and 90 million pounds.

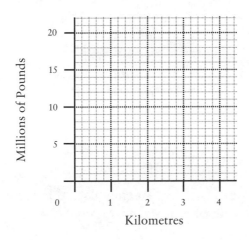

c) Use your graph to calculate the cost of building:
   i) a 12 km stretch of motorway,
   ii) a 4 km stretch of motorway.

4 The Rick Dastardly Detective Agency charges £40 a day to hire one of their detectives. This can be expressed as the equation:

$$C = 40d$$

161

where C is the total cost and d is the number of days the detective is hired for.

a) i) Copy and complete this table showing the cost of hiring a detective for up to 7 days.

Days (d)	0	1	2	3	4	5	6	7
Cost (£C)	0		80					280

ii) Plot these points and draw a graph to represent the cost of hiring a Rick Dastardly detective. Use axes which start like this and go up to 7 days and £280.

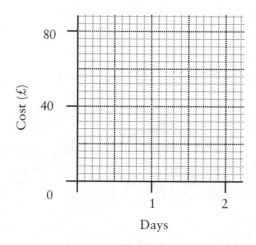

b) The Purple Panther Detective Agency uses this formula to work out the cost of hiring one of its detectives:

$$C = 20d + 80$$

where C is the total cost and d is the number of days the detective is hired for.

i) Copy and complete this table showing the cost of hiring a detective for up to 7 days.

Days (d)	0	1	2	3	4	5	6	7
Cost (£C)	0		120					220

ii) Plot these points and draw a graph to represent the cost of hiring a Purple Panther detective.

c) What advice would you offer somebody who intended to hire a detective from one of the two companies?

5 Nadia wants to hire a disco for her club.
She gets two leaflets about the charges.

a)

> ## 'ROBIN DISCO'
>
> To hire our disco:
>
> We charge £30 plus 50p per person.

i) Complete the table for the charges made by 'Robin Disco'.

Number of people	10	30	50	70	90
Charge (£)	35	45			

ii) Plot these points and draw a graph to represent charges made.
Use axes which start like these and go up to 90 people and £80.

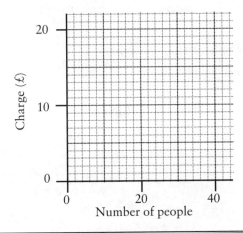

b)

> ## 'OWL DISCO'
>
> To hire our disco:
>
> the charges are calculated from the formula
>
> $$C = \frac{N}{4} + 50$$
>
> where N is the number of people at the disco.
>
> C is the charge in £.

i) Complete the table for the charges made by 'Owl Disco'.

Number of people	0	20	40	80	100
Charge (£)			60		75

ii) On the grid opposite, plot the points and draw a graph to represent the charges made.

c) What do the two graphs tell you about which disco is the cheaper?

(NEAB)

REWIND

1 Write each of the following statements in standard mathematical shorthand.

a) The number y is always 5 more than the number x.

b) 3 times the number t, minus 4 times the number s is equal to the number r.

2 If $a=6$, $b=3$ and $c=5$, find the value of:

a) $a+b$ c) $2a+3b$ e) ab g) ab^2 i) $17+2cb^2$

b) $b-c$ d) $5c-2b$ f) $2ac-ab$ h) a^3b j) $a(b+c)$

3 If $a=-2$, $b=-1$ and $c=5$, find the value of:

a) $a+b$ b) $b-c$ c) $2a+3b$ d) ab e) ab^2

4 Simplify each of the following expressions:

a) $17x+y+3x+5y$ c) $x-12y+7x+9y$

b) $3x+2y-2x+6y$ d) $-x+2y+7x+5y$

5 Expand the brackets and simplify:

a) $4(3r+5)$ c) $3(4p-1)$

b) $4(7r-5)$ d) $5(4-3q)$

6 A boat leaves harbour with 12 000 litres of fuel oil on board. Each day the engines use 800 litres of oil. Write down a formula to calculate the oil that is left after the boat has been at sea for t days.

7 Factorise completely each of the following expressions.

a) $20x+35$ c) $8-12p$

b) $14y+7$ d) $b-6ab$

8 Solve:

a) $6m=36$ d) $t+45=104$ g) $\dfrac{t}{5}=-13$ j) $\dfrac{x}{4}-5=1$

b) $108=12t$ e) $18=r-7$ h) $2x+7=11$ k) $3(2x-1)=51$

c) $12x=-24$ f) $15=r+5$ i) $13+7m=48$ l) $4(2x-1)=8$

9 Solve:

a) $9p+4=5p-12$ b) $x-25=5-5x$ c) $5m+13-m=3m-23$

10 Find the rule which links each term in the following sequences with the one before it. Use the rule to write down the next 2 numbers in each sequence.

a) 24, 27, 30, 33, ...   c) 1, 2, 1, 2, 1, ...

b) 360, 180, 90, 45, ...   d) 3, 4, 7, 11, 18, ...

11 Draw diagrams to show each of the following mappings applied to the set of numbers $-3,-2,-1, 0, 1, 2, 3$

a) $x \rightarrow x+5$ b) $x \rightarrow 4x$

12 Draw a graph and mark on it the lines with equation:

a) $x=3$ b) $y=-2$ c) $x=0$ d) $y=0$ e) $x=-3.5$ f) $y=2.5$

13 Make a table and draw a graph to illustrate each of the following equations. Use x values from -4 to 4 (y will go from -10 to 11). Write down the coordinates of the point where each graph cuts the y-axis.

a) $y=x+5$ b) $y=x-6$ c) $y=\dfrac{1}{2}x$ d) $y=2x+3$

14 Make a table and draw a graph to illustrate each of the following equations using x values from -3 to 3 (y will go from -2 to 11).

a) $y=x^2$ b) $y=x^2+2$ c) $y=x^2-2$

15 Peter went on a cycle ride from his aunt's house. He had a rest on his way there. The travel graph shows his journey.

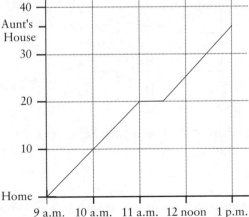

165

a) How far is Peter's aunt's house from his home?
b) For how long did Peter rest?
c) How far had Peter cycled when he stopped to rest?
d) How long did it take Peter to reach his aunt's house?

16 The Hire-A-Heap car hire company offer an executive saloon at two different daily hiring rates.

Scheme A: £20 per day plus 4 pence per mile

Scheme B: £25 per day plus 2 pence per mile.

a) The daily cost of hiring a car under Scheme A can be represented by the equation:

$$C=20+\frac{m}{25}$$

where C is the daily cost and m is the number of miles covered.

Copy and complete this table of values.

Miles (m)	0	100	200	300	400	500
Cost (£)	20	24			36	

b) Plot these points and draw a graph to represent the cost of hiring a car using Scheme A. Use axes which start like this and go up to 500 miles and £40.

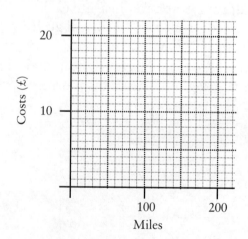

c) The daily cost of hiring a car under Scheme B can be represented by the equation:

$$C=25+\frac{m}{50}$$

where C is the daily cost and m is the number of miles covered.

166

Copy and complete this table of values

Miles (*m*)	0	100	200	300	400	500
Cost (£)	25	27			33	

d) Plot these points on your grid and draw a graph to represent the cost of hiring a car using Scheme B.

e) Susan Taylor wants to hire a car for a holiday during which she anticipates she will travel an average of 300 miles each day. Which hiring scheme will be the cheapest for Susan?

f) Aruna Patel wants to hire a car for a day to make a round trip of 200 miles. Which hiring scheme will be the cheapest for Aruna?

FASTFORWARD

1 a) Write, in symbols, the rule:

'to find *y*, double *x* and add 1'.

b) Use your rule from part a) to calculate the value of *x* when $y=9$.

(ULEAC)

2 Theatre tickets cost £7 each.

a) Write an equation to find the cost of *n* theatre tickets.

b) The total cost is reduced by £10 when more than ten tickets are purchased.

Write an equation to find the cost of *n* theatre tickets when *n* is more than ten.

(SEG)

3 Use the values $x=9$ and $y=5$ to work out:

a) $x+y$ b) $2y-3$ c) y^3

(MEG)

4 a) $S=180n-360$.

Find the value of S when $n=10$.

b) $T=\dfrac{a+m}{2}$.

Find the value of T when $a=6$ and $m=81$.

(MEG)

167

5 A formula connecting T, f and g is $T=4f-5g$.
   Work out the value of T when $f=6.4$ and $g=3.9$.   (MEG)

6 The cost, C pence, of a newspaper advertisement of n words is
   given by the formula

$$C=12n+32$$

   Find the cost of an advertisement of 16 words.   (MEG)

7 The price £P, charged by 'Motif Shirts' for making sweat shirts of
   your own design is given by the formula $P=3N+20$, where P is the
   price in pounds and N is the number of shirts ordered.
   a) Work out the price of 40 shirts.
   b) Work out the price per shirt when 40 shirts are ordered. (MEG)

8 Fran, Jo and Tom share some money.
   Jo gets 50p more than Tom.
   Fran gets twice as much as Jo.
   Let x be the number of pence Tom gets.
   Write expressions in terms of x for the number of pence given to:
   a) Jo,
   b) Fran,
   c) all three together.
   The money shared is £6.70.
   d) Write down an equation in x and solve it to find x.

                                                            (NICCEA)

9 The diagram shows a square and a rectangle. The square has sides
   of length $2y$ metres. The rectangle has length $3y$ metres and breadth
   3 metres.

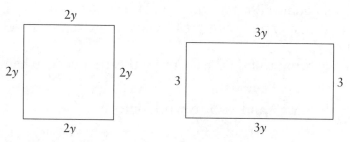

   a) i) Find, in terms of y, the perimeter of the square.
      ii) Find, in terms of y, the perimeter of the rectangle.
   b) The perimeter of the square is equal to the perimeter of the
      rectangle.
       i) Form an equation in y.
      ii) Work out the value of y.   (SEG)

10 The sides of a triangle are a cm, $(a-2)$ cm and $(a+3)$ cm, as shown.

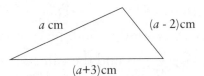

a cm $(a-2)$cm

$(a+3)$cm

a) What is the perimeter of the triangle in terms of a?
b) The triangle has a perimeter of 19 cm. Calculate the value of a.
(MEG)

11 Solve:

$$3x-4=11 \qquad \text{(ULEAC)}$$

12 This picture shows some packets of rice in the pans of a weighing machine.
Each packet of rice weighs x kg.

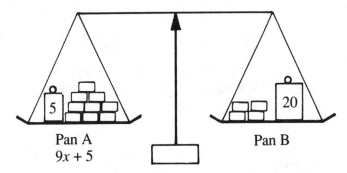

Pan A   Pan B
$9x+5$

In Pan A there are 9 packets of rice and a weight of 5 kg.
An expression for the total weight in kg in Pan A is $9x + 5$.
In Pan B there are 4 packets of rice and a weight of 20 kg.
a) Write down in terms of x an expression for the total weight in Pan B.
The total weight in each pan is the same.
b) Write down an equation in terms of x to represent this information.
c) Use your equation to calculate the weight, x kg, of one packet of rice.
(ULEAC)

13 Solve these equations:
a) $3x+2=18-5x$
b) $2(x+3)=18-6x$ (SEG)

14 Solve the equation $4(x-3)=22$ (MEG)

15 Solve the equation

$$11x+5=x+25 \qquad \text{(ULEAC)}$$

169

16 Solve the equations:

a) $x+7=18$ b) $5y=45$ c) $3z+2=14$ (MEG)

17 a) Use the formula $S=180n-360$ to find the value of S when $n=10$.

b) Use the formula $n=\dfrac{S+360}{180}$ to find the value of n when $S=720$.

(ULEAC)

18 Here is a formula for working out the perimeter of a rectangle.

$$P=2(l+w)$$

Use the formula to work out the value of P when $l=6$ and $w=4$.

(ULEAC)

19 Here is a formula:

$$v=u+10t$$

Find the value of v when:

a) $u=6$, $t=8$

b) $u=5$, $t=0$

(ULEAC)

20   3 4 9 13 15 23 25 28 64

Copy each statement below. Choosing numbers from the list above, fill in the blank spaces to make the statements true.

a) ____, ____ and ____ are prime numbers.

b) ____ and ____ are factors of 200.

c) ____ is a multiple of 7.

d) ____ is a cube.

e) $5 \div$ ____ $=\frac{1}{3}$.   (NICCEA)

21 Find the next two numbers in each of these simple number patterns.

a) 10, 35, 60, 85, ..., ...

b) 29, 22, 15, 8, ..., ...   (ULEAC)

22 Here are the first four lines of a number pattern.

Line 1   5 → 11

Line 2   10 → 16

Line 3   15 → 21

Line 4   20 → ☐

a) What is the missing number in the box?

b) Explain how you found the missing number.

c) Write down Line 20 of the pattern.   (ULEAC)

23 Here are the first four numbers of a number pattern

7, 14, 21, 28, ..., ...

a) Write down the next two numbers in the pattern.

b) Describe, in words, the rule for finding the next number in the pattern.   (ULEAC)

24

1				Sum $=1$	$=1^3$
3	5			Sum $=8$	$=2^3$
7	9	11		Sum $=27$	$=3^3$
.....	.....	.....	.....	Sum $=.....$	$=.....$

a) Complete the fourth line of the number pattern above.

b) Calculate which line will have a sum equal to 729.   (ULEAC)

25 This is part of a sequence of shapes that Imran has made from matchsticks.

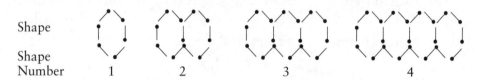

Shape				
Shape Number	1	2	3	4

Imran counted how many matchsticks he needed to make each shape. He then drew the table below.

Shape number (p)	1	2	3	4	5	6
Number of matchsticks (n)	6	11	16	21		

a) Copy and complete the table to show how many matchsticks he would use for shape 5 and for shape 6.

b) Work out which shape number would need 281 matches.

Let p, stand for the shape number.

Let n stand for the number of matchsticks needed to make that shape.

c) Complete the formula connecting n and p.   (ULEAC)

26 a) Copy and complete the next line of the following sequence.

$$3^2 - 2^2 = 3 + 2 = 5$$
$$4^2 - 3^2 = 4 + 3 = 7$$
$$.....-......=....+....=....$$

b) Two more lines of the same sequence are shown below. Copy and complete them.

i) $.....-......=....+....=13$

ii) $.....-......=....+....=35$ (MEG)

171

27 Here are the first four terms of a number sequence:

$$7, 11, 15, 19.$$

Write down the nth term of the sequence. (ULEAC)

28 The rule for a sequence is:

> Multiply the previous number by 3, then add 2.

The first four numbers of the sequence are:

$$3, 11, 35, 107$$

a) Work out the next two numbers in the sequence.
   x represents a number in this sequence.
b) Write down, in terms of x, an expression for the next number
   after x in this sequence. (ULEAC)

29 a) Write down the next term in the series

$$x, x^3, x^5, x^7,$$

b) What is the value of this term when $x=1$? (MEG)

30 a) On a grid, plot and label the points

   P(4,1)   Q(3,−2)   R(−3,−2)   S(−2,1).

b) Give the geometrical name of quadrilateral PQRS. (ULEAC)

31 Copy and complete the following table for the rule.
   a) 'To find y, double x and add 1'.

x	y
0	
1	
3	

b) Plot the values from the table on to a coordinate grid. Join your
   points with a straight line.
c) Write, in symbols, the rule:

   'to find y, double x and add 1'.

d) Use your rule from part c) to calculate the value of x when $y=9$.
   (ULEAC)

32 a) Draw a graph and plot the points (1,3) and (4,6).
   Join the points with a straight line.
b) The point P $(a, 5)$ lies on the line.
   What is the value of a?
c) The line is extended.

172

Complete the following mapping for points on the line.

$$1 \rightarrow 3$$
$$5 \rightarrow 7$$
$$10 \rightarrow \ldots\ldots\ldots$$
$$x \rightarrow \ldots\ldots\ldots$$
(SEG)

33 a) Complete this table of values for $y=x+2$.

x	−3	−2	−1	0	1	2	3
y			1		3	4	

b) Draw an x-axis from −4 to 4 and a y-axis from −3 to 6.
   Plot the points given by the values in your table.

c) Work out the value of x when $y=2.5$. (ULEAC)

34 a) Given that $y=x^2$, copy and complete the following table.

x	−3	−2.5	−2	−1.5	−1	−0.5	0	0.5	1	1.5	2	2.5	3
y	9	6.25			1		0		1			6.25	9

b) Using a scale of 2 cm to represent 1 unit on each axis, draw the
   graph of $y=x^2$ for values of x from −3 to 3.

c) Using the same scales and axes as in part b), draw the graph of
   the straight line $y=3-x$.

d) Write down the coordinates of the point where the graphs cross.
   (MEG)

35 The graph of $y=x^2+1$ is drawn by plotting the points given in the
following table and joining these points with a smooth curve.

x	0	1	2	3	4	5	6
y	1	2	5	10	17	26	37

a) Using 2mm graph paper draw the graph of $y=x^2+1$. Use a
   scale of 2cm = 1 unit on the x-axis and 2cm = 10 units on
   the y-axis.

b) Add the points A (1, 25) and B (5, 5) to your graph.

c) Draw the straight line joining the points A and B. This line
   meets the curve $y=x^2+1$ at C.
   i) Mark the position of C on the diagram.
   ii) Write down the coordinates of C. (WJEC).

36 The numbers 4, 6 and 9 are all factors of 36.
  a) Explain why 5 is not a factor of 36.
  b) i) Complete these pairs of whole numbers which multiply to
         give 36.
         (2, ...),   (3, ...),   (4, 9),
         (6, 6),   (9, 4),   (12, ...)
     ii) Copy the grid opposite. Plot these six pairs of whole
         numbers as points on the grid and join them with a
         smooth curve.

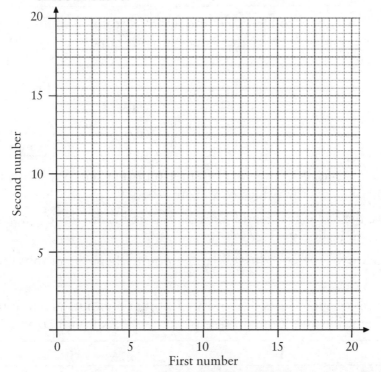

     iii) By drawing lines on your graph show how to find the
          number which multiplied by 5 gives 36.   (SEG)

37 This graph can be used to change between £'s and French Francs.

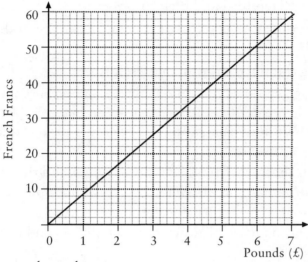

Use the graph to change:
a) i) £6 to French Francs,   ii) £2.90 to French Francs,
b) i) 55 French Francs to £s   ii) 40 French Francs to £s (ULEAC)

38

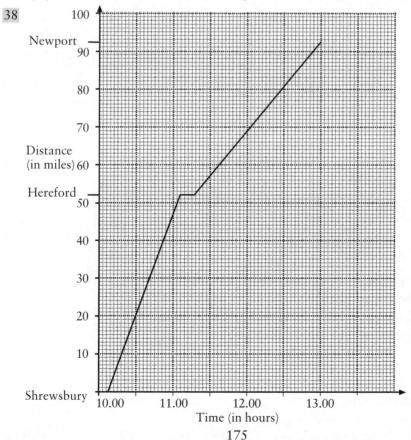

175

The graph represents the journey of a train that travels from Shrewsbury to Hereford and then to Newport.

a) What was the average speed of the train from Shrewsbury to Hereford?

b) How long did the train wait at Hereford?

c) The average speed of the train between Shrewsbury and Hereford is greater than its average speed between Hereford and Newport. Without calculating any average speed, explain how the graph shows this.

d) Another train starts from Newport at 11.15 and travels non-stop to Shrewsbury at an average speed of 60 mph. Copy the graph and add this train's journey.

e) Use your graph to write down the time this second train arrived at Shrewsbury.

f) Write down how far from Hereford the trains were when they passed each other. (WJEC)

 39

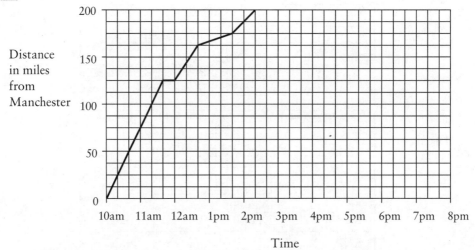

Time

The graph represents part of Mrs Hinton's journey from Manchester to London.
Mrs Hinton stopped for a rest at a service station.

a) ii) Write down the time at which she stopped.
   ii) For how long did she stop?

For part of her journey Mrs Hinton had to slow down because of a traffic queue.

b) For how many miles did she travel at this slower speed?

c) Make a copy of the graph.

Mrs Hinton spent an hour at a meeting in London. She then returned home to Manchester, travelling at a steady speed of 50 miles an hour.

Use this information to complete the graph of her journey.

(ULEAC)

Shape and Space

As civilisations developed, more and more practical mathematical knowledge was needed. The construction of buildings required accurate measurement of length and angle.

The ownership of land required surveying techniques and the measurement of area. The spread of trade required the development of arithmetic and the measurement of weights and volumes.

Horizontal, vertical and parallel

This is a picture of a group of teachers on holiday.

The waiter is **vertical**. The boat is **horizontal** in the water. The sides of a beach towel are **parallel**.

PAUSE

1 List 5 more things in the picture which are horizontal.

2 List 5 more things in the picture which are vertical.

3 List 5 more things in the picture which are parallel.

4 Damien has capsized his sail-board. These pictures show him pulling it from a horizontal to a vertical position.

a) Sort the pictures into the correct order.
b) Through what fraction of a whole turn does Damien turn the sail-board?

■■■■■■■■■■■■■■■■■■■■■■■■■■■■■■■■■■■■

Acute, obtuse, reflex and right angles

A quarter turn is called a *right* angle.

A turn which is less than a quarter turn is called an *acute* angle.

A turn which is more than a quarter turn is called an *obtuse* angle.

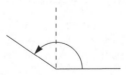

A turn which is more than a half turn is called a *reflex* angle.

Example
We can describe a turn from E to SW like this:

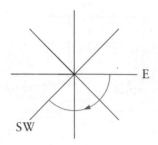

$\frac{3}{8}$ of a full turn clockwise which is an obtuse angle.

PAUSE

1 Write a similar description for these *clockwise* turns:

  a) E to SE   d) S to NW   g) E to W   j) SW to N
  b) NW to NE   e) NW to SW   h) SW to SE
  c) SW to NE   f) W to NW   i) SE to S

2 Here is the logo of the 'Flying A' pizza company.
  On a copy of the drawing mark:

  a) a right angle with an R,
  b) two parallel lines each with a P,
  c) an obtuse angle with an O.
    CD is a vertical line.
  d) Mark another vertical line with a V.
    AB is a horizontal line.
  e) Mark another horizontal line with an H.

(ULEAC)

Measuring angles

We have inherited our system of angle measurement from the Babylonians. The mathematics of this ancient civilisation, as they mapped the stars, measured *direction* with a circle divided into 360 parts. These parts of a circle are called *degrees*.
There are 360 degrees in a full circle, 180 degrees in half a circle and 90 degrees in a quarter of a circle.

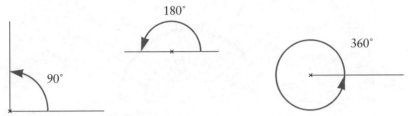

The abbreviation for 'degree' is a small circle. 180 degrees is abbreviated as 180°.
The marked angle can be called angle *x*, angle AOB, ∠ AOB or AÔB.

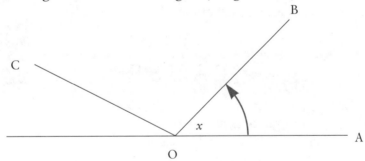

Angles are measured with a protractor, or angle measurer.

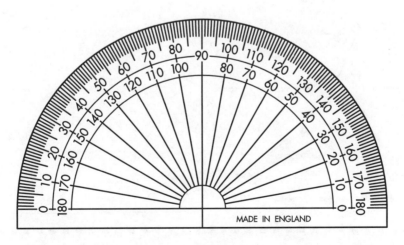

183

These have two scales. One scale measures clockwise angles. The other scale measures anticlockwise angles.
This protractor shows that angle AOB is 40° and angle AOC is 150°.

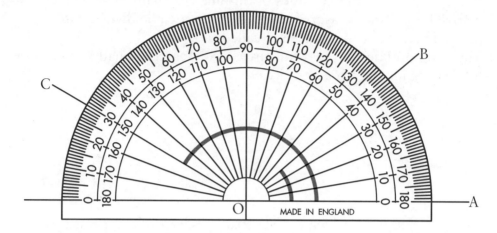

Measuring using the anticlockwise scale, ∠ AOB is an acute angle of 40° and ∠ AOC is an obtuse angle of 150°.

PAUSE

a) Decide if each angle is acute or obtuse.
b) Measure each angle accurately. Use your answer to part a) to help you choose the correct scale.

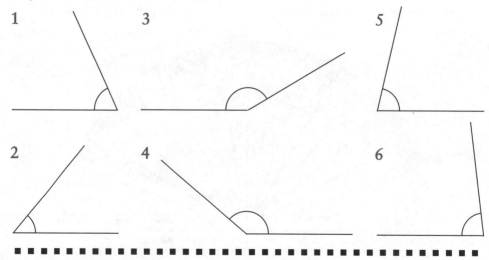

Drawing angles

A protractor can be used to draw an angle. This diagram shows the stages in drawing an angle of 40°

1.

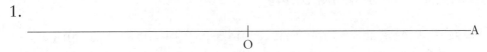

2.

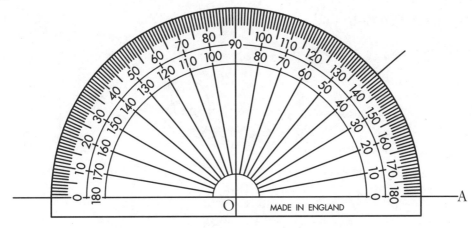

3.

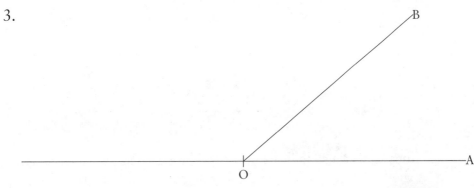

PAUSE

1 Draw clockwise angles of:
  a) 50°   b) 160°   c) 15°   d) 105°   e) 33°   f) 167°

2 Draw anticlockwise angles of:

   a) 80°   b) 110°   c) 45°   d) 145°   e) 42°   f) 126°

■ ■

Bisecting a line or an angle

These diagrams show how a ruler and a pair of compasses can be used to cut a line or an angle in half. This is called *bisecting* the line or the angle.

To bisect a straight line.

   1.   2.    3.   4.

To bisect an angle.

   1.   2.   3.   4.    5.

■ ■

PAUSE

1 Draw lines with these lengths and then bisect them. Measure each half of the line to check the accuracy of your construction.

   a) 10 cm   c) 11 cm
   b) 12 cm   d) 8.6 cm

2 Draw the angles and then bisect them. Measure each half of the angle to check the accuracy of your construction.

   a) 60°   c) 120°
   b) 40°   d) 136°

■ ■

Constructing triangles

This diagram shows the stages in drawing a triangle with sides of 5 cm, 3 cm and 4 cm.

1.

5 cm

2.

4 cm

5 cm

3.

3 cm

5 cm

4.

4 cm

3 cm

5 cm

PAUSE

1 Use a ruler and compasses to draw these triangles.
   a) 4 cm, 4 cm and 5 cm   c) 12 cm, 13 cm and 5 cm
   b) 8 cm, 6 cm and 9 cm   d) 9 cm, 9 cm and 9 cm

2 The villages of Smidgley, Widgley and Ridgley form a triangle with sides 4 km, 7 km and 9.5 km. This is a rough sketch map of the villages.

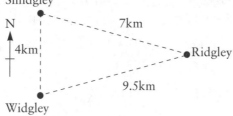

Smidgley

N

4km

7km

Ridgley

9.5km

Widgley

Using a scale of 1 cm = 1 km, draw an accurate map showing the three villages.

Scale drawings

Examples

1. Standing 25 m from the base of a cliff, a student measures the angle of elevation of the top of the cliff as 60°. If the student makes this measurement with an instrument held 1.5 m from the ground, how high is the cliff?

   Use a scale of 1 cm = 5 m.
   We can draw this diagram, using the scale given.

   The height of the triangle is 8.7 cm.
   8.7 cm represents $5 \times 8.7 = 43.5$ m

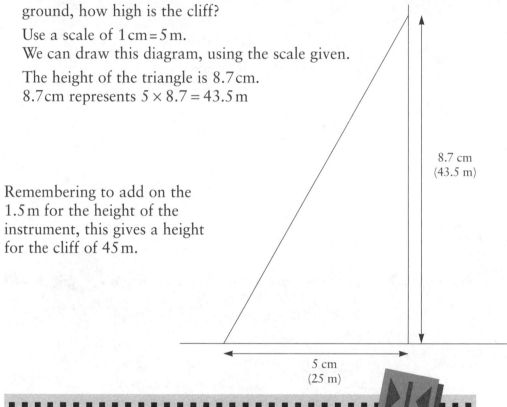

8.7 cm
(43.5 m)

Remembering to add on the 1.5 m for the height of the instrument, this gives a height for the cliff of 45 m.

5 cm
(25 m)

PAUSE

1 A ladder 6 metres long rests against a wall with the foot of the ladder 1.5 metres from the base of the wall.

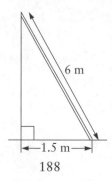

6 m

1.5 m

Make an accurate drawing using a scale of 2 cm = 1 m. How far does the ladder reach up the wall?

2 Make an accurate full size drawing of the triangle. Measure and write down the length of the side AB.

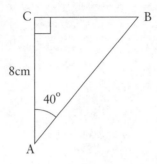

3 On a sunny day, a flagpole casts a shadow 8.5 metres long when the sun rays are at an inclination of 56° to the ground.

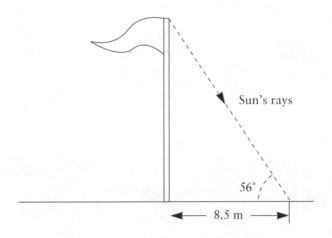

Make an accurate drawing using a scale of 1 cm = 1 m. How high is the flagpole?

4 Chelmsford is 30 km to the west and 25 km to the south of Ipswich.

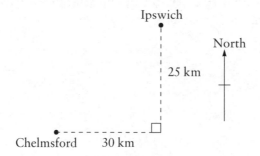

Make an accurate scale drawing using a scale of 1 cm = 5 km and find the direct distance from Chelmsford to Ipswich.

5 This is a sketch of a field where some treasure is hidden.

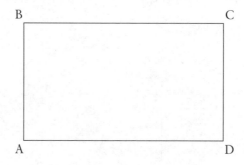

AB is 60 m and AD is 100 m.

a) Using a scale of 1 cm = 10 m draw an accurate scale diagram of the field.
b) Bisect the side AB.
c) Bisect the side AD.
   The treasure was hidden at a point which is the same distance from A and B and the same distance from A and D.
d) Mark the position of the treasure with an X on your diagram.

■ ■

Reading map scales

This is a map of part of Guernsey drawn to a scale of $1\,cm = 1\,km$.

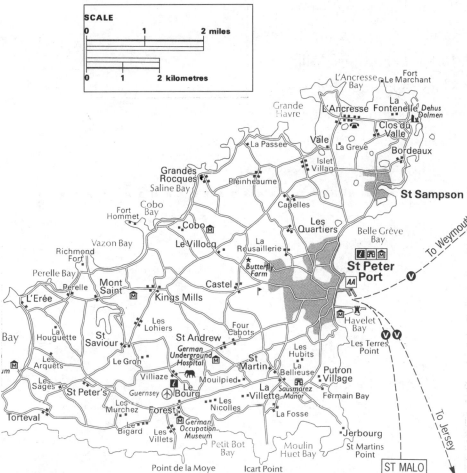

Example

Find the direct distance between St Andrew and Icart Point.

On the map the distance is 3.5 cm.

So, the distance between St Andrew and Icart Point is 3.5 km.

PAUSE

Find the direct distance between:

1 Grandes Rocques and Vale,

2 Vale and Bordeaux,

3 Bordeaux and Putron Village,

4 Putron Village and Grandes Rocques,

5 Grandes Rocques and Torteval,

6 Torteval and Kings Mills,

7 Kings Mills and St Peter's,

8 St Peter's and Jerbourg,

9 Jerbourg and Fort Hommet,

10 Fort Hommet and Point de la Moye.

■ ■

Map scales

This is a map of East Anglia and the East Midlands drawn to a scale of 1 cm = 20 km.

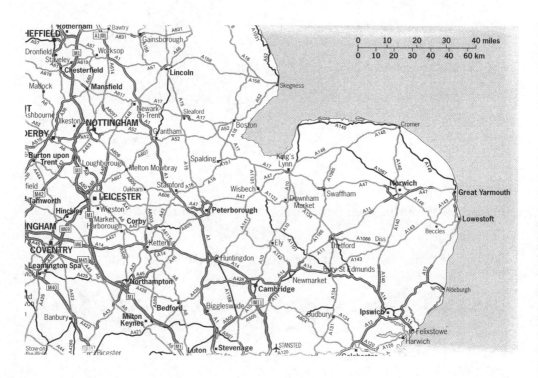

Examples

1. Estimate the direct distance between Norwich and Peterborough.

   On the map the distance is 5.5 cm.

   So, the distance between Norwich and Peterborough = $5.5 \times 20 = 110$ km.

2. If two towns are 136 km apart, what will be the distance between them on the map?
   Distance = $136 \div 20 = 6.8$ cm.

PAUSE

Estimate the direct distance between:

1 King's Lynn and Swaffham,

2 Swaffham and Lowestoft,

3 Lowestoft and Felixstowe,

4 Felixstowe and Lincoln,

5 Lincoln and Leamington Spa,

6 Leamington Spa and Sleaford,

7 Sleaford and Boston,

8 Boston and Cambridge,

9 Cambridge and Worksop,

10 Worksop and Skegness.

What will be the distance on the map between towns which are:

11 178 km apart,

12 286 km apart,

13 34 km apart,

14 58 km apart,

15 242 km apart?

This is a map of part of London drawn to a scale of 1 cm = 100 m.

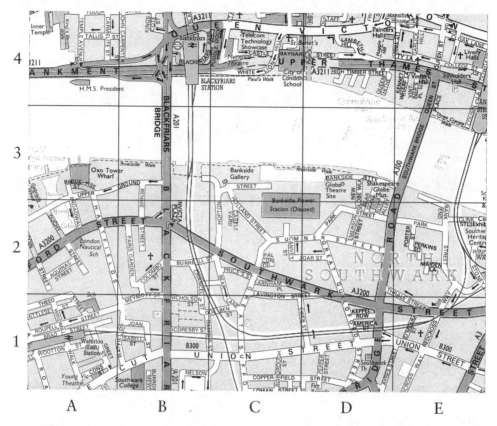

A   B   C   D   E

Examples

1. Estimate the length of Southwark Bridge.

   Southwark Bridge is 2 cm long on the map.

   The length of Southwark Bridge $= 2 \times 100 = 200$ m.

2. If a street is 480 metres long, how long will it be on the map?

   Length $= 480 \div 100 = 4.8$ cm.

PAUSE

Estimate the length of:

1 Scoresby St., B1

194

2 Sumner St., C2/D2

3 Holland St., C2/C3

4 Blackfriars Bridge, B3/B4

5 Union St., B1/C1/D1/E1

6 Great Guildford St., D1/D2

7 Hatfields, A2/A3/B1/B2

8 Park St., D2/E2

9 Temple Avenue, A4

How long will a street be on the map if its real length is:

10 597 m,

11 147 m,

12 831 m,

13 1 km,

14 1.3 km?

■ ■

Bearings

Bearings are used to measure the direction in which one location lies from another. For example, this sketch map shows the locations of Cambridge and Norwich.

Three steps are needed to measure the bearing of Norwich from Cambridge.

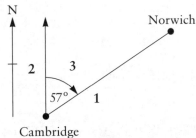

1 Draw in a line connecting Cambridge to Norwich.
2 Draw in a line through Cambridge pointing due North.
3 Measure the clockwise angle between the North line and the line connecting the two places.

Bearings are always written with three figures. The bearing of Norwich from Cambridge is 057°.

The bearing of *Cambridge from Norwich* is *not* the same as the bearing of *Norwich from Cambridge*. This map shows the necessary construction to measure the bearing of Cambridge from Norwich.

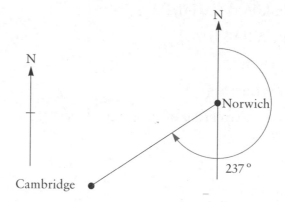

The bearing of Cambridge from Norwich is 237°.

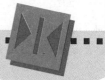

PAUSE

1 Newcastle-on-Tyne is 70 miles to the north and 50 miles to the east of Kendal.

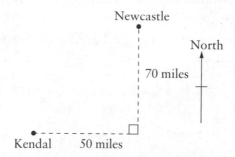

   a) What is the bearing of Newcastle from Kendal?
   b) What is the bearing of Kendal from Newcastle?

2 Manchester is 40 miles to the north and 40 miles to the west of Nottingham.

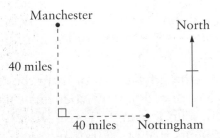

a) What is the bearing of Manchester from Nottingham?
b) What is the bearing of Nottingham from Manchester?

3 Bradford is 150 miles to the north and 40 miles to the west of Chelmsford.

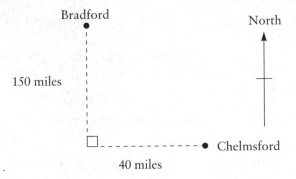

a) What is the bearing of Bradford from Chelmsford?
b) What is the bearing of Chelmsford from Bradford?

4

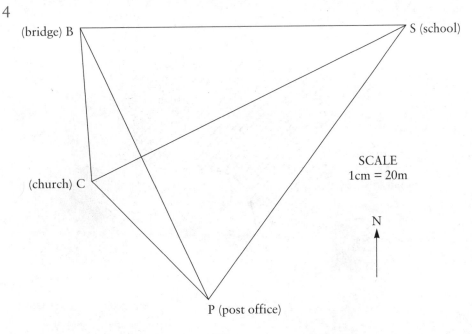

197

The diagram is an accurate scale drawing showing some features of a village. The bridge is due north of the church.

a) i) Measure the size of angle BCS.
   ii) What is the bearing of the school from the church?
b) i) Measure the length of PS. Give your answer in centimetres.
   ii) How far is the school from the post-office?
c) Taking measurements from the drawing, find:
   i) the distance, BP, of the post-office from the bridge,
   ii) the bearing of the post-office from the bridge.   (NICCEA)

5 In the village of Little Marsh, the church is 100 m due north of the post office.

a) Use a scale of 1 cm to 20 m to draw the positions of the church and post office.
b) The village Hall, H, is south-east of the church and 130 m from the post-office. On your drawing find by construction the position of H.

6 The map shows part of a coastline and a coastguard station.
1 cm on the map represents 2 km.
A ship is 12 km from the coastguard station on a bearing of 160°.
Copy the map and plot the position of the ship from the coastguard station, using a scale of 1 cm to represent 2 km.

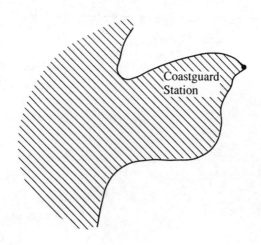

Coastguard Station

(ULEAC)

7 The map shows the position of a lighthouse, L, and a coastguard station, C. Copy the map on to squared paper.

The bearing of a ship, S, from the coastguard station, C, is 065 degrees and the distance CS is 16 km.

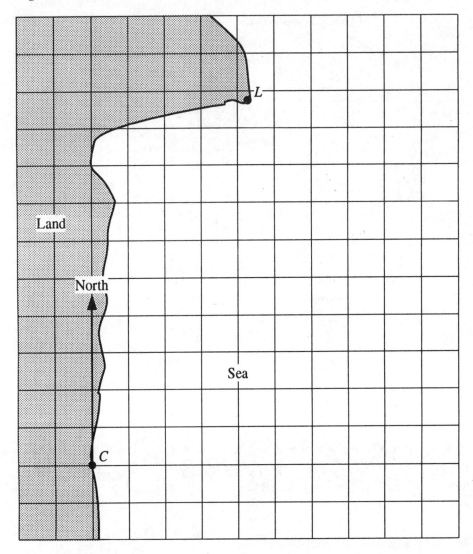

a) Using a scale of 1 cm to 2 km mark the position of S.
b) Describe the position of the ship from the lighthouse, L.

(SEG)

Solids

There are some common solids, with some words we use to describe them. Hidden edges are often shown by dotted lines to make the diagrams clearer. Isometric grid paper helps to draw these solids.

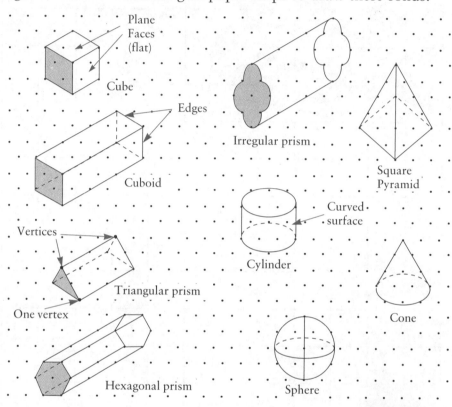

PAUSE

1 List the names of each basic solid which have been used to build up the diagram.

   Use isometric grid paper to copy the diagram.

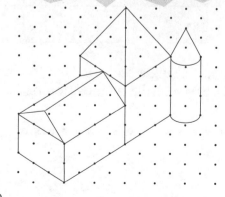

2 A sugar lump is an example of a cube. A can of beans is an example of a cylinder. Give 3 different examples of each of these solids.

a) cube   c) triangular prism   e) cone
b) cuboid   d) pyramid   f) sphere

3 Copy and complete this table:

Solid	Curved surfaces	Plane faces	Vertices	Edges
Cube	0	6	8	12
Cuboid				
Triangular prism				
Hexagonal prism				
Square-Pyramid				
Cylinder				
Cone				
Sphere				

Using an isometric grid

Isometric grid paper helps to draw solids.
These are shapes drawn on an isometric grid.

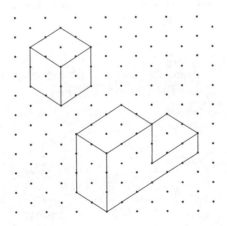

201

1 Make a copy of each diagram on isometric grid paper.

2 Use isometric grid paper to copy this diagram.

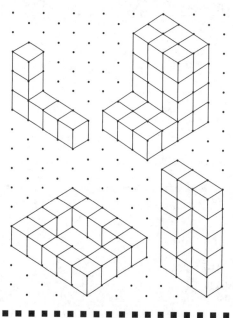

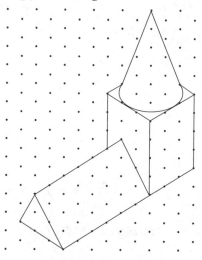

3 Draw an imaginary building on isometric grid paper.

Nets for solids

A net when cut out and folded forms the outside of a hollow solid. For example, this is one possible net for a cube.

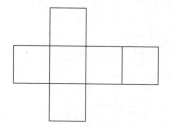

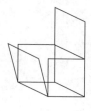

1 a) Here are two more patterns of six squares:

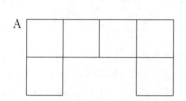

   Which one is the net of a cube?
   b) Draw on squared paper five more nets for a cube. Check each
   one by cutting it out and folding it.

2 Diagram A is part of the net of the cuboid B.

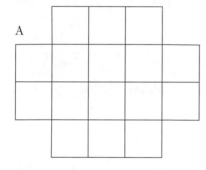

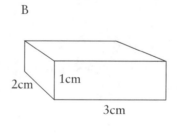

   a) Copy diagram A on to squared paper.
   b) Complete diagram A to make a net for the cuboid.

3 Draw a net for a cuboid which is 3 cm wide, 3 cm high and
   4 cm long. Check your net by cutting it out and folding it.

4 Draw a net for a cuboid which is 2 cm wide, 2.5 cm high and 3 cm
   long. Check your net by cutting it out and folding it.

5 This is the net for a solid drawn on a grid.

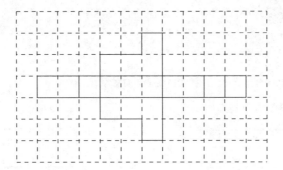

   a) Describe the solid.
   b) Check your description by copying the net, cutting it out and
      folding it.

6 This diagram shows three open topped boxes, A, B and C and
   three nets, D, E and F. Match each box to one of the nets.

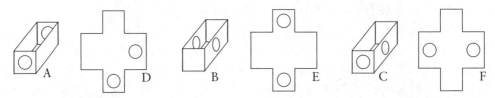

7 Describe the solids that you think each of the following nets will
   make.

   a)

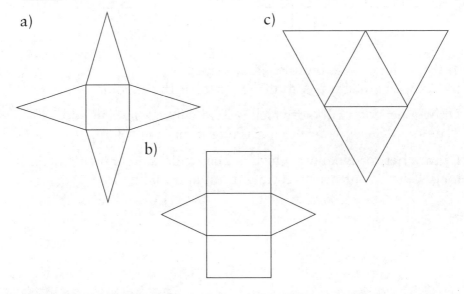

   b)

   c)

Plans and elevations

This diagram shows three different views of the same car.

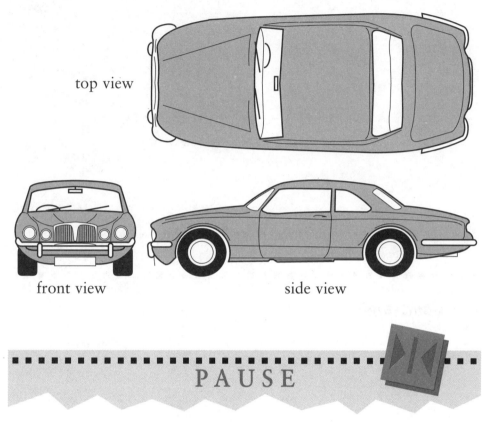

top view

front view

side view

PAUSE

1 A, B and C are three views of the triangular prism.

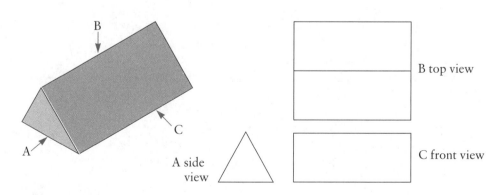

B top view

C front view

A side view

Sketch the required view in each of these questions.

a) Show a side view of this cuboid.

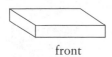

front

b) Show a top view of this cube.

front

c) Show a top view of this hexagonal prism.

d) Show a side view of this cylinder.

2 Select a simple object. Draw a top view, a side view and a front view of the object.

■ ■

Lines and angles

Examples

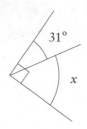

angle $x = 90° - 31° = 59°$

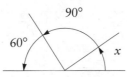

$x = 180° - (90° + 60°)$

$x = 180° - 150°$

$x = 30°$

angle $y = 360° - (174° + 47° + 50°)$

angle $y = 360° - 271° = 89°$

206

1 Find the size of each unknown angle in these diagrams:

a)

f)

k)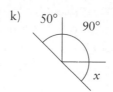

p)

b)

g)

l)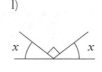

q)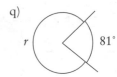

c)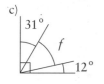

h)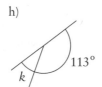

m)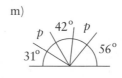

r)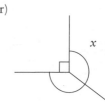

d)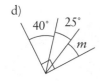

i)

n)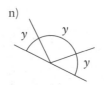

s)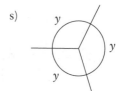

e)

j)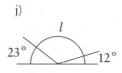

o)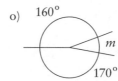

t)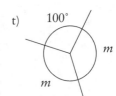

When a pair of lines intersect, then opposite angles are equal.

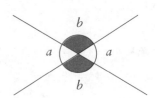

Example
Find the angles marked with letters.

$a = 180 - 50 = 130°$ (*a* and 50° are on a straight line)
$b = 50°$ (*b* and 50° are opposite angles)
$c = a = 130°$ (*c* and *a* are opposite angles)
$a = 130°$, $b = 50°$ $c = 130°$

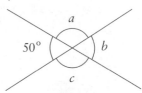

PAUSE

Find the angles marked with letters.

1
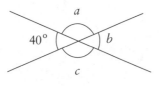

2
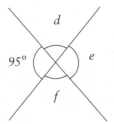

3
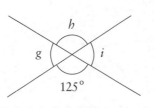

4
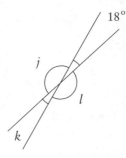

5

6
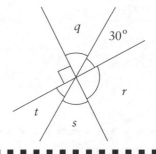

This diagram shows a third line crossing a pair of parallel lines.

The 'top set' of four angles is the same as the 'bottom set' of four angles.

All the angles marked with the letter *a* are equal.

All the angles marked with the letter *b* are equal.

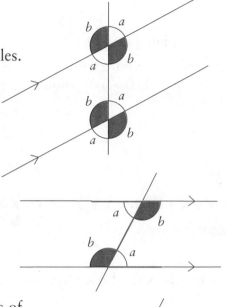

This diagram shows two pairs of *alternate angles*, *a* and *a* are on alternate sides of the crossing line.

Alternate angles (sometimes called 'Z' angles) are equal.

This diagram shows two of the pairs of *corresponding angles*, *b* and *b* are in corresponding places in the 'top set' and 'bottom set' of angles.

There are four pairs of corresponding angles altogether.

Corresponding angles (sometimes called 'F' angles) are equal.

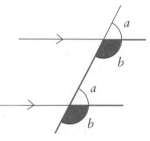

a and *b* are *interior angles*. Interior angles add up to 180°. There are two pairs of interior angles.

Examples

1. Calculate angles *a*, *b*, *c*, *d*, *e*, *f* and *g*.

   $a = 60°$
   $b = 120°$
   $c = 60°$
   $d = 120°$
   $e = 60°$
   $f = 120°$
   $g = 60°$

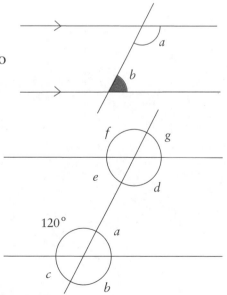

2. Find angles *a* and *b*.

a = 40° (alternate angles)
b = 180° − 110° = 70° (interior angles)

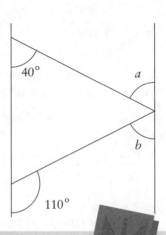

▪ ▪

PAUSE

1 Find the size of each unknown angle in these diagrams.

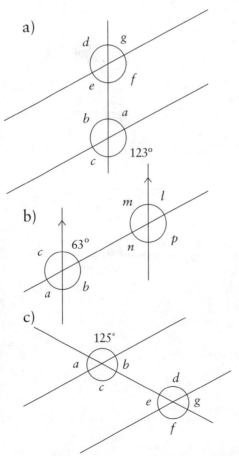

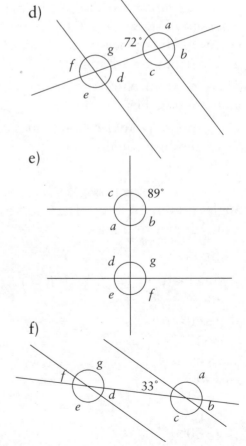

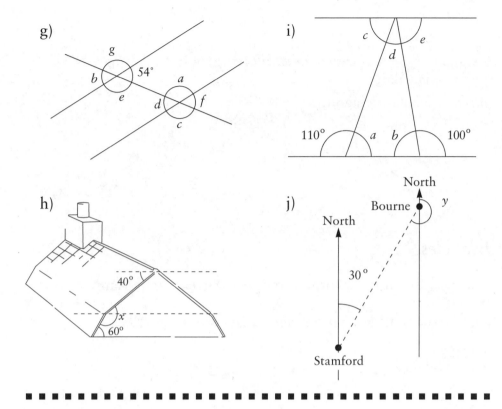

Polygons

A *polygon* is a shape made from straight lines.
These are all examples of polygons:

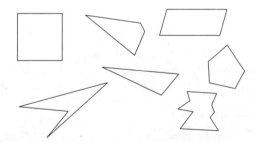

Number of sides	Name of polygon
3	triangle
4	quadrilateral
5	pentagon
6	hexagon
7	heptagon
8	octagon

211

If a polygon has all its sides and all its angles equal it is called a
regular polygon.

A regular triangle is called an **equilateral triangle**. A square is a
regular quadrilateral.

This is a regular octagon.

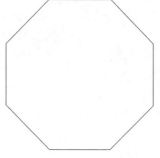

Triangles

Triangles, the simplest form of polygon, have an important angle
property.

The three angles inside a triangle always add up to 180°.

Example

   Find angle x.

   angle $x = 180° - (75° + 63°)$
   angle $x = 180° - 138°$
   angle $x = 42°$

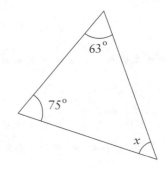

An *isosceles* triangle has two equal sides.
The equal sides are usually marked
on a diagram by dashes.

The angles formed between the
equal sides and the third side are
always equal. In this isosceles triangle,
AB and AC are the equal sides and
angles ABC and ACB are the equal
angles.

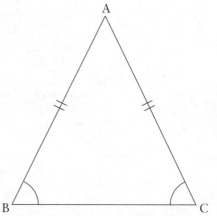

A *scalene* triangle has no equal
sides or angles.

Example
Find angle x and angle y.
As the triangle is isosceles:

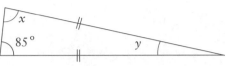

angle $x = 85°$
$$y = 180° - (85° + 85°)$$
$$= 10°$$

■ ■

PAUSE

1 Find the size of each unknown angle in these diagrams.

a)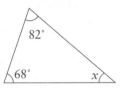

b)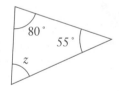

c)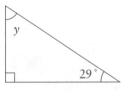

d)

e)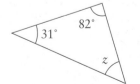

f)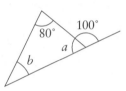

g)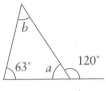

h)

i)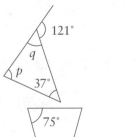

j)

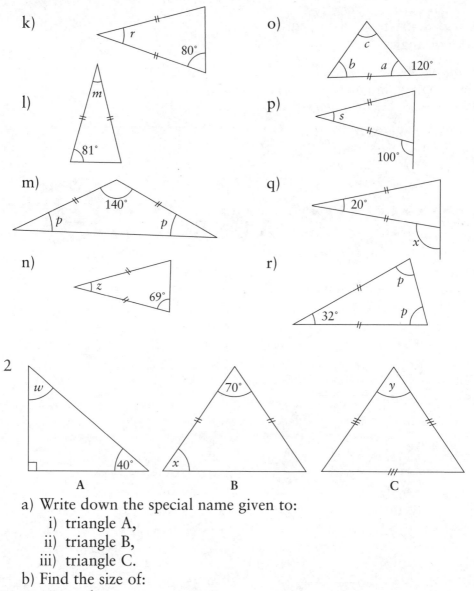

k)

l)

m)

n)

o)

p)

q)

r)

2

A   B   C

a) Write down the special name given to:
   i) triangle A,
   ii) triangle B,
   iii) triangle C.
b) Find the size of:
   i) angle *w*,
   ii) angle *x*,
   iii) angle *y*.

(NEAB)

3

A   B

Not to
scale

85°

55°

P   Q

a) Work out the size of angle ABP.

b) AB is parallel to PQ.

Work out the size of angle BPQ. (SEG)

4

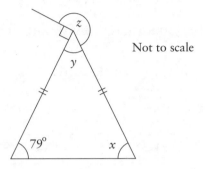

Not to scale

Work out the sizes of angles x, y and z.

(MEG)

5

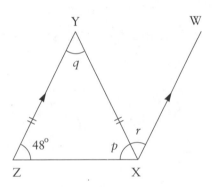

In the diagram $XY = ZY$ and ZY is parallel to XW.

a) Write down the size of angle p.

b) Calculate the size of angle q.

c) Write down the size of angle r. (SEG)

■■■■■■■■■■■■■■■■■■■■■■■■■■■■■■■■■■■■

Quadrilaterals

Any four-sided polygon is called a *quadrilateral*.

There are several different types of quadrilateral, each with its own name and special properties. You are asked to discover some of these properties in the next exercise.

1 A *trapezium* is a quadrilateral with one pair of parallel sides.

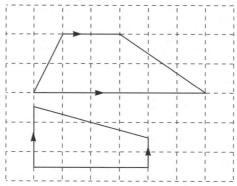

Draw three different trapeziums on squared paper.

2 A *parallelogram* is a quadrilateral with two pairs of parallel sides.

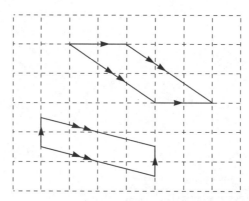

a) Draw three different parallelograms on squared paper.
b) By making measurements on your drawings, what can you discover about:
- the angles of a parallelogram,
- the diagonals of a parallelogram?

3 A *rhombus* is a quadrilateral with four equal sides.

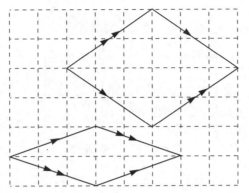

a) Draw three different rhombuses on squared paper.
b) By making measurements on your drawings, what can
   you discover about:
   • the angles of a rhombus,
   • the diagonals of a rhombus?

4 A *rectangle* is a quadrilateral with two pairs of parallel sides and
   interior angles of 90°.

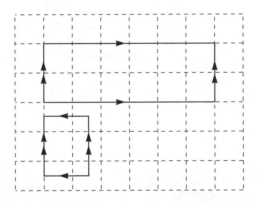

a) Draw three different rectangles on squared paper.
b) By making measurements on your drawings, what can you
   discover about:
   • the angles of a rectangle,
   • the diagonals of a rectangle?

5 A *square* is a quadrilateral with four equal sides and interior angles of 90°.

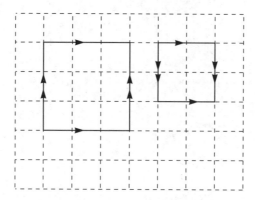

a) Draw three different squares on squared paper.
b) By making measurements on your drawings, what can you discover about:
  • the angles of a square,
  • the diagonals of a square?

6 A *kite* is a quadrilateral with two pairs of equal sides arranged in adjacent pairs.

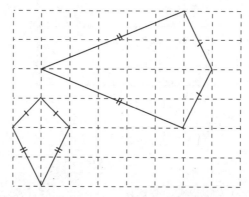

a) Draw three different kites on squared paper.
b) By making measurements on your drawings, what can you discover about:
  • the angles of a kite,
  • the diagonals of a kite?

The angles in a polygon

The angles formed inside a polygon are called *interior* angles.

If each side of a polygon is extended, the angles formed are called the *exterior* angles of the polygon.

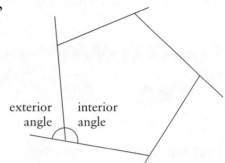

We know that the three interior angles of any triangle always add up to 180°. The interior angles of any other type of polygon also always add up to a fixed total.

Examples

1. Find the sum of the interior angles of the pentagon below.

   Starting at any corner point, divide the pentagon into triangles.

   The interior angles of the pentagon are equal to the angles of three triangles. The interior angles of the pentagon must add up to 180° × 3 or 540°.

2. Find the size of the interior and exterior angles in a regular pentagon.

   From the last example, we know that the five interior angles in any pentagon total 540°.

   In a regular pentagon, all the interior angles are equal.

   Each interior angle must be equal to 540° ÷ 5 = 108°.

   Each pair of interior and exterior form an angle of 180°.

So, each exterior angle must be equal to 180° − 108° = 72°.

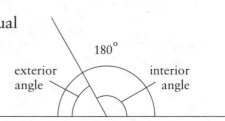

If you go round the outside of any polygon, turning through each exterior angle you make a complete turn of 360°.
So we have the rule:
Sum of the exterior angles of *any* polygon = 360°

PAUSE

1 Find:

    a) the total of the interior angles in a quadrilateral,
    b) the size of each interior angle in a regular quadrilateral,
    c) the size of the exterior angles in a regular quadrilateral,
    d) calculate angle x.

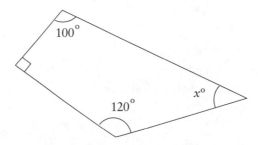

2 Find:

    a) the total of the interior angles in a decagon (ten sides),
    b) the size of each interior angle in a regular decagon,
    c) the size of the exterior angles in a regular decagon.

3 Find:

    a) the total of the interior angles in a hexagon,
    b) the size of each interior angle in a regular hexagon,
    c) the size of the exterior angles in a regular hexagon,
    d) calculate angle x.

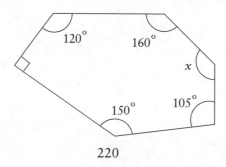

4 Find:

   a) the total of the interior angles in an octagon (eight sides)
   b) the size of each interior angle in a regular octagon,
   c) the size of the exterior angles in a regular octagon.

5 Find the number of sides of each of these regular polygons, given exterior angles of:

   a) 15°   b) 30°   c) 12°   d) 10°

6 If a regular polygon has interior angles of 162°, how many sides does it have?

7

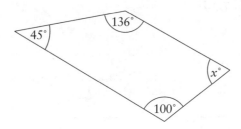

   Work out the value of x.

                                                    (ULEAC)

8

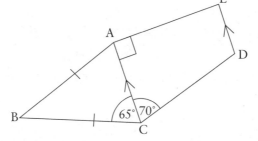

   Not to scale

   The pentagon ABCDE is the frame for Ibrahim's mountain bike.
   ABC is an isosceles triangle in which AB=BC and angle BCA=65°.
   In the quadrilateral ACDE, angle ACD=70°, angle CAE=90° and AC is parallel to ED.

   a) Calculate angle ABC, giving a reason for each step of your working.
   b) Calculate angle CDE, giving a reason for your answer.

                                                    (MEG)

221

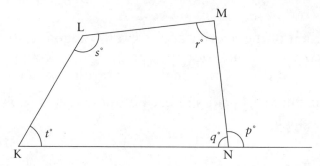

9

The diagram shows a quadrilateral KLMN drawn on a straight line KNX.

Complete the formula:

a) $p+q=$

b) $q+r+s+t=$

(ULEAC)

10 A workbench is standing on a horizontal floor.
The side view of the workbench is shown.

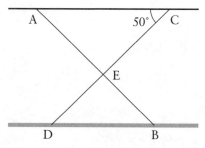

The legs AB and CD are equal in length and joined at E.
AE=EC.

a) Which two lines are parallel?
   Angle ACD is 50°.

b) Work out the size of angle BAC giving a reason for your answer.

(SEG)

11 A regular octagon, drawn below, has eight sides. One side of the octagon has been extended to form angle p.

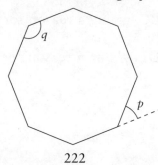

a) Work out the size of angle p.

b) Work out the size of angle q. 　　　　　　　　　　　(SEG)

Tessellations

A *tessellation* is a pattern of shapes which cover a flat surface leaving no gaps or overlaps. For example, it is possible to fit regular hexagons together in this way to form a tessellation.

PAUSE

1 This is the start of a tessellation of equilateral triangles and hexagons.

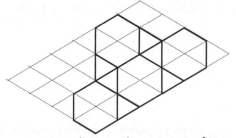

a) Copy the diagram on to isometric paper and extend the tessellation.

b) Draw a different tessellation of equilateral triangles and hexagons.

2 Use squared paper to draw a tessellation of squares.
Can you discover more than one possible tessellation of squares?

3 On squared paper, draw a tessellation of this shape.

Transformation geometry describes the ways in which the position of an object can be changed.

All changes in position can be described in terms of three basic movements, *translations, rotations* and *reflections*.

Translations

A *translation* changes the position of an object by moving every point on the object through the same distance in the same direction.

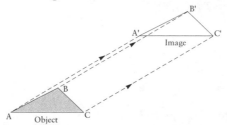

The shape in the new position is usually called the *image*.

If the object is labelled ABC the image is labelled A′B′C′.

Translations are usually applied to objects drawn on a square grid or a graph.

A translation is described using the *horizontal movement* and the *vertical movement*.

These movements are written in a bracket underneath each other so they do not look like coordinates.

This diagram shows how four translations applied to a shaded quadrilateral are described.

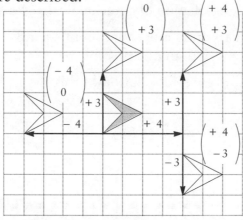

PAUSE

1 This diagram shows a shaded triangle moved to eight new positions.

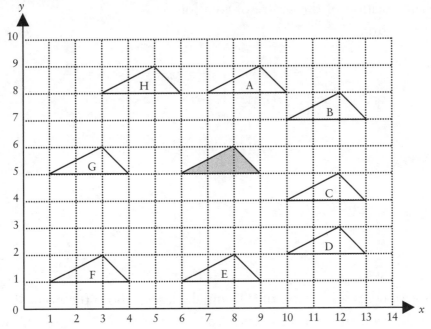

a) Copy the diagram.
b) Beside each image write the translation which moves the shaded triangle to that position.

2 Draw a graph with x- and y-axes from −6 to +6. Plot the triangle with corner points at (0,1), (−3,1) and (−3,2). Show on your graph the new position of this triangle after each of the following translations.

a) $\begin{pmatrix} +5 \\ +4 \end{pmatrix}$ c) $\begin{pmatrix} +5 \\ +0 \end{pmatrix}$ e) $\begin{pmatrix} -4 \\ -0 \end{pmatrix}$ g) $\begin{pmatrix} -3 \\ -7 \end{pmatrix}$

b) $\begin{pmatrix} +3 \\ -2 \end{pmatrix}$ d) $\begin{pmatrix} 0 \\ -4 \end{pmatrix}$ f) $\begin{pmatrix} -3 \\ +3 \end{pmatrix}$ h) $\begin{pmatrix} +4 \\ -6 \end{pmatrix}$

Rotations

A **rotation** changes the position of an object by turning it about a fixed point called the **centre of rotation**.

We describe a rotation by stating three facts.

- ◾ The angle that the object has been rotated through.
- ◾ The direction of rotation (anticlockwise or clockwise).
- ◾ The position of the centre of rotation.

This rotation

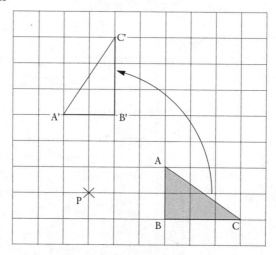

is described as a rotation of 90° anticlockwise about the point P.

This diagram shows rotations of 90°, 180° and 270° completed on squared paper.

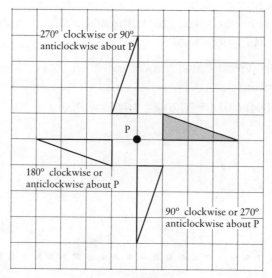

1 Copy each of the following diagrams. Use tracing paper to help you draw the image of the object after the stated rotation about the marked point.

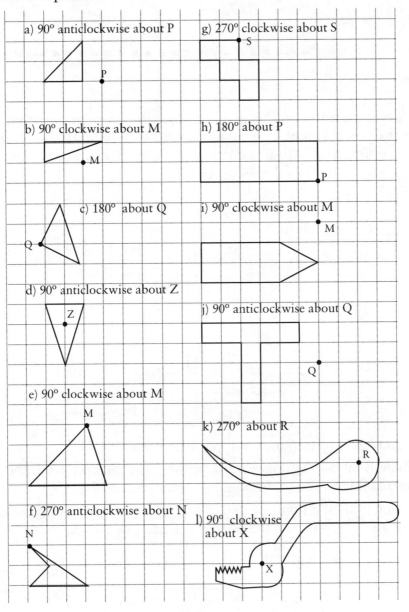

2 Draw a graph with x- and y-axes from −6 to +6. Plot the triangle with corner points at (0,1), (−3,1) and (−3,2). Show on your graph the new position of this triangle after each of the following rotations.

a) 90° clockwise about (0,0)
b) 180° about (0,0)
c) 90° anticlockwise about (0,0)
d) 270° anticlockwise about (−3,2)
e) 270° clockwise about (0,6)
f) 180° about (−1,2)

■ ■

Reflections

A reflection creates an image of an object in the same way that a mirror does. If you place a small mirror along the reflection line in this diagram, you will see an image in the mirror which is identical to the one that has been drawn on the page.

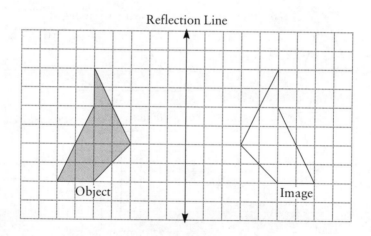

To complete a reflection, we apply two rules:

1. Each point on the image must be the same distance from the mirror line as the corresponding point on the object.

2. A line joining a point on the object to the corresponding point on the image must cross the mirror line at right angles.

Example

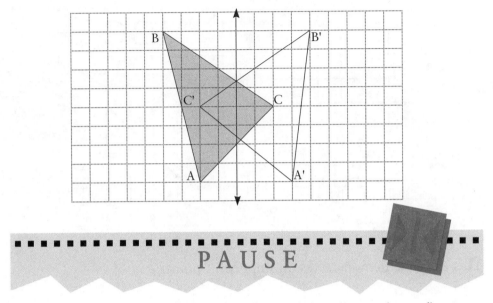

Copy each diagram and draw the image of the object after reflection in the mirror line.

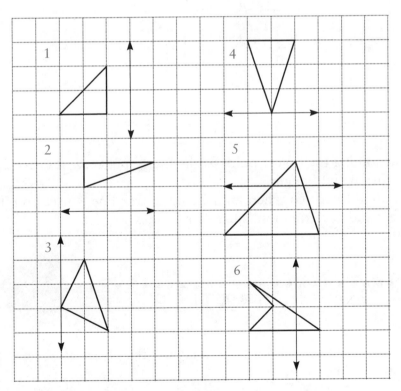

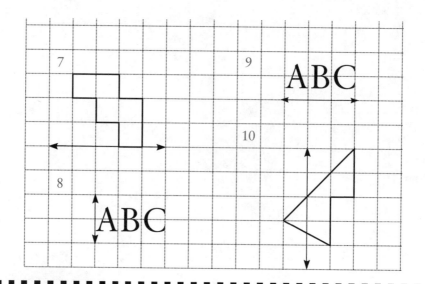

This example demonstrates an important point.

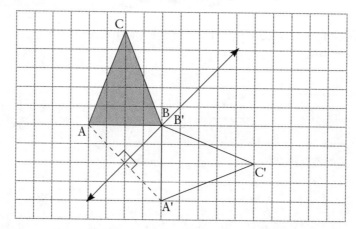

The line joining the object point to the image point *must* cross the mirror line at right angles.

This is often forgotten when an inclined mirror line is used to reflect an object and is a common cause of mistakes.

PAUSE

Copy each diagram and draw the image of the object after reflection in the mirror line.

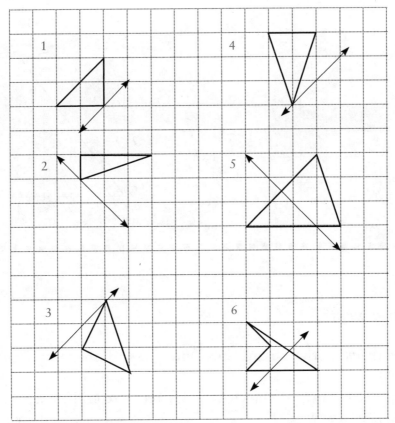

7 Copy each graph and reflect the object in the line with the given equation.

a)

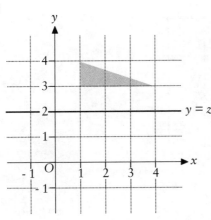

b)

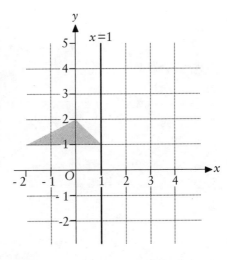

c)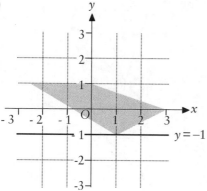

d)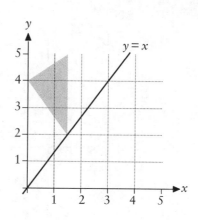

■ ■

Enlargements

An **enlargement** changes an object into one with the same *shape* but a different *size*.

Enlargements can be completed on different size grids.

Example

This is a shape drawn on a 1 cm grid.

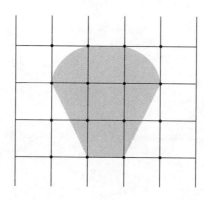

This is the same shape drawn on a 2 cm grid.

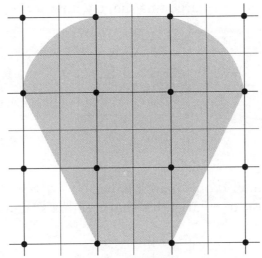

The shape has been *enlarged* by a *scale factor of 2.*

PAUSE

1 a) Draw a 2 cm grid on squared paper.
   b) Use your grid to enlarge this shape with a scale factor of 2.

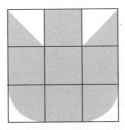

2 a) Draw a 2 cm grid on squared paper.
   b) Use your grid to enlarge this shape with a scale factor of 2.

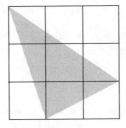

3 a) Draw a 3cm grid on squared paper.
  b) Use your grid to enlarge this shape with a scale factor of 3.

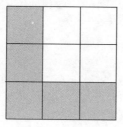

4 a) Draw a 4cm grid on squared paper.
  b) Use your grid to enlarge this shape with a scale factor of 4.

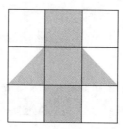

5

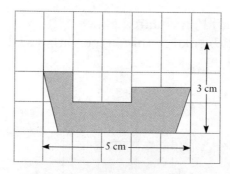

The shaded part of the diagram represents the end view of a piece
of metal. The view is drawn inside a rectangular framework
measuring 5cm by 3cm. An enlarged drawing of the end view is to
be made inside a framework measuring 10cm by 6cm.

a) What will be the scale factor of the enlargement?
b) Draw the enlarged framework.
c) Draw and shade the enlargement of the end view inside the
   framework you have drawn.   (ULEAC)

We can also complete an enlargement, by drawing lines outwards from a centre of enlargement through the main points on the object.

Along each of these lines, we first measure the distance of the object point from the centre of enlargement.

Multiplying this distance by the scale factor gives us the distance on that line of the image point from the centre of enlargement.

Examples
1. Enlargement, centre P, scale factor 2.

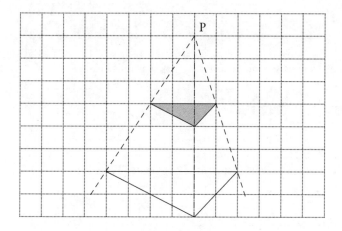

2. Enlargement, centre Q, scale factor 3.

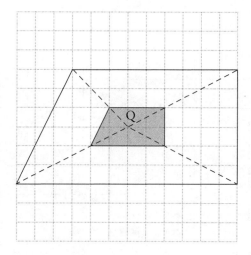

PAUSE

1 Copy each of the following diagrams and draw in the image of the object after the stated enlargement.

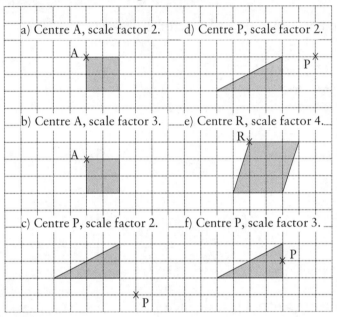

a) Centre A, scale factor 2.   d) Centre P, scale factor 2.

b) Centre A, scale factor 3.   e) Centre R, scale factor 4.

c) Centre P, scale factor 2.   f) Centre P, scale factor 3.

2 Copy the diagram and, using the point O as the centre of enlargement, enlarge the shaded rectangle with scale factor 3.

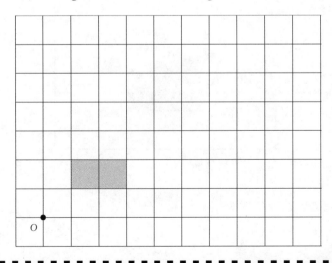

(MEG)

Mixed transformations

Many examination questions will require a mixture of translation, rotation, reflection and enlargement. The following exercise contains questions like this.

■ ■

PAUSE

1 This diagram shows a tessellation of irregular quadrilaterals drawn on a square grid.

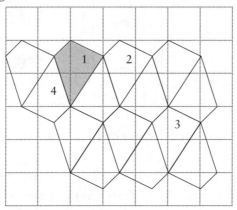

What transformation will move:
a) quadrilateral 1 on to quadrilateral 2,
b) quadrilateral 1 on to quadrilateral 3,
c) quadrilateral 1 on to quadrilateral 4?

2

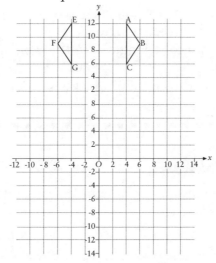

a) Describe, fully, the transformation that maps triangle ABC to triangle EFG.

b) Copy the diagram and draw the image of triangle ABC after translation 4 right and 2 down.

c) Draw the image of triangle ABC after a half turn about centre 0.

(ULEAC)

3

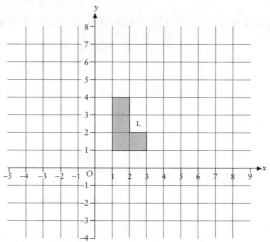

Copy the grid and show the results of the following transformations of the shape L.

a) A reflection of L in the x-axis. Label your answer A.

b) A half turn of L centre (0,0). Label your answer B.

c) An enlargement of L scale factor 2, centre (0,0). Label your answer C.   (ULEAC)

4 Draw a pair of axes from −6 to 6.

a) Plot the points (1, 2), (5, 2) and (5, 4).
Join them up to form a triangle.
Write the letter A in the triangle.

b) Draw the reflection of triangle A in the y-axis. Write the letter B in this triangle.

c) Rotate triangle A through 90° clockwise about the origin. Write the letter C in this triangle.

Rotational symmetry

Shapes which have rotational symmetry fit back into their original position as they are rotated.

The shape below fits back into its original position three times as it is rotated through 360°.

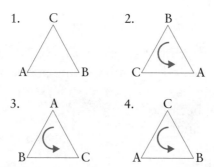

The shape has *rotational symmetry of order three*.

All shapes must fit back into their original position after a full rotation of 360°, so all shapes must have an order of rotational symmetry of at least one.

Sometimes a shape which has a rotational symmetry of order one may be called a shape with no rotational symmetry. This shape has rotational symmetry of order one (no rotational symmetry).

PAUSE

1 What is the order of rotational symmetry of each of the following shapes?

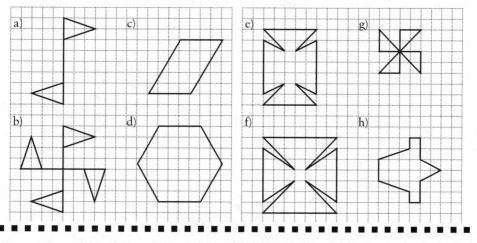

Reflectional symmetry

Shapes which have reflectional symmetry fit back into their original
position if they are reflected in a mirror line across the shape.
For example this shape has
reflectional symmetry because
it fits back into its original
position after a reflection
in the dotted mirror line.

The mirror line is called *an axis
of symmetry* or *a line of symmetry*.
Some shapes have several different
lines of symmetry. For example,
this shape has four lines of symmetry.

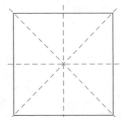

PAUSE

1 Copy each of the diagrams in the previous exercise. Mark on your
   diagrams all the lines of symmetry of each shape.

2 Which of the designs below have line symmetry?

a)

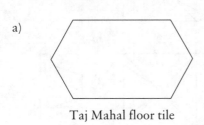

Taj Mahal floor tile

b)

Asian carpet design

c)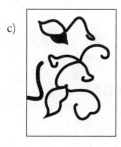

Contemporary art

d)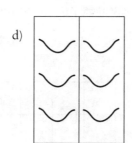

Wallpaper pattern

e)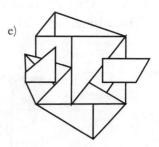

Tile design

(ULEAC)

3

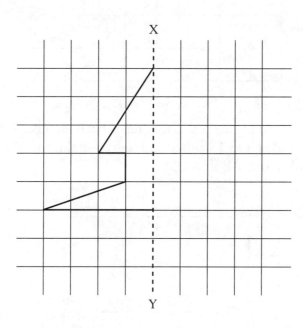

Copy and complete the diagram so that line XY is a line of symmetry of the complete diagram.

(ULEAC)

4 A crossword has shaded squares placed symmetrically about the two lines AB and CD.

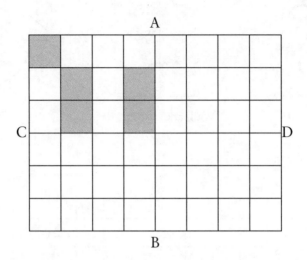

In the crossword above 5 squares have been shaded. Copy the crossword and shade 15 other squares to make the crossword symmetrical about AB and CD.

(MEG)

5

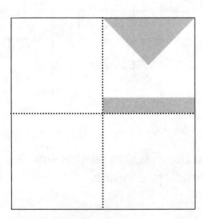

The picture shows a large tile with only part of its pattern filled in.
a) Copy and complete the picture so that the tile has rotational symmetry order 2.
b) How many lines of symmetry has the completed tile? (NEAB)

6 Copy this diagram:

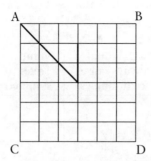

a) Draw extra lines on the grid so that the completed pattern has line symmetry about both of the lines AC and BD.
b) State the order of rotational symmetry of your completed pattern. (ULEAC)

7 a) Write down the number of lines of symmetry of a regular hexagon.
b) Copy this diagram and shade two triangles of the regular hexagon so that the resulting figure has only one line of symmetry.

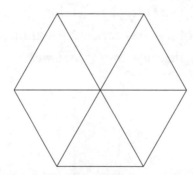

c) Make a new copy of the diagram and shade two triangles of the regular hexagon so that the resulting figure has rotational symmetry of order two. (MEG)

8 Copy and complete this table. The names of the quadrilaterals may be chosen from the following list: square, parallelogram, rhombus, kite and trapezium.

	Name of quadrilateral	Diagonal always cut at right angles	Number of axes of symmetry	Order of rotational symmetry
a)	rectangle			
b)		yes		2
c)			0	2
d)		yes	1	
e)				4

(NICCEA)

■■■■■■■■■■■■■■■■■■■■■■■■■■■■■■■■■■■■

Reflectional symmetry in solid objects

It may be possible to imagine a 'slice' through a solid object leaving two parts which are exact mirror reflections of each other.

In this case the solid object has reflective symmetry.

The mirror 'slice' is called a *plane of symmetry*.

Example
Draw diagrams to show all the planes of symmetry for this cuboid.

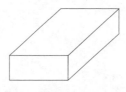

These are the required diagrams.

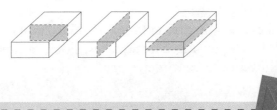

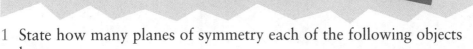

PAUSE

1 State how many planes of symmetry each of the following objects has.

a)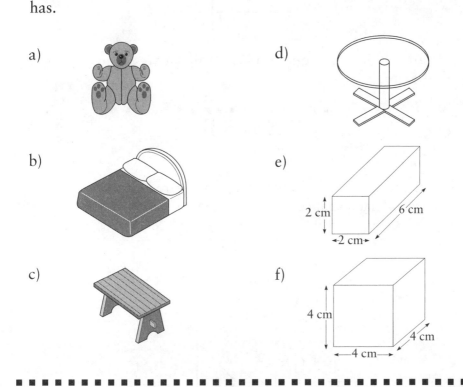

b)

c)

d)

e)

f)

SECTION 3 Perimeter, Area and Volume

Measuring area

The *area* of a shape is a measurement of the size of its surface.
In the metric system of measurements, the standard squares used to

measure area are the square millimetre, the square centimetre, the square metre and the hectare.

Other shapes cannot be divided into standard squares, but we can find their area by counting part squares. For example, this is a picture of a shape drawn on a centimetre grid.

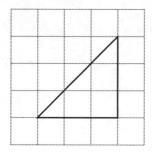

It has an area of 3 whole squares plus 3 half squares. The area of the shape is 4.5 cm².

PAUSE

This is a picture of shapes drawn on a centimetre grid.
Find the area of each shape.

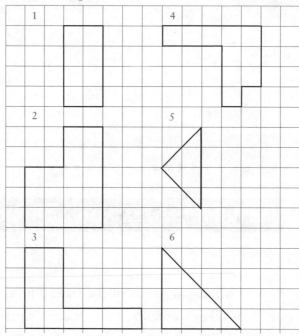

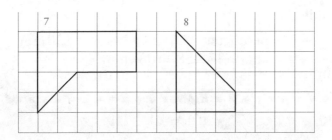

■■

Area and perimeter of a rectangle

The area of a rectangle can be calculated by multiplying the base length by the height.

The perimeter of a shape is the distance all the way round the outside of a shape.

Examples

1. Find the perimeter and area of this rectangle.

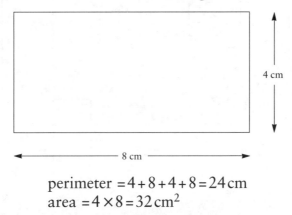

$$\text{perimeter} = 4+8+4+8 = 24\,\text{cm}$$
$$\text{area} = 4\times8 = 32\,\text{cm}^2$$

2. Find the perimeter and area of this rectangle.

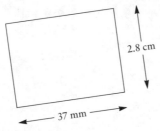

There is a mixture of units in the measurements given. We must therefore first convert all the measurements into either centimetres or millimetres.

Using millimetres:

$$\text{perimeter} = 37 + 28 + 37 + 28 = 130\,\text{mm}$$
$$\text{area} = 37 \times 28 = 1036\,\text{mm}^2$$

■■■■■■■■■■■■■■■■■■■■■■■■■■■■■■■■■

PAUSE

1 These rectangles are drawn on a centimetre grid. For each rectangle:

a) find the area by counting whole squares, half squares and quarter squares,

b) write down the height and base of each rectangle,

c) calculate the area by multiplying the height by the base.

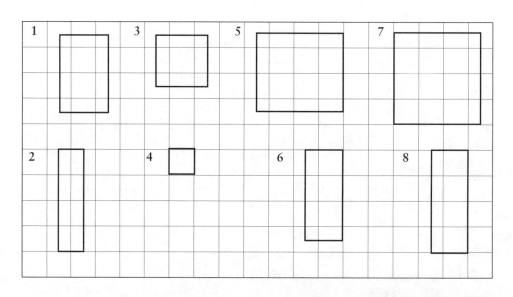

■■■■■■■■■■■■■■■■■■■■■■■■■■■■■■■■■■

Areas of shapes made from rectangles

Example

Fine the perimeter and area of this shape.

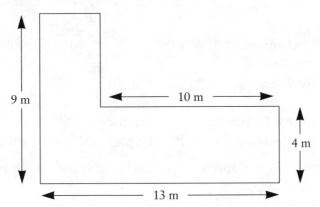

First, we must fill in all the missing measurements.

By comparing the length of 13 m and 10 m, we see that the missing length is 3 m.

By comparing the 9 m and the 4 m, we see that the missing height is 5 m.

The area is found by dividing the shape into rectangles, calculating their areas and then adding these areas together to find the area of the whole shape.

This diagram shows the extra measurements and has been divided into rectangles.

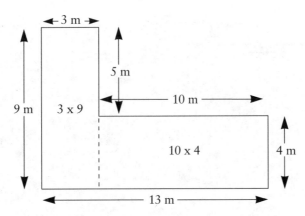

$$\text{Perimeter} = 3 + 5 + 10 + 4 + 13 + 9 = 44$$
$$\text{Area} = (3 \times 9) + (10 \times 4) = 27 + 40 = 67 \, \text{m}^2$$

1 Find the perimeter and area of rectangles with the following measurements.

a) 2cm by 16cm   e) 2.1m by 4.5m

b) 23m by 60m   f) 34mm by 7.3cm (in cm and cm²)

c) 165mm by 113mm   g) 125cm by 2.7m (in m and m²)

d) 8.9cm by 4.0cm   h) 24cm by 0.89m (in cm and cm²)

2 Find the perimeter and area of each of the following shapes.

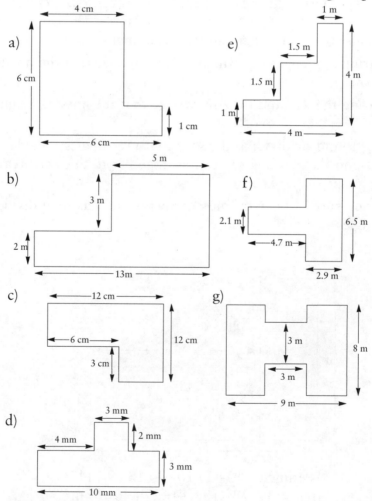

3 By making measurements correct to the nearest tenth of a centimetre, find the perimeter and area of each of the following shapes.

a)　　　　　　　　　　b)　　　　　　　　　　c)

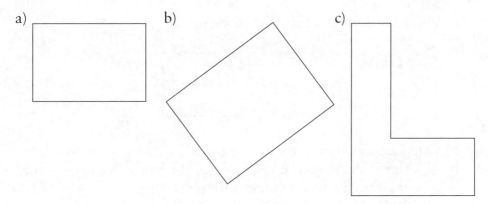

4 The carpet that Julie Hasdell wants to buy for her lounge is only available from a roll with a width of 4 m. The carpet shop will only sell a length cut from this roll, they will not sell carpet cut to any particular shape. These diagrams show the carpet roll and the measurements of Julie's lounge. Julie does not want any joins in the carpet.

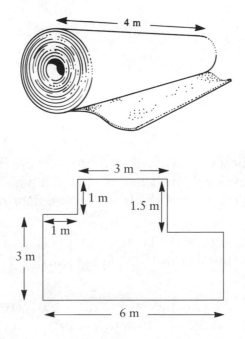

a) What length of carpet does Julie need to buy?
b) What is the area of the piece of carpet Julie buys?

c) If the carpet costs £9.99 per square metre, how much will Julie pay?

d) What area of the carpet will be wasted after it has been cut to fit Julie's lounge?

e) What is the cost of this wasted carpet?

5

14.4 cm

2.5 cm

Not to scale

a) Calculate the area of the rectangle.

b) i) What is the length of each side of the square which has the same area as the rectangle above?

ii) Draw this square accurately.

(MEG)

6

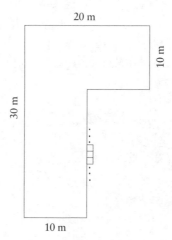

20 m

10 m

30 m

10 m

The diagram shows a lawn. All of its corners are right angles. Using flagstones which are 1 metre square, a path 1 metre wide is laid all around the edge of the lawn. (Three flagstones are drawn in place.)

a) Calculate the area of the lawn.

b) Calculate the number of flagstones needed.

(NICCEA)

7 Abrahim has broken a window and must buy glass to mend it. The window is in the shape of a rectangle 180 cm long and 120 cm wide.

a) Change the measurements to metres.

b) Work out the area of the window. Give your answer in square metres.

Glass costs £14.50 per square metre.

c) Work out the cost of the glass that Abrahim must buy.

(ULEAC)

■ ■

Area and perimeter of a parallelogram

Any parallelogram has the same area as a rectangle with the same base length and height.

Example
Find the area of this parallelogram.

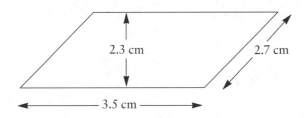

$$\text{area} = 3.5 \times 2.3 = 8.05 \, \text{cm}^2$$

■ ■

PAUSE

1 Calculate the area of these parallelograms drawn on a centimetre grid.

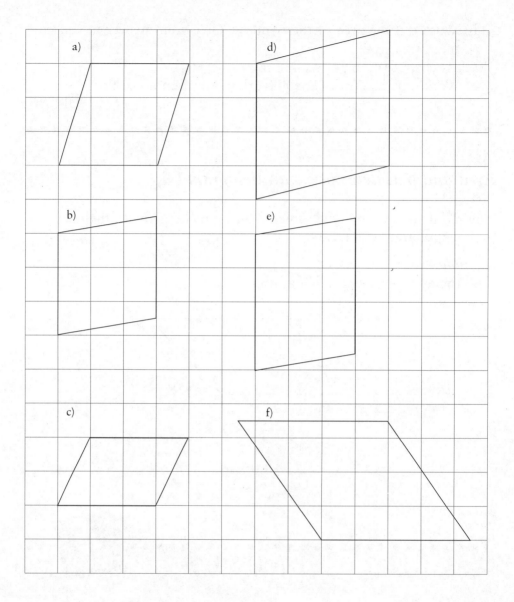

a)
b)
c)
d)
e)
f)

2 Find the area of parallelograms with the following measurements.
   a) base = 5 cm   height = 8 cm
   b) base = 5.4 m   height = 9.4 m
   c) base = 3.7 mm   height = 8.9 mm
   d) base = 5.4 m   height = 94 cm (in m^2)
   e) base = 456 mm   height = 0.89 m (in cm^2)

3 Find the area of each of the following shapes.

a)   b)

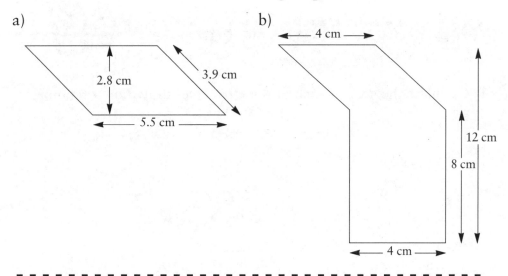

Area and perimeter of a triangle

Any triangle with a base b and a height h is half of a parallelogram with a base b and a height h.

Because the area of the parallelogram is $b \times h$, the area of the triangle is $\dfrac{b \times h}{2}$, or $\dfrac{bh}{2}$.

Example
Find the perimeter and
area of this triangle.

4.2 cm   3.6 cm   4.0 cm

3.7 cm

$$\text{perimeter} = 4.2 + 4.0 + 3.7 = 11.9 \, \text{cm}$$
$$\text{area} = \frac{3.6 \times 3.7}{2} = \frac{13.32}{2} = 6.66 \, \text{cm}^2$$

255

1 Calculate the area of each of these triangles drawn on a centimetre grid.

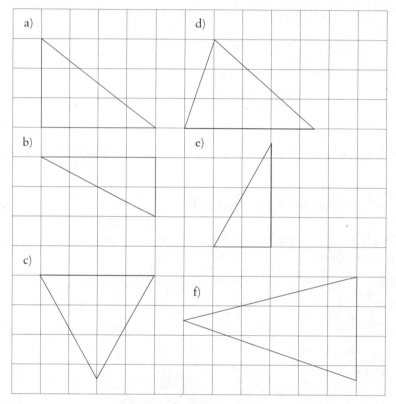

2 Find the area of triangles with the following measurements.

a) base = 5 cm height = 8 cm

b) base = 5.4 m height = 9.4 m

c) base = 3.7 mm height = 8.9 mm

d) base = 5.4 m height = 94 cm
   (in m²)

e) base = 456 mm height = 0.89 m
   (in cm²)

3 Find the area of each of the following shapes.

a)

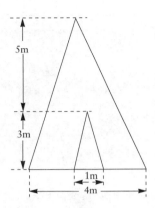

b)

4 An arrow for a traffic diversion
sign is made using an isosceles
triangle and a rectangle.

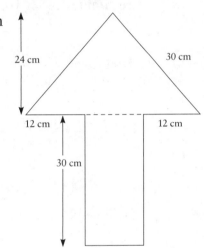

Calculate:

a) the perimeter of the arrow,
b) the area of the triangle,
c) the total area of the arrow.
                    (NICCEA)

5

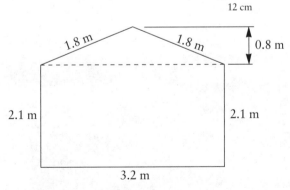

a) Calculate the perimeter of this shape.
b) This shape is made up of a rectangle and a triangle.
    i) Calculate the area of the rectangle.
    ii) Calculate the area of the triangle.   (SEG)

Area of a shape with cut out sections

Example

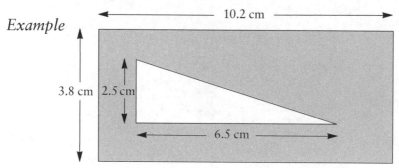

This shape is a rectangle with a triangle cut out.

area of rectangle $= 3.8 \times 10.2 = 38.76\,\text{cm}^2$

area of triangle $= \dfrac{6.5 \times 2.5}{2} = 8.125\,\text{cm}^2$

area of shape $= 38.76 - 8.125 = 30.635\,\text{cm}^2$

area of shape $= 30.6\,\text{cm}^2$ (correct to 1 decimal place)

PAUSE

Find the area of each shape.

1
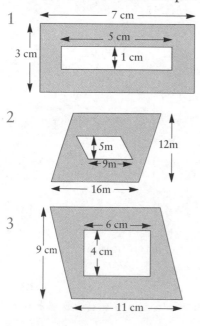

2

3

4
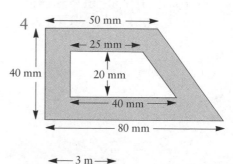

5
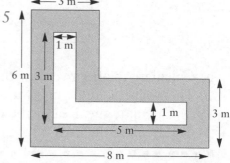

6 The diagram shows a special board for a game.

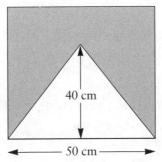

It has a triangle on a square of side 50 cm.

a) What is the area of the square?
b) What is the area of the shaded part of the board?
c) Find the ratio of the shaded area to the area of the whole board.

■ ■

The circumference of a circle

The *radius* of a circle is a line joining the centre to a point on the circle.

The *diameter* of a circle is a line which joins two points on the circle and passes through the centre.

The *circumference* of a circle is its perimeter, the distance around the outside of the circle.

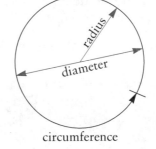

A rule to link the diameter and the circumference

An approximation for the circumference can be calculated by multiplying the diameter by a number between 3.1 and 3.2.

The numbers 3.1, 3.14 and 3.142 will give better and better approximations.

The Greek letter π (Pi) is used to stand for these different multipliers.

This allows us to write the formula:
$$C = \pi d$$
In most examination questions you will be told which value of π to use.

Example

Find the circumference of this circle using $\pi = 3.14$.

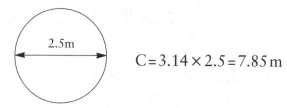

$$C = 3.14 \times 2.5 = 7.85 \, m$$

If you have a scientific calculator, it will have a special button to give a value for π.

The π button on an eight digit calculator gives the value 3.1415927.

We can use the formula 'in reverse' to find the diameter, if we are given the circumference. The reverse formula is:
$$d = \frac{C}{\pi}$$

Example

Find, correct to one decimal place, the diameter of a circle with a circumference of 36.5 cm ($\pi = 3.14$).
$$\text{diameter} = \frac{36.5}{3.14} = 11.6 \, cm$$

■ ■

PAUSE

1 Find, correct to one decimal place, the circumference of the following circles.

Use $\pi = 3.14$ or use the π button on your calculator.

a) diameter = 8 cm
b) radius = 8 cm
c) diameter = 3.5 m
d) radius = 10.8 mm
e) diameter = 240 m
f) radius = 43 mm

2 Using the value 3.14 for π or the π button on your calculator, find, correct to one decimal place, the diameter and radius of the following circles.

a) circumference = 314 cm
b) circumference = 100 mm
c) circumference = 59.5 cm
d) circumference = 37.2 mm

3 A bicycle is fitted with wheels which have a diameter of 65 cm.

a) What is the circumference of a wheel? (π = 3.14)
b) How far would you expect the bike to travel as the wheels turn 10 times?

4

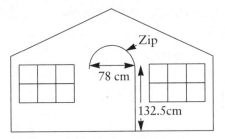

A flap door is made for a tent by using a zip as shown in the diagram. The zip is made up of a semicircle and a straight line.

What length of zip is required? (you may take π = 3.14)

(NICCEA)

5

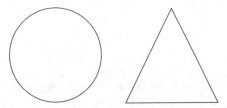

a) Calculate the circumference of a circle of radius 18 cm. (you may take π as 3.14)
b) An equilateral triangle has the same perimeter as the circle. Calculate the length of one side. (NICCEA)

261

6 Andre is rolling a hoop along the ground.

The hoop has a diameter of 60 cm.
a) What is the circumference of the hoop?
   Take π to be 3.14 or use the π key on your calculator.
b) What is the minimum number of times the hoop must rotate to cover a distance of 5 m?

(SEG)

7 The diagram below is a map of Megtown.

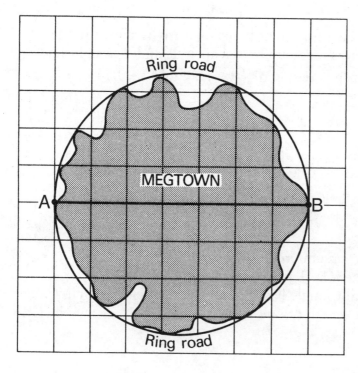

SCALE:
1 cm represents

a) By counting squares, estimate as accurately as you can the area of Megtown (the shaded area).
b) i)   What is the direct distance, in miles, from A to B?
   ii)   I travel from home, A, to work, B, along a straight road through the centre of Megtown. The journey takes me $\frac{1}{4}$ hour. What is my average speed?

(MEG)

c) A ring road is built around Megtown. It is a circle with AB as diameter.
   i)   What will be the total length of the ring road? Give your answer to the nearest mile. Take the value of π to be 3.14.
   ii) What is the distance from A to B around the ring road?
   iii) I travel from home to work around the ring road at an average speed of 60 mph. How long will this journey take? Give your answer in minutes.
d) How much time will I save on my journey from A to B by using the ring road rather than by going along the direct road?

8

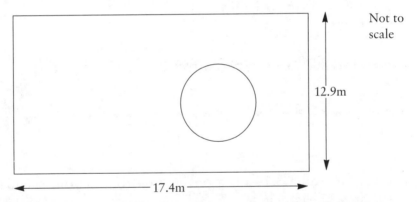

12.9m

Not to scale

17.4m

A rectangular lawn contains a circular pond of radius 3 metres.

a) Calculate the circumference of the pond. Take the value of π to be 3.14.
b) Calculate the perimeter of the rectangle.
c) An edging strip is to be placed around the circumference of the pond and the perimeter of the rectangle.
   i)   Calculate the total length of edging strip required.
   ii) Edging strip costs 68p per metre.
        Calculate the total cost of the edging strip, correct to the nearest penny.

(MEG)

■ ■

The area of a circle

The *area* of a circle can be found with the formula:
$$A = \pi \times r \times r$$
which can be written:
$$A = \pi r^2$$

Example

1. Find the area of this circle, correct to 2 decimal places, using the value 3.14 for π.

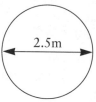

2.5m

radius = $2.5 \div 2 = 1.25$
area = $3.14 \times 1.25 \times 1.25 = 4.91 \, \text{m}^2$ (correct to 2 decimal places)

2. Find, correct to 2 decimal places, the radius of a circle with an area of $49.55 \, \text{m}^2$ ($\pi = 3.14$)

$r^2 = \dfrac{49.55}{3.14} = 15.780255$

$r = \sqrt{15.780255} = 3.97 \, \text{m}$ (correct to 2 decimal places).

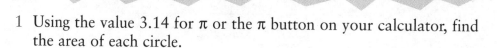

PAUSE

1 Using the value 3.14 for π or the π button on your calculator, find the area of each circle.

a)
2 cm

c)
5.5 cm

e)
55 cm

g)
3 cm

i)
6 m

b)
3.5 cm

d)
13.5 m

f)
2 cm

h)
9 cm

j)
15 mm

2 A cardboard party plate has a diameter of 22 cm.

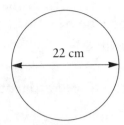

a) Calculate the circumference of the plate.
   Take π to be 3.14 or use the π key on your calculator.
b) i) What is the radius of the plate?
   ii) Calculate the area of the plate correct to the nearest whole
       number.

3 The instructions for a garden fertilizer state:

'Apply 100 grams per square metre'.

Estimate how many kilograms of fertilizer should be applied to a
circular flower bed with a diameter of 12 m (π = 3).

4 A circular plaque with a radius of 13.7 cm is to be plated with
silver.

a) Find the area of the plaque (π = 3.14).
b) Silver plating costs 35p per square centimetre. Find the total
   cost of silver plating the plaque.

5

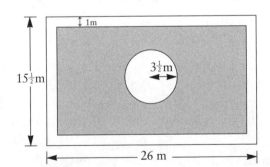

The diagram represents a rectangular garden measuring 26 m by
$15\frac{1}{2}$ m.

The garden is to be sown with grass seed except for a 1 m strip
around the edge and a circular rose bed of radius $3\frac{1}{2}$ m in the
centre.

(You may take π to be 3.14 or use the π button on your calculator.)
a) What are the length and breadth of the inner rectangle?
b) What is the area of the rose bed?
c) What is the area to be sown with grass seed?

A box of grass seed covers 25 m².

d) How many boxes of grass seed are required?

(NICCEA)

6

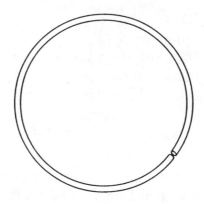

A piece of rope is 12 m long. It is laid on the ground in a circle, as shown in the diagram.

a) Using 3.14 as the value of π calculate the diameter of the circle.
b) Explain briefly how you would check the answer to part a) mentally.

The cross-section of the rope is a circle of radius 1.2 cm.

c) Calculate the area of the cross-section.

■ ■

Volume of a prism

The *volume* of an object is a measurement of the space that it occupies.

In the metric system of measurement the standard cubes used to measure volumes are the cubic millimetre (mm³), the cubic centimetre (cm³) and the cubic metre (m³).

The volumes of liquids are usually measured in litres (l).

A litre is 1000 cubic centimetres. The cubic centimetre is also called a *millilitre* (ml).

Find the volume of each of these solids built from centimetre cubes.

1

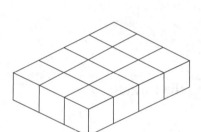

3

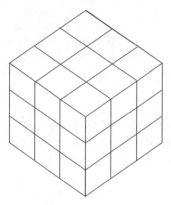

2

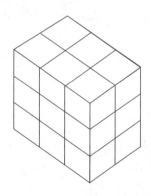

4

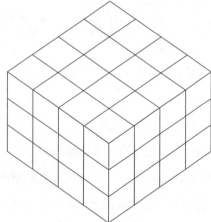

■ ■

Volume of a cuboid

This is a cuboid.

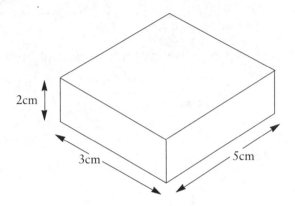

The volume of a cuboid is found using the formula:
Volume = length × width × height
The volume of the cuboid = $5 \times 3 \times 2 = 30\,\text{cm}^3$.

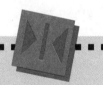

PAUSE

Find the volume of cuboids with these measurements.

1 length = 4 cm, width = 4 cm, height = 7 cm

2 length = 3 cm, width = 6 cm, height = 9 cm

3 length = 2.5 cm, width = 4 cm, height = 1 cm

4 length = 10 cm, width = 1.5 cm, height = 2 cm

5 length = 2.5 m , width = 1 m, height = 10 m

6

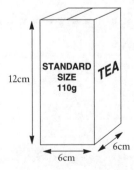

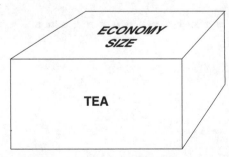

a) Calculate the volume of the Standard Size packet of tea.
b) The volume of the Economy Size packet is 1296 cm³. Calculate the weight of tea in the Economy Size packet, assuming both packets are completely filled.

(MEG)

Surface area of a cuboid

Look at this cuboid.

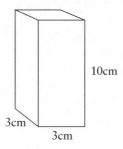

This is a sketch of the net of the cuboid.

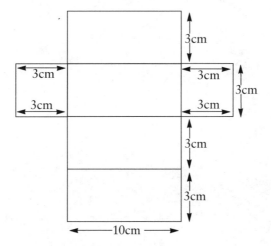

The surface area of the cuboid = $(10 \times 12) + (3 \times 3) + (3 \times 3)$
$$= 120 + 9 + 9$$
$$= 138 \, \text{cm}^2$$

In questions 1–5:

    a) Sketch the net of the cuboid.
    b) Calculate the surface area of the cuboid.
    c) Calculate the volume of the cuboid.

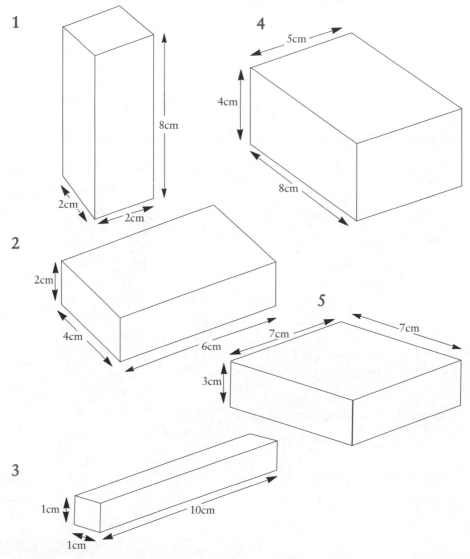

6

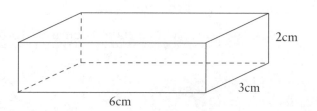

2cm
3cm
6cm

a) Calculate the volume of the cuboid shown.
b) Make an accurate drawing of a net of this cuboid.
c) Calculate the surface area of the cuboid.

(NICCEA)

■ ■

◀ ◀

REWIND

◀ ◀

1 Make an accurate drawing of these triangles.

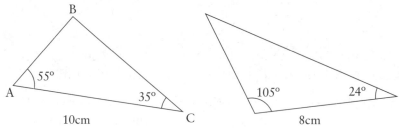

2 Chelmsford is 30 km to the west and 25 km to the south of
   Ipswich. Draw a map using a scale of 1 cm = 5 km. Find the
   bearing of Ipswich from Chelmsford and the bearing of
   Chelmsford from Ipswich.

3 a) Make an accurate drawing of this sketch using a scale of
      1 cm = 1 m.

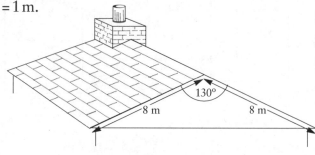

b) Use your sketch to find the width of the roof.

4 List the names of the solids which have been used to build up the picture.

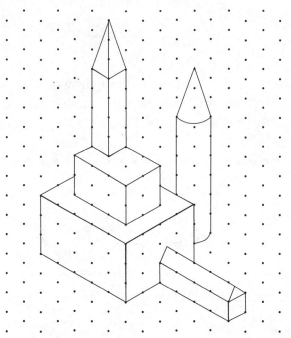

5 Draw a net for a cuboid which is 6 cm wide, 4 cm high and 7 cm long. Check your net by cutting it out and folding it.

6 Describe the solids that you think each of the following nets will make. Check your answers by copying the nets, cutting them out and folding them.

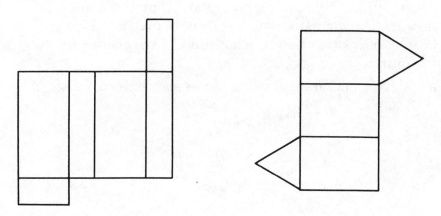

7 Draw a top view of this object and side elevations from the directions shown by the arrows.

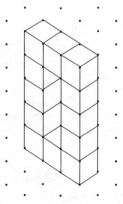

8 i) Find the size of each unknown angle in these diagrams.

ii) State whether each angle is acute, obtuse or reflex.

a)

72°

a

c)

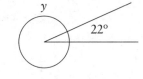

y

22°

b)

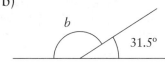

b

31.5°

d)

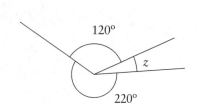

120°

z

220°

9 Find the size of each unknown angle in these diagrams:

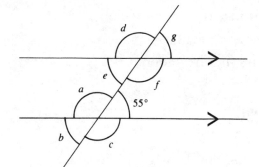

d   *g*

e   *f*

a

55°

b   *c*

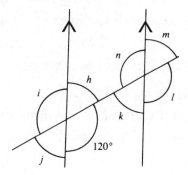

m

n

h

i

k

l

120°

j

10 Find the size of each unknown angle in these diagrams:

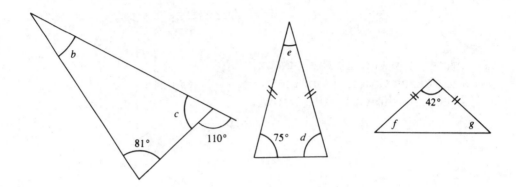

11 Write down the correct name of each of the quadrilaterals.

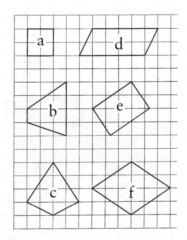

12 A heptagon is a seven sided polygon. Find:
   a) the total of the interior angles in a heptagon,
   b) the size of the interior angles in a regular heptagon,
   c) the size of the exterior angles in a regular heptagon,
   d) the total of the exterior angles in a heptagon.

13 Repeat question 12 for:
   a) a decagon (ten sided polygon),
   b) a dodecagon (twelve sided polygon).

14 Only three of the regular polygons can be used on their own to form a tessellation. Write down the names of the polygons.

15 Write down the translation which moves the shaded triangle to each position.

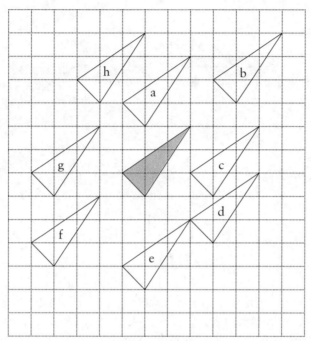

16 Draw a graph with *x*-and *y*-axes from −6 to +6. Plot the triangle with corner points at (0,1), (−3,1) and (−3,2). Show on your graph the new position of this triangle after each of the following translations.

a) $\begin{pmatrix} +6 \\ 0 \end{pmatrix}$ b) $\begin{pmatrix} +6 \\ -4 \end{pmatrix}$ c) $\begin{pmatrix} -3 \\ +4 \end{pmatrix}$ d) $\begin{pmatrix} 0 \\ +4 \end{pmatrix}$

17 Copy each of the following diagrams and draw in the image of the object after the stated rotation about the marked point.

a) 90° anticlockwise about P

b) 90° clockwise about P

c) 180° about P

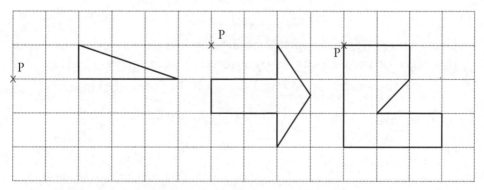

18 Copy each of the following diagrams and draw in the image of the object after a reflection in the mirror line.

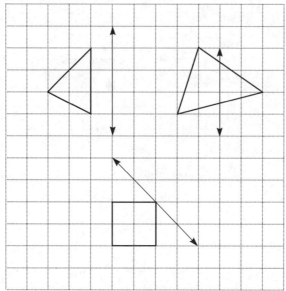

19 Draw a graph with x-and y-axes from -12 to $+12$. Plot the object with corner points at (2,2), (2,3), (4,2). Show on your graph the image of this object after an enlargement with centre (0,0) and scale factor:
a) 2   b) 3

20 Tina is designing a pattern in a rectangle 4 squares by 3 squares.

She draws the small design which then has to be enlarged into a rectangle 12 squares by 9 squares.

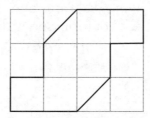

Draw an enlargement of the small shape so that its edges lie along the edges of the 12 squares by 9 squares rectangle.   (SEG)

21 a) Copy the shapes below and draw all the lines of symmetry.

i) Square

ii) Equilateral triangle

b) Write down the order of rotational symmetry of:
  i) the square,
  ii) the equilateral triangle. (ULEAC)

22 a) Copy each of the quadrilaterals and draw in all lines of symmetry. If no lines can be drawn, state on the figure 'no lines possible'.

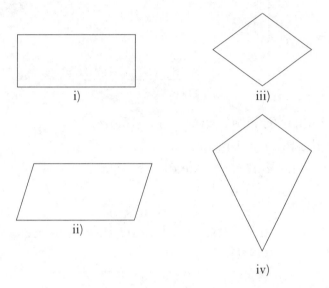

i)

ii)

iii)

iv)

b) Each of the quadrilaterals can be given a distinct name. Give the name of each of the quadrilaterals as precisely as possible. (ULEAC)

23 Find the perimeter and area of a rectangle with a height of 5 cm and a base of 6.5 cm.

24 Calculate the area of this shape.

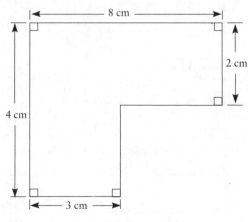

8 cm

2 cm

4 cm

3 cm

25 Work out the area of these shapes.

a)

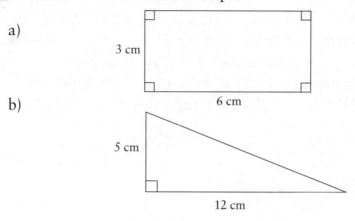

3 cm

6 cm

b)

5 cm

12 cm

(ULEAC)

26 The floor of a hall is in the shape of a square.
The area of the floor is 144 m².
a) What is the length of each side of the square?
b) What is the perimeter of the square?

(ULEAC)

27 ABCDE represents the shape of the end wall of a house. It is
drawn accurately on a 1 cm square grid.

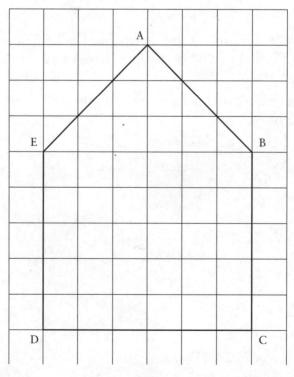

a) i) Name two edges of the shape that are parallel.

   ii) Name two edges of the shape that are perpendicular.

b) i) Measure and write down the length of AB.

   ii) Find the perimeter of the shape ABCDE.

c) Find the area of the shape ABCDE.

(MEG)

28 Find the area of a parallelogram with a height of 5.3 cm and a base of 7.5 cm.

29 Find the perimeter and area of this shape:

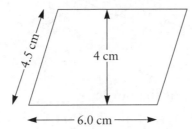

30 Find the area of a triangle with a height of 8 m and a base of 7.5 m.

31 Find the perimeter and area of this shape:

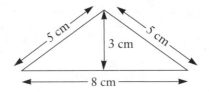

32 Find the area and circumference of a circle with a radius of 5.3 cm ($\pi = 3.1$).

33 Find the area and circumference of a circle with a diameter of 4.25 m ($\pi = 3.14$).

34 Find the diameter and radius of a circle with a circumference of 37.68 cm ($\pi = 3.14$).

35 Find the volume and surface area of the following cuboid.

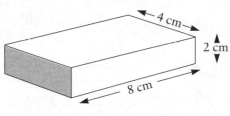

1

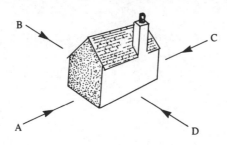

This is a model of a house.

Here are two views of the house.

Which arrow do you look along to see each view?

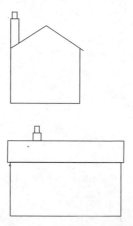

(MEG)

2 Using a scale of 1 cm to represent 2 m, mark the positions of 3 boys so that each boy is 12 m from the other two. (MEG)

3

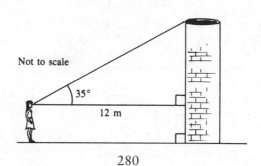

Not to scale

35°

12 m

A girl, whose eyes are $1\frac{1}{2}$ metres above the ground, stands 12 metres away from a tall chimney. She has to raise her eyes 35° upwards from the horizontal to look directly at the top of the chimney.

Using a scale of 1 cm to represent 1 metre, find the height of the chimney by scale drawing. (MEG)

4 On a map 1 cm represents $\frac{1}{2}$ km on the ground.

a) State the distance in kilometres represented by 5 cm on the map.

b) Two villages are 7 km apart. How far apart are they on the map?

c) This diagram shows three villages and their distances apart on the map. It also shows two bearings. It is not drawn accurately. Draw the diagram accurately. (SEG)

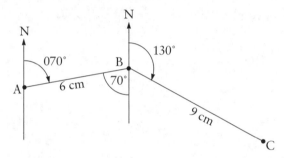

5 The diagram shows the net of a cardboard carton. The carton holds a chocolate bar.

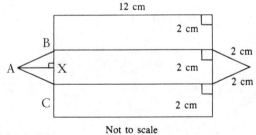

Not to scale

a) i) What type of triangle is ABC?

  ii) What is the size of angle BCA?

b) The length of AX is 1.73 cm. Calculate the area of

  i) triangle ABC,

  ii) the complete net.

c) The chocolate bars (in their cartons) are packed in layers in a box. The box is 10 cm wide, 5.4 cm high and 24 cm long. Some bars are shown in the following full-size diagram.

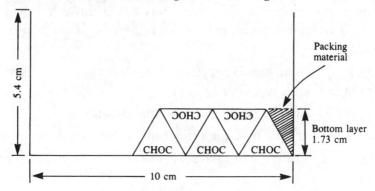

i) How many chocolate bars will there be in the complete bottom layer?

ii) How many layers will there be inside the box?

iii) How many chocolate bars will be packed inside the box?

(MEG)

6 The sum of the exterior angles of any polygon is 360°.

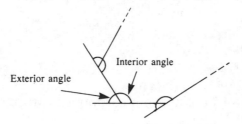

a) Calculate the interior angle of a regular

i) hexagon   ii) pentagon

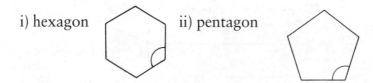

b) i) Another regular polygon has x sides. Find a formula for y, the interior angle, in terms of x.

ii) Rearrange this formula to express x in terms of y.

c) An artist is designing wallpaper patterns. She wants to cover the whole paper with a single repeated regular shape, leaving no gaps. Figure 1 shows her pattern using a regular hexagon. Figure 2 shows that she cannot use a regular pentagon.

282

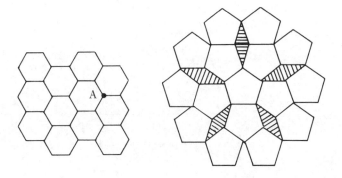

Figure 1   Figure 2

i) How many hexagons meet at point A in Figure 1?

ii) Use your two answers to the interior angles in part a) to explain why the artist can use a hexagon but not a pentagon.

iii) Can she use a regular octagon? Explain your answer.

(SEG)

7 Three pupils were asked to draw nets for a cube. These were their diagrams.

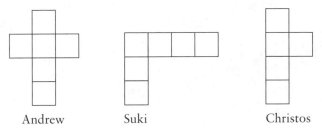

Andrew   Suki   Christos

For each of these, write down whether the net is correct or incorrect.

(SEG)

8

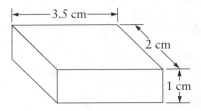

a) Calculate the volume of a cuboid which has dimensions 3.5 cm by 2 cm by 1 cm.

The diagram below shows part of the net of the cuboid which has dimensions 3.5 cm by 2 cm by 1 cm.

283

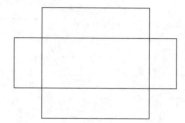

b) i) Copy and complete the net accurately.

   ii) Calculate the surface area of the cuboid.

(SEG)

9 This is a framework of a gate.

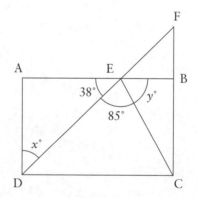

ABCD is a rectangle. Calculate the values of x and y.

(MEG)

10 The diagram below, *not* drawn to scale, shows a quadrilateral.

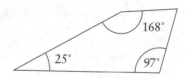

Three of the interior angles are 25°, 168° and 97°. Calculate the size of the fourth angle.

(SEG)

11 a) Name the type of triangle shown below.

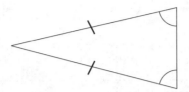

b) The diagram shows a parallelogram.

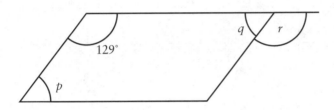

Calculate the value of:

  i) p,

 ii) q,

iii) r.   (ULEAC)

12 Draw a tessellation of the shape given on a grid. The shape should be repeated at least eight times.

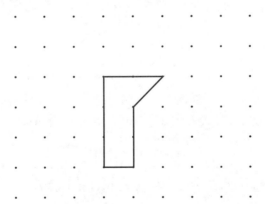

(MEG)

13

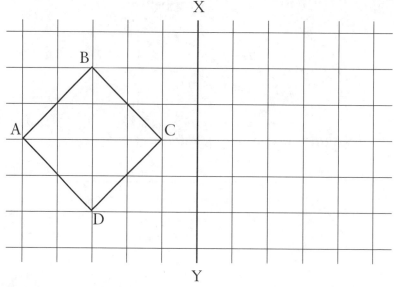

Copy the diagram.

a) Draw the reflection ABCD in the mirror line XY.

b) ABCD has rotational symmetry.
Mark with a cross its centre of rotation.

14

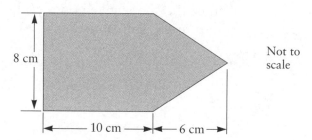

The diagram shows a flag.
The design on the flag consists of a rectangle and a triangle.
Calculate the area of the design. (MEG)

15 To answer this question use a centimetre square grid.

a) Rectangle A is 7 cm long. Its perimeter is 20 cm.

Complete a drawing of rectangle A.

b) Rectangle B is 4 cm wide. Its area is 32 cm².

Complete a drawing of rectangle B.

c) Rectangle D has the same area as square C, which is 6 cm by
6 cm. Complete a drawing of rectangle D, if it has a height of
4 cm. (WJEC)

16

The picture is in a square of area $25 \, cm^2$. Calculate:

a) the length of a side of the square,

b) the perimeter of the square. (NEAB)

17

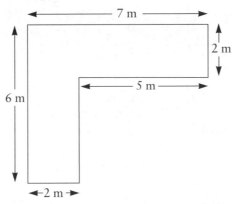

a) The diagram shows a corridor 2 m wide. Calculate the area of the floor of the corridor.

b) The floor of this corridor is covered with square carpet tiles which have a side of 0.5 m as shown.

   i) How many carpet tiles are needed to cover 1 square metre?

   ii) How many tiles are needed to cover the corridor? (SEG)

18

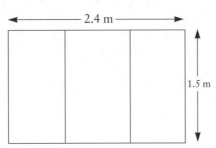

The rectangular window in the diagram (width 2.4 m and length 1.5 m) has to be glazed with three pieces of glass.

Each of the pieces is the same size.

a) Work out the width and length of one of the pieces of glass needed.

b) Work out the area of the piece of glass whose dimensions you found in a).

Glass costs £2.40 a square metre.

c) Calculate the total cost of the glass needed to glaze the window.

(ULEAC)

19

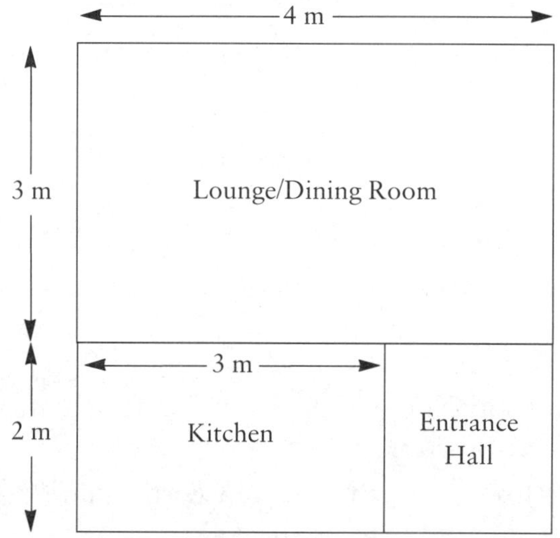

The above diagram, which has not been drawn to scale, shows the ground floor of a house.

a) What is the floor area of the lounge/dining room?

b) David covers the floor of the kitchen using $\frac{1}{2}$m by $\frac{1}{2}$m carpet tiles. How many of these tiles are needed?

c) Write down the length and breadth of the entrance hall of the house.

(MEG)

20

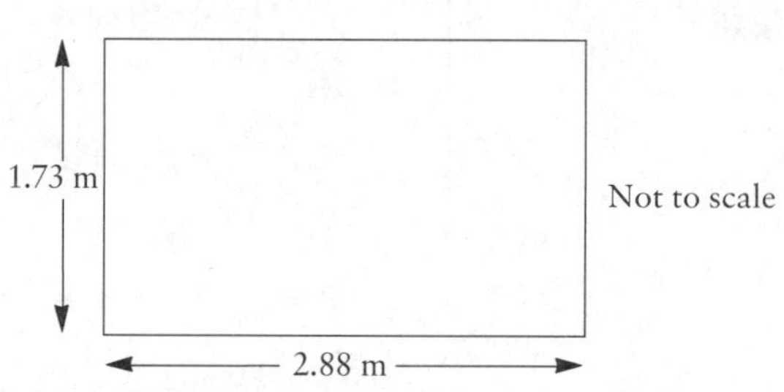

The diagram is of a sheet of glass which has been cut to fit a large rectangular window.

a) Calculate the exact value of

   i) the perimeter of the glass (in m),

   ii) the area of one side of the glass (in m²).

b) Write down your answers to part a) correct to the nearest whole number. (MEG)

21

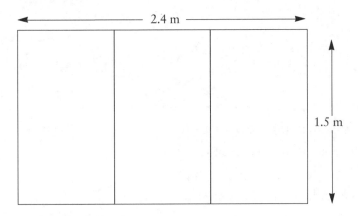

The rectangular window in the diagram (width 2.4 m and length 1.5 m) has to be glazed with three pieces of glass. Each of the pieces is the same size.

a) Work out the width and length of one of the pieces of glass needed.

b) Work out the area of the piece of glass whose dimensions you found in a).

c) Glass costs £2.40 a square metre.

Calculate the total cost of the glass needed to glaze the window.

(ULEAC)

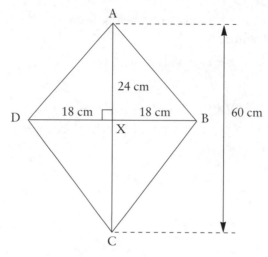

22

The diagram shows a kite ABCD.

a) i) Calculate the area of triangle ABX.

ii) Calculate the area of triangle ABD.

b) Calculate the area of triangle BCD.

c) Calculate the total area of the kite. (MEG)

23 The diagram represents a chocolate box in the shape of a pyramid.

The box has a square base and four triangular faces.

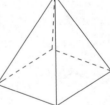

The net of the chocolate box is shown below.

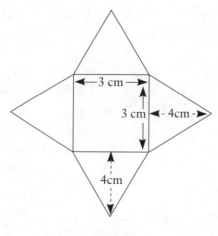

a) Work out:
   i) the area of the base,
   ii) the area of a triangular face,
   iii) the total surface area of the box.   (ULEAC)

24

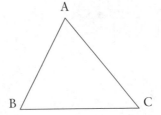

ABC is an accurately drawn triangle.
a) Measure and write down the size of
   i) angle A,
   ii) angle B.
b) Find the length of the perimeter of the triangle, in mm.
c) Find the area of the triangle in mm².   (ULEAC)

25 A circle has a radius of 9 cm.
   a) Work out, to the nearest centimetre, the circumference of the circle.
   b) An equilateral triangle is drawn with the same perimeter as the circle. Work out the length, to the nearest centimetre, of one of the sides of the triangle.   (ULEAC)

26 The diameter of a bicycle wheel is 40 cm.

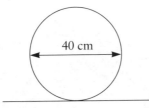

40 cm

a) Calculate the circumference of the wheel. Give your answer in centimetres.
b) Calculate how far along a road the bicycle travels while the wheel is making 50 complete turns. Give your answer in metres, to the nearest metre. (You may use π = 3.14.)   (MEG)

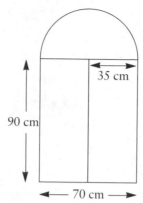

27

A metal frame, shown in the diagram, is made for a window. The lower part consists of two rectangles, each 90 cm by 35 cm, and the upper part is a semi-circle with radius 35 cm. Calculate the length of metal used in making

a) the straight pieces,

b) the curved piece, (Take π to be 3.14 or use the π button on your calculator. Give your answer correct to the nearest whole number.)

c) the total frame. (SEG)

28

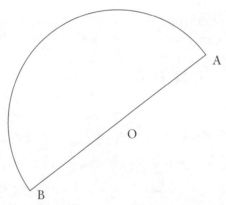

The diagram shows a semi-circular shape.

a) Measure and write down the length in cm of the radius OA.

b) Use the formula

$$\text{perimeter} = (\pi + 2) \times \text{radius}$$

and π = 3.14 to find the perimeter of the semi-circular shape.

Give your answer in centimetres correct to the nearest whole number. (NEAB)

29 Below are five familiar objects, all shaped differently.

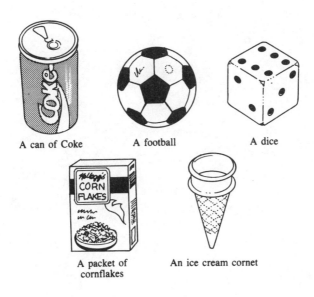

A can of Coke   A football   A dice

A packet of   An ice cream cornet
cornflakes

a) Which of the above objects is a sphere?

b) What mathematical shape is the can of coke?

c) Which one of the following shapes is *not* shown amongst the objects above?

a cone; a cuboid; a square-based pyramid; a cube.   (NEAB)

30

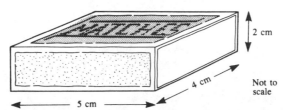

2 cm

4 cm

Not to scale

5 cm

The diagram shows a matchbox measuring 5 cm by 4 cm by 2 cm.

a) Calculate the volume of the matchbox.

12 similar matchboxes fill a carton with base dimensions of 10 cm by 8 cm.

Calculate:

b) the volume of the carton,

c) the height of the carton,

d) the total number of matches in the carton, if each box contains 48 matches.   (MEG)

Data Handling

Data Handling has been developed over the past 200 years. It is a systematic, mathematical way to answer questions about the world we live in.

To answer questions like these, we collect and organise data, present and illustrate data and make comparisons between different sets of data.

Types of variable

We collect data about *variables*. There are three types of variable.
A *qualitative variable* takes *non-numerical* values. These are some
examples of qualitative variables.

Colour of coat

Favourite dog food

Breed

Colour of paintwork

Maker's name

Type of fuel used

A *discrete variable* takes one of a range of *specific numerical values*. For
example, in a survey the number of children in a family may range from 0
to 6. Only whole numbers are possible, values like 1.6 or 5.78 children are
impossible. These are some more examples of discrete variables.

Number of legs

Number of brothers and sisters

Number of walks each week

Number of wheels

Number of gears

Number of cylinders

A *continuous variable* can take *any value* between the start and end
of a range. For example, if the weights of the players in a team are
measured, a team member could weigh 67 kg, or 67.3 kg, or 67.37 kg
depending on the accuracy of the weighing scales. These are some
more examples of continuous variables.

Height
Length of tail
Body temperature

Top speed
Weight
Average fuel consumption

To record continuous variables we must decide on the level of accuracy required. For example, we might measure the length of a ladybird to the nearest millimetre, the length of a worm to the nearest centimetre and the height of an apple tree to the nearest metre.

PAUSE

1 This multi-choice question was designed to record a person's religion.

Religion	*Please tick*:
Church of England	_____
Catholic	_____
Other Christian	_____
Muslim	_____
Hindu	_____
Sikh	_____
Jewish	_____
Other	_____

· Design a multi-choice question to record:

a) A person's favourite type of pop music.
b) The method of transport a pupil uses to come to school.
c) A person's favourite breakfast cereal.

2 This multi-choice question was designed to record the number of people living in each house on an estate.

How many people live in your house?	Please tick:
1	_____
2	_____
3	_____
4	_____
5	_____
6	_____
7	_____
8	_____
More than 8	_____

Design a multi-choice question to record:

a) The number of pints of milk delivered to each house in a street.

b) The number of days a pupil was absent from school last week.

c) The shoe size of each member of your mathematics group.

3 This multi-choice question was designed to record the number of times a pupil had been absent from school in one year.

How many days absence did you have last year?	Please tick.
0 days	_____
1–5 days	_____
6–10 days	_____
11–15 days	_____
16–20 days	_____
More than 20 days	_____

Design a multi-choice question to record:

a) The number of apples that a person eats each month.

b) The number of books a person owns.

c) The number of cigarettes that a person smokes each week.

4 This multi-choice question was designed to record the length of an earthworm.

Design a multi-choice question to record:

a) The length of a ladybird (to the nearest millimetre).

b) The weight of a new-born baby (to the nearest kilogram).

c) The time taken by a Year 7 pupil to run 100 metres (to the nearest second).

Length of the worm (to the nearest centimetre)	
1	_____
2	_____
3	_____
4	_____
5	_____
6	_____
7	_____
8	_____
9	_____
10	_____
Over 10	_____

5 State whether the following are qualitative, discrete or continuous variables.
a) A person's eye colour.
b) The number of pints of milk delivered to each house in a street.
c) The number of apples that a person eats each month.
d) The shoe size of each member of your mathematics group.
e) The time taken by a Year 7 pupil to run 100 metres.
f) A person's favourite breakfast cereal.
g) The number of days holiday that an employee gets each year.
h) The height of an apple tree (to the nearest metre).
i) The number of days a pupil was absent from school last week.
j) The weight of a new-born baby.
k) The number of books a person owns.
l) The method of transport a pupil uses to come to school.

■■

Frequency tables

Data is often organised into *frequency tables*.

For example, some data has been collected to answer the question:

'Do the families on Housing Estate A have more children than the families on Housing Estate B?'

A door to door survey was done on each estate to discover the number of children in 40 families.

This is the 'raw' data. It is difficult to compare unless it is put into frequency tables.

Estate A	Estate B
Number of children per family	Number of children per family
0 1 2 3 2 2 2 1 1 2	4 6 5 2 4 2 2 2 1 2
1 0 0 0 2 2 3 4 3 1	3 3 1 0 4 3 2 2 2 2
1 2 1 3 0 4 2 2 2 3	1 4 2 2 3 0 2 2 2 2
0 2 2 2 4 3 2 4 0 0	5 6 6 6 2 3 5 3 1 3

A *tally table* is often used to complete a frequency table. The tally marks are done in groups of five. The fifth tally mark is used to cross out the previous four marks.

No. of children per family	Estate A Tally	Frequency
·0	||||| |||	8
1									7
2																	15
3								6
4						4
5		0
6		0
	Total	40

No. of children per family	Estate B Tally	Frequency
0				2
1						4
2																		16
3									7
4						4
5					3
6						4
	Total	40

Some variables have so many different values that we must arrange them into groups. For example, if we collect data on the weekly earnings of a sample of 500 people, we can expect a large number of different results. We might use a *grouped table* like this:

Earnings per week	Frequency
Less than £100	
£101 – £150	
£151 – £200	
£201 – £250	
£251 – £300	
Over £300	

When we collect continuous data we need to decide how accurate the measurements are going to be. For example, in an experiment to measure the lengths of 200 slugs, we decide to measure each slug and record the results correct to the nearest centimetre. We might use a table like this:

Length of slug (nearest cm)	Tally	Frequency
1		
2		
3		
...		

The table makes the length look like a discrete variable. We must remember that the headings are correct to the nearest centimetre.

Any slug from 1.5 cm to 2.5 cm goes in the 2 cm group. A slug which is exactly equal to 2.5 cm, goes in the 2.5 cm to 3.5 cm group. Inequality signs are sometimes used to state the exact range of a continuous variable.

For example, if the letter L represents the length of a slug, the table above could be written like this.

Length of slug (L cm)	Frequency
$0.5 \leq L < 1.5$	
$1.5 \leq L < 2.5$	
$2.5 \leq L < 3.5$	

$1.5 \leq L < 2.5$ means L is between 1.5 and 2.5, but could be equal to 1.5 as $\leq$ includes an equal sign.

P A U S E

1 This table shows the membership of organisations for young people (source: Social Trends 1994).

Youth organisation	Members (in thousands)	
	1971	1994
Cub, Scouts and Venture Scouts	480	540
Brownies, Guides and Rangers	692	642
Sea, Army and Combined Cadets Force, Air Training Corps	135	132
Boys Brigade and Girls Brigade	237	173
NABC – Clubs for Young People	164	198
Youth Clubs UK	319	715
Methodist Youth Clubs	115	60
YMCA (males and females)	48	80

a) How many members did the Cub Scouts have in 1971?
b) How many members did the Cub Scouts have in 1994?
c) How many members did the Youth Clubs UK have in 1971?
d) How many members did the YMCA have in 1994?
e) Copy the table and add a third column for 'Change in Membership 1971–1994 (in thousands)'.
f) In e) most clubs changed to have more members. A few like Methodist Youth Clubs changed to have fewer members. Think of a way of marking those with fewer members in the 'Change in Membership column'.

2 These tables show details of people killed and seriously injured in road accidents (source: Annual Abstract of Statistics 1994).

Type of road user	Number
Child Pedestrians	4901
Adult Pedestrians	9119
Child Pedal Cyclists	1195
Adult Pedal Cyclists	2751
Moped Riders	807
Motor Scooter Riders	152
Motor Scooter Passengers	11
Motor Cycle Riders	5784
Motor Cycle Passengers	569
Car and Taxi Drivers	15406
Car and Taxi Passengers	9718
Users of Buses and Coaches	655
Users of Goods Vehicles	1967
Users of Other Vehicles	214

Age group	Number
0–4	1141
5–9	2588
10–14	3328
15–19	7509
20–24	8016
25–29	6133
30–39	7383
40–49	5194
50–59	3746
60 and over	7748

a) How many people aged from 20–24 were killed or seriously injured?

b) How many people aged from 30–39 were killed or seriously injured?

c) How many motor cycle riders were killed or seriously injured?

d) 569 motor cycle passengers were killed or seriously injured, compared to 9718 car or taxi passengers. Does this mean that travelling as a passenger on a motor cycle is safer than travelling as a passenger in a car or taxi?

e) 1141 people aged 0–4 were killed or seriously injured, compared to 2588 people aged 5–9. Does this mean that children aged 4 years and under are more careful road users than children aged 5 years to 9 years?

f) Are insurers right to charge more to insure drivers under 30? Use the numbers in the table to help you with your answer.

3 These are the final scores in some cup matches. Complete a table with tally marks to show the frequency with which teams scored no goals, 1 goal, 2 goals etc.

FA Cup Third Round			
Barnsley	4	Chelsea	0
Birmingham	0	Wimbledon	1
Blackpool	0	Bournemouth	1
Bradford	1	Tottenham	0
Brighton	1	Leeds	2
Cardiff	1	Hull	2
Carlisle	0	Liverpool	3
Charlton	2	Oldham	1
Crewe	2	Aston Villa	3
Derby	1	Southampton	1
Hartlepool	1	Bristol City	0
Huddersfield	0	Sheffield Utd	1
Kettering	1	Halifax	1
Manchester City	1	Leicester	0
Manchester United	0	QPR	0
Middlesbrough	1	Grimsby	2

4 Some letters of the alphabet occur more frequently than others. The letter *e*, for example, occurs far more frequently than the letter

z. If a large sample of English is checked, the order of frequency of each letter is usually:

ETOANIRSHDLCWUMFYGPBVKXQJZ

Carry out your own survey to check this order of frequency. Use a paragraph chosen from any book. Design a tally chart table and use it to collect your results. Comment on your results. How well do they match the predictions?

5　Two groups of 40 pupils take a Mathematics test marked out of 100. These are the raw results.

GROUP 1

```
75 67 34 91 23 32 45 63
82 71 63 44 87 31 92 55
45 67 87 98 37 64 63 59
56 67 89 93 63 54 45 29
65 83 66 82 67 81 66 83
```

GROUP 2

```
23 47 56 73 66 49 34 22
37 62 29 17 36 63 37 22
41 29 42 28 34 27 43 26
51 36 50 37 49 38 48 39
47 40 46 41 26 55 61 12
```

a) Copy and complete this tally chart table for the pupils in Group 1.

Mark	Tally	Frequency
0–10		
11–20		
21–30		
31–40		
⋮		

b) Complete a similar tally chart table for the pupils in Group 2.
c) Comment on any differences between the two groups of pupils.

6　Two different samples of 50 apples were weighed. These are the raw results.

Sample 1 (weights to the nearest gram)

```
83    87    92    103   121   107   88    94    103   112
90    93    108   117   123   122   89    98    100   120
129   84    95    96    99    120   115   118   117   121
116   109   108   119   118   122   127   125   130   131
93    125   94    124   95    123   125   116   112   123
```

Sample 2 (weights to the nearest gram)

117	119	125	143	131	144	132	145	147	151
132	115	107	99	122	125	141	134	137	138
132	139	141	145	151	98	107	105	118	119
112	124	127	128	139	130	138	137	136	152
120	134	145	146	137	138	141	133	132	137

a) Copy and complete this tally chart table for the apples in Sample 1. Remember that an apple weighing exactly 90 g would go in the group $90 \leq w < 100$.

Weight (*w* grams)	Tally	Frequency
$80 \leq w < 90$		
$90 \leq w < 100$		
$100 \leq w < 110$		
$110 \leq w < 120$		
$120 \leq w < 130$		
$130 \leq w < 140$		
$140 \leq w < 150$		
$150 \leq w < 160$		

b) Complete a similar tally chart table for the apples in Sample 2.

c) Comment on any differences between the two samples of apple.

■ ■

Hypothesis testing and bias

An *hypothesis* is a statement that could be true but has not been proved, for example 'More people would use public transport for going to work if the services were better.'

Questionnaires are often written to see if hypotheses are true.

We have to be careful of false results through bias. This can happen if we do not ask a fair sample. Consider the question, 'Would you use a new leisure centre?'. Suppose the person doing the survey asked every tenth person coming out of a supermarket on a Tuesday morning. The people shopping at that time would be mostly retired or mothers with young children. They would not form a fair sample.

There are other reasons for bias. A Year 11 pupil is testing the hypothesis 'More girls than boys in Year 11 smoke.' Year 11 pupils may not admit to smoking if their teacher is listening. The questions also have to be worded carefully. 'You don't smoke, do you?' is more likely to get the answer 'No' than 'Do you smoke?'.

Sometimes we need our sample to come from a particular group. If we want to test the hypothesis 'More people would use public transport for going to work if the services were better', we need to ask people who use their cars for going to work at present.

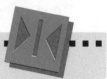

PAUSE

In questions 1–8, write a question or questions that could be used to test the hypothesis. Suggest different samples that could be used. What precautions do you need to take against bias?

1 'More mothers than fathers take their children to school.'

2 'School dinners contain plenty of vegetables and salad.'

3 'More people would use a bicycle for short journeys if there were special routes for bicycles.'

4 'The pavements would be cleaner if there were more dog toilet bins.'

5 'Women usually have to wait longer than men when using a public toilet.'

6 'Most school pupils would prefer not to wear a uniform.'

7 'Most school pupils would like more PE lessons.'

8 'Girls have to help more with housework than boys.'

9 Jean carried out a survey. She asked three sets of 100 people 'Do you think that the number of vehicles on the road should be reduced?'
   Set A Yes 74 No 26   **Set B** Yes 13 No 87   **Set C** Yes 99 No 1
   She asked one set coming from an anti-pollution rally, one set coming from a factory producing cars and one set coming out of a cinema.

   a) Which set do you think is which? Give a reason for your answer.
      Anti-pollution rally
      Factory
      Cinema
   b) Which of the three sets do you think is likely to be the most representative of public opinion?   (WJEC)

Graphs and diagrams can be used to illustrate data. They make data easier to understand. These are the different types of graphs and diagrams that are commonly used.

Bar charts and vertical line graphs

Bar charts are used to illustrate qualitative data and discrete quantitative data.

Example

Number of children per family	0	1	2	3	4	5	6
Frequency	10	9	18	8	5	0	0

This is the completed bar graph.

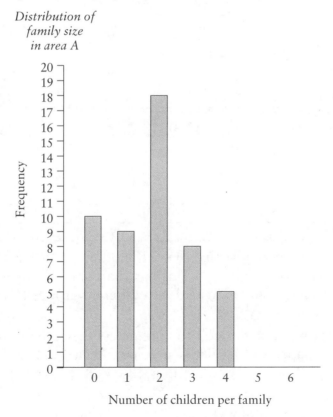

Distribution of family size in area A

307

Sometimes the bars are replaced with single lines like this:

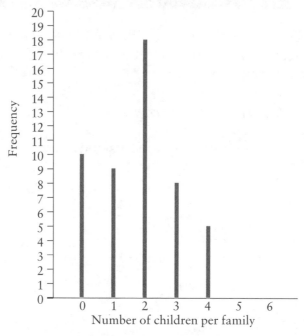

Number of children per family

This is called a vertical line graph.

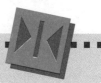

PAUSE

1 Draw a bar chart to show the information in this table:

Number of children per family	0	1	2	3	4	5	6
Frequency	3	4	20	9	5	4	5

2 A survey in 1992 revealed that 21% of all families with children were lone parent families. This bar chart shows how each 100 of those families can be divided into different groups (source: General Household Survey 1994).

Bar charts can be difficult to read unless they are printed on squared paper. Use a ruler as a guide to help you.

a) How many out of each 100 lone parent families are headed by:
   i) a single mother,   iv) a lone father,
   ii) a divorced mother,   v) a widow,
   iii) a separated mother,   vi) a woman?

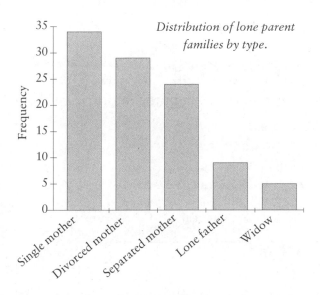

Distribution of lone parent families by type.

b) Write two comments about the information the bar chart shows.

3 This bar chart shows how male school pupils who smoke are affected if their parents smoke.

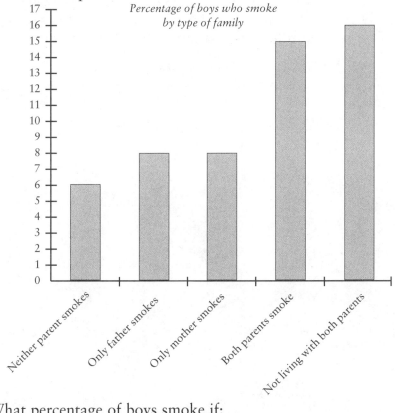

Percentage of boys who smoke by type of family

a) What percentage of boys smoke if:

i) only their father smokes,
ii) only their mother smokes,
iii) both parents smoke,
iv) they are not living with both parents?

b) Write two comments about the information the bar chart shows.

4 This table shows how female school pupils who smoke are affected if their parents smoke.

	Neither parent smokes	Only father smokes	Only mother smokes	Both parents smoke	Not living with parents
Percentage of girls who are regular smokers	7	8	11	14	17

a) Draw a vertical line graph to show the information in the table.

b) Write two comments about the information the bar chart shows.

5 This double bar graph shows the results of a survey when 2176 Year 11 pupils were asked, 'When choosing what to eat, do you consider your health?' (source: Young people in 1993).

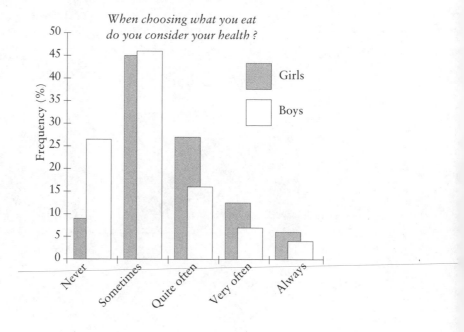

a) When asked this question, what percentage of girls replied:
  i) never,
  ii) sometimes,
  iii) quite often,
  iv) very often,
  v) always?
b) When asked this question, what percentage of boys replied:
  i) never,
  ii) sometimes,
  iii) quite often,
  iv) very often,
  v) always?
c) Write two comments about the information the double bar chart shows.

6 This table shows the GCSE Maths grades obtained by Year 11 pupils in two different schools.

GCSE maths grade	A	B	C	D	E	F	G	U
Frequency (school A)	3	12	10	17	1	3	4	1
Frequency (school B)	10	11	27	13	5	0	3	0

a) Draw a double bar chart to show the information in this table.
b) Compare the results of the two schools.

7 This bar chart shows the number of deaths from solvent abuse each year from 1971 to 1991 (source: Re-solv 1994).

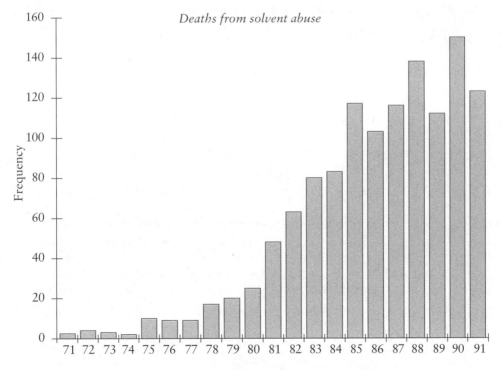

Deaths from solvent abuse

311

a) Estimate the number of deaths in:
   i) 1971,   iv) 1986,
   ii) 1976,   v) 1991.
   iii) 1981,

b) Write two comments about the information the bar chart shows.

■■■■■■■■■■■■■■■■■■■■■■■■■■■■■■■■■

Pictograms

A pictogram is a variation of the bar chart, using lines of symbols to replace the solid bar.

This is data on the number of drinks sold by a vending machine in a one hour period:

Type of drink	Number sold
Tea	5
Coffee	9
Soup	3
Chocolate	4

The table can be illustrated with this pictogram:

Drinks sold by vending machine in one hour

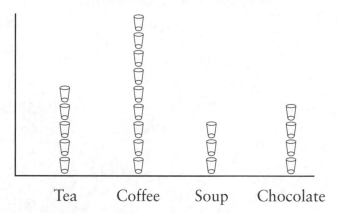

      Tea   Coffee   Soup   Chocolate

Note: one cup represents one drink.

This table gives the number of drinks sold by a vending machine in a one week period.

312

Type of drink	Number sold
Tea	120
Coffee	125
Soup	73
Chocolate	85

It would take too long to draw lines with 120 or 135 cups. We use a scale and let one cup symbol represent 10 cups of drink sold. If a number sold does not divide exactly by 10, we draw part of a cup. This is the completed pictogram drawn horizontally this time.

Drinks sold by vending machine in one week

Tea	🥤🥤🥤🥤🥤🥤🥤🥤🥤🥤🥤🥤
Coffee	🥤🥤🥤🥤🥤🥤🥤🥤🥤🥤🥤🥤◡
Soup	🥤🥤🥤🥤🥤🥤🥤◡
Chocolate	🥤🥤🥤🥤🥤🥤🥤🥤◡

PAUSE

Choose very simple symbols for your pictograms. You have to draw the symbols several times.

1 This table illustrates the types of pets owned by a class. Draw a pictogram to illustrate the data.

Pet	Frequency
Dogs	12
Cats	15
Rabbits	6
Fish	7
Snakes	1

This table illustrates the type of footware worn by a group on pupils on a school trip. Draw a pictogram to illustrate the data.

Footware	Frequency
Shoes	11
Trainers	10
Boots	8
Sandals	2

3 This table illustrates the transport used by groups of Year 7 and Year 11 pupils to come to school.

Draw two separate pictograms to illustrate the data.

Transport	Year 7	Year 10
Car	30	13
Bus	38	34
Cycle	25	29
Walk	52	66

■ ■

Pie charts

Bar charts are very useful for picking out the most or least common variable. *Pie charts* give a better display of the way that a variable is 'shared out.'

For example, this pie chart illustrates the reasons given for not truanting in a survey of Year 10 and Year 11 students (source: Truancy in English secondary schools 1994).

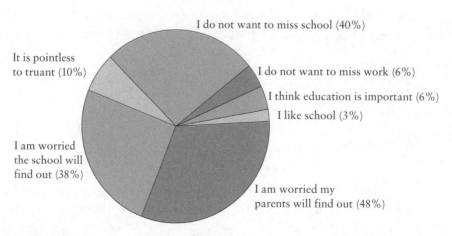

Reasons for not truanting

I do not want to miss school (40%)

It is pointless to truant (10%)

I do not want to miss work (6%)

I think education is important (6%)

I like school (3%)

I am worried the school will find out (38%)

I am worried my parents will find out (48%)

When drawing our own pie charts there are two methods we can use:

Method 1: Using a pie chart scale.

Example:
An international committee has 18 members, 6 from Great Britain, 7 from America, 3 from France and 2 from Japan. Illustrate this data with a pie chart.

Country	Number of members
Great Britain	6
America	7
France	3
Japan	2
Total	18

In any pie chart, we start with a full circle or 100% to share out. We add a column to the table showing the percentage represented by the members from each country.

Country	Number of members	Percentage
Great Britain	6	33.3%
America	7	38.9%
France	3	16.7%
Japan	2	11.1%
Total	18	100%

The percentages are worked out by dividing each number by the total and then multiplying by 100.

For example, for Great Britian, the percentage = $6 \div 18 \times 100 = 33.3\%$.

We can now draw the pie chart. Draw a circle of a suitable size. Start at any point to divide it up into slices. Use a pie chart scale and the percentages in the table. Give the pie chart a title and label the slices.

Nationality of Committee Members

315

Method 2: Using a protractor

Example

An international committee has 18 members, 6 from Great Britain, 7 from America, 3 from France and 2 from Japan. Illustrate this data with a pie chart.

Country	Number of members
Great Britain	6
America	7
France	3
Japan	2
Total	18

In any pie chart, we start with a full circle or 360° to share out. We add a column to the table showing the angle represented by the members from each country.

Country	Number of members	Pie chart angle
Great Britain	6	120°
America	7	140°
France	3	60°
Japan	2	40°
Total	18	360°

The angles are worked out by dividing each number by the total and then multiplying by 360.

For example, for Great Britian, the angle = $6 \div 18 \times 360 = 120°$.

We can now draw the pie chart. Draw a circle of a suitable size. Start at any point to divide it up into slices. Use a protractor and the angles in the table.

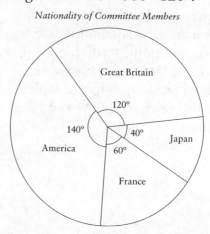

Nationality of Committee Members

316

Questions 1, 2 and 3 are suitable for a Pie Chart Scale (Method 1).

1 This table shows how every 100 households in Great Britain can be divided up into different types of dwelling (source: General Household Survey 1994).

Type of dwelling	Frequency in every 100 dwellings
Detached House	20
Semi-Detached House	31
Terraced House	28
Flat or Maisonette (purpose built)	15
Flat or Maisonette (converted)	5
With Business or Shop	1
Total	100

Draw a pie chart to show the information in the table.

2 In a survey, Year 7 pupils were asked whether, when choosing what to eat, they thought about their health. This table shows the results for every 100 boys or girls who answered the questions.

When choosing food do you think about your health?	Boys	Girls
Always	8	7
Very Often	8	11
Quite often	24	27
Sometimes	44	47
Never	16	8
Total	100	100

a) Draw two separate pie charts to illustrate this information.
b) Write two comments about the information the pie charts show.

3 This diagram was drawn to show the breakdown of the cost of a bottle of mineral water (source: trade estimates).

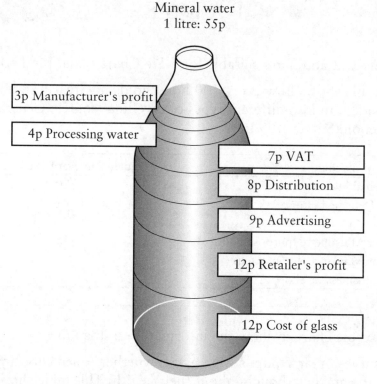

Mineral water
1 litre: 55p

3p Manufacturer's profit

4p Processing water

7p VAT

8p Distribution

9p Advertising

12p Retailer's profit

12p Cost of glass

Draw a pie chart to illustrate the breakdown of the cost of a bottle of mineral water.

Questions 4, 5 and 6 are suitable for an angle measurer (Method 2).

4 This table shows the numbers of each type of drink sold from a vending machine in a one week period. Illustrate this data with a pie chart.

Type of drink	Number sold
Tea	120
Coffee	90
Chocolate	75
Tomato soup	60
Chicken soup	15

5 A local council did a survey in their area of pre-school provision for under fives. The results are shown in the table.

Type of provision	Private nursery schools	Council nursery schools	Nursery class in infant school	Playgroup
Frequency	6	1	4	9

Draw a pie chart to illustrate the data.

6 Each year, a game warden in East Anglia checks on the contents of 60 nests of the Egyptian Goose, a bird introduced from Africa in the eighteenth century. The table below shows her results for two successive years.

Number of eggs	0	1	2	3	4	5	6	7	8	9
Number of nests (Year 1)	12	0	0	3	0	12	17	12	4	0
Number of nests (Year 2)	17	0	1	5	0	19	12	6	0	0

a) Draw a pie chart to represent the results for Year 1.
b) Draw a pie chart to represent the results for Year 2.
c) Write some comments about the differences between the two years.

7 A shop sells four flavours of crisps; Cheese and Onion, Plain, Salt and Vinegar, Chicken.

This pie chart represents the weekly sales.

Weekly sales of crisps

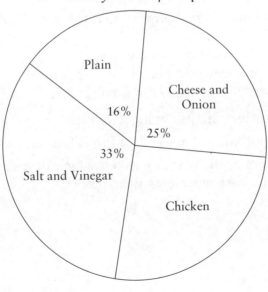

a) What percentage of the crisps sold were chicken flavour?
b) Which was the most popular flavour?
c) The shop sold 200 bags of crisps. How many of these were cheese and onion flavour?
d) Show the same information as a bar chart.

8 The cost of a litre of petrol was checked at 50 garages in a city. This pie chart shows the result.

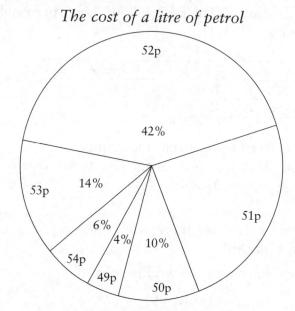

The cost of a litre of petrol

a) What percentage of the garages sold the petrol for 51p per litre?
b) Which was the most common price?
c) How many garages sold petrol for 50p a litre?
d) Show the same information in a bar chart.

9 A youth club offers the following activities:

      Football   Snooker   Table Tennis   Disco

All the members of the club are asked which of these activities they prefer. The pie chart represents their replies.

Activities chosen by members of a youth club

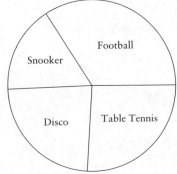

a) What is the size of the angle which represents snooker?
b) Which of these activities is the most popular?
c) The club has 180 members.
   How many members prefer the disco?
d) Show the same information as a bar chart.   (SEG)

10 720 students were asked how they travelled to school.

The pie chart shows the results of this survey.

How students travel to school

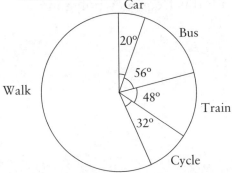

Work out:

a) how many of the students travelled to school by bus,
b) how many of the students walked to school.   (ULEAC)

■ ■

Frequency polygons

This table:

Length of earthworm (nearest cm)	1	2	3	4	5	6	7	8	9	10
Number of earthworms	3	7	12	19	18	18	11	10	2	0

can be illustrated with this *frequency polygon*:

321

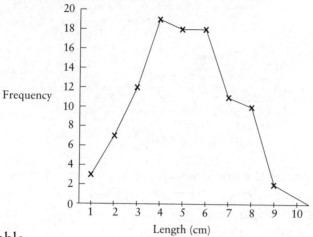

Distribution of length in a sample of 100 earthworms

This table:

Time (minutes)	$0 \leq T < 5$	$5 \leq T < 10$	$10 \leq T < 15$	$15 \leq T < 20$	$20 \leq T < 25$
Frequency	5	8	4	2	1

can be illustrated with this frequency polygon:

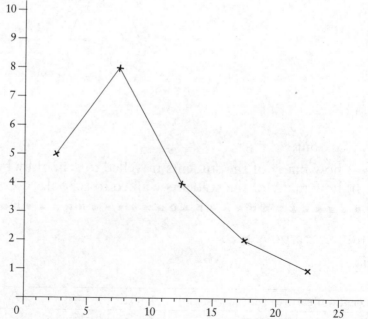

Notice that the points are plotted over the *middle value* of each group.

PAUSE

1 The weights of two samples of 100 piglets are recorded. The first sample have spent 10 weeks on Diet A and the second sample have spent 10 weeks on Diet B. The results are shown in this table.

Weight (nearest kg)	Frequency (Diet A)	Frequency (Diet B)
25	20	17
26	23	20
27	31	30
28	19	23
29	7	8
30	0	2

a) Draw, on one graph, two frequency polygons to illustrate the table. Go up to 30 kg and a frequency of 35. Use 2 mm graph paper and start your graph like this:

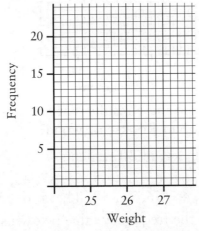

b) Which diet do you consider is the most successful?

2 Michelle Jackson, the film star, owns a country estate to 'get away from it all'. She is interested in preserving nature and asks for a survey into the size of trees in two pieces of woodland she owns. The circumferences of 100 selected trees are measured in Rooksend and Streamside.

Circumference C (cm)	Rooksend	Streamside
$0 \leq C < 20$	3	5
$20 \leq C < 40$	17	3
$40 \leq C < 60$	22	6
$60 \leq C < 80$	25	11
$80 \leq C < 100$	19	18
$100 \leq C < 120$	7	24
$120 \leq C < 140$	5	26
$140 \leq C < 180$	2	7

a) Draw, on one graph, two frequency polygons to illustrate the table. Go up to 180mm and a frequency of 30. Use 2mm graph paper and start your graph like this:

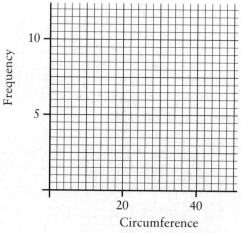

b) Can we conclude from these results that Streamside Wood contains older trees than Rooksend Wood?

3 Here are the weights, in kg, of 30 students.

45, 52, 56, 65, 34, 45, 67, 65, 34, 45, 65, 87, 45, 34, 56, 54, 45, 67, 84, 45, 67, 45, 56, 76, 57, 84, 35, 64, 58, 60.

a) Copy and complete the frequency table below using a class interval of 10 starting at 30.

Weight range (w)	Tally	Frequency
$30 \leq w < 40$		

b) Which class interval has the highest frequency?
c) Draw a frequency polygon representing this information.

(ULEAC)

4 The table gives information about the weight of the potato crop produced by 100 potato plants of two different types.

Weight of potatoes per plant w kg	Number of plants Type X	Number of plants Type Y
$0 \leq w < 0.5$	0	0
$0.5 \leq w < 1.0$	3	0
$1.0 \leq w < 1.5$	12	6
$1.5 \leq w < 2.0$	55	39
$2.0 \leq w < 2.5$	23	32
$2.5 \leq w < 3.0$	7	23
$3.0 \leq w < 3.5$	0	0

a) Using a scale of 1 kg = 4 cm on the horizontal axis and 10 plants = 2 cm on the vertical axis. Go up to 4 kg and 60 plants. Draw a frequency polygon for each type of potato.
b) Which type of potato produces the heavier crop?
c) i) Which type of potato has more variation in the weight of the crop?
   ii) Give a reason for your answer.

(SEG)

■ ■

Visual misrepresentation of data

It is claimed that the Nineteenth Century English Prime Minister Disraeli once said,

'There are lies, damned lies and statistics.'

Unfortunately Disraeli had a point. It is possible to use statistics to both confuse and delude the general public.

Sometimes mistakes in statistical presentations may be genuine. However, 'mistakes' happen frequently, and in work by expert statisticians. The intention to deceive is often deliberate.

We will look at some of the methods that are used to present results in a misleading way.

Graphs drawn without a scale

A graph without a scale means little but such graphs are found in advertising. For example, the graph below shows the 'goodness' of Zappo Flakes.

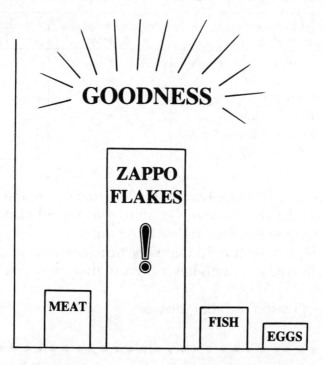

The graph is meant to show that Zappo Flakes are better for you than meat, fish or eggs. Looking at the graph we might ask these questions.

- What is 'goodness', the graph gives no hint of things like vitamin or fibre content.
- Whatever 'goodness' is, were equal amounts of the foods compared? For example, were 2 tons of Zappo Flakes compared with one egg or a single sardine?
- Why is the Zappo Flakes bar twice as wide as the other bars?
- Why is there an exclamation mark on the Zappo Flakes bar?

There are no answers to any of these questions. The 'graph' is a statistical trick to get you to buy the product. Sometimes numbers may be added to a graph without saying what they mean. We can add numbers to the Zappo graph, but it will still be worthless.

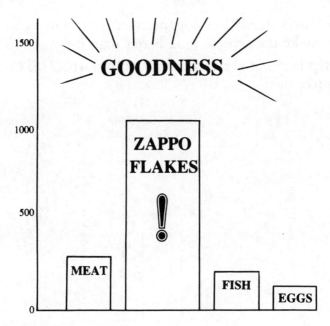

The exaggerated graph

Our previous example was an easily spotted misrepresentation. Graphs like this are usually only found in advertising and publicity material and few people will take them seriously.

The exaggerated graph, on the other hand, crops up all the time. It is hard to spot and is even found in material produced by large companies and government departments.

Here is an honest and fair bar chart drawn to illustrate the sales of Zappo Flakes over a three year period.

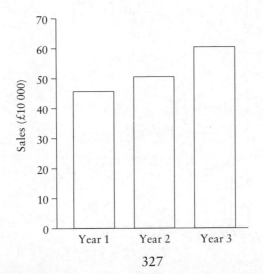

The graph shows steady but not spectacular growth. Now, suppose we wish to make the growth look better than it is.

The first step is to cut the vertical axis and start at 35. Our graph now looks like this:

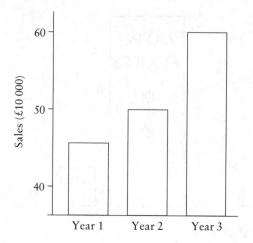

The graph now makes the sales growth look more impressive.

Visually the graph now gives an exaggerated impression of the sales growth. The third bar is over twice as high as the first bar and, at a glance, we may think the sales have more than doubled.

We can stretch the vertical axis and make the graph look like this.

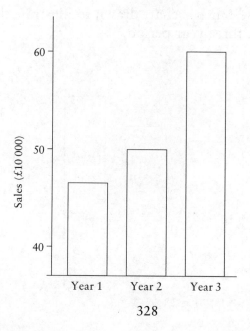

Now that really is dramatic and spectacular sales growth, a company well worth investing in!

So, a respectable sales growth can easily be presented as a really spectacular sales growth by simple adjustment to the frequency axis on the graph. If the axis is correctly labelled, the graph is still 'honest' because it does contain accurate information. There is however little justification for using a representation like this unless the intention is deliberately to deceive and exaggerate results.

Remember, if you want to draw a deceptive graph.

- Don't start your frequency axis at zero, select the starting value that shows your results in the best light.
- Exaggerate your results still further by 'stretching' the frequency axis.

Using solid images to deceive the eye

Our third trick is developed from the pictogram.

We will start with this honest representation of the sales of two brands of coffee in a supermarket.

Sales of instant coffee in Sainsco supermarkets

Tasteless Wonder
English Coffee

Imported Dutch
Mud Coffee

Each jar represents 1000 jars sold each week

As you can see, the best selling brand is 'Tasteless English' which easily outsells the imported Dutch brand.

Suppose you are the director of 'Tasteless English Foods PLC' and want to make these results look even better.

Your coffee sells four times as many jars as the imported brand. So why not draw a different pictogram, showing just two jars of coffee, one drawn four times as large as the other. This is the graph:

We can argue that since the second jar is drawn four times as wide as the first jar this is a fair representation.

There is something wrong though because if you look at the diagram, it gives the impression that sales of 'Tasteless English' are much greater than sales of 'Dutch Mud'.

The trick is in the phrase 'four times as large'. The second jar is certainly four times as wide, but it is also four times as high and four times as thick. This means that it will have sixty-four times the volume of the smaller jar.

When you look at the illustration, it is this difference in volume that your eye measures. The result is a great exaggeration of the real difference between the sales figures for the two brands.

Remember, if you want to draw a deceptive pictogram.

- Use single symbols drawn so that their lengths and heights represent their frequencies.

- Turn the symbols into three dimensional objects. The effect will be to greatly exaggerate any differences represented in the heights or lengths.

1 Invent a product. It might be a new brand of washing powder, a new car, a better mouse trap or whatever. Draw a meaningless graph without scales which 'demonstrates' that your new wonder product is far better than its rivals.

2 Look carefully at the graph behind this politician. Comment on the way that the graph represents the jobless figures.

3 You are the director of Zapper Cars. In the last four years your Supersport model has sold 5400, 5500, 5600 and 5900 cars respectively. Present this information graphically. Try to create the best possible impression of your company.

4 In 1983, the average yearly incomes per head in Switzerland, the UK, Trinidad and Chile were $16000, $8000, $4000 and $2000 respectively. This data is illustrated in the pictogram below. Redraw the pictogram using single symbols drawn to a length scale and comment on the results.

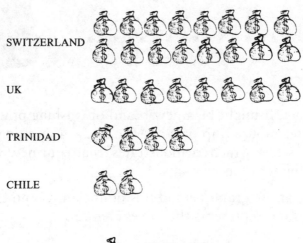

SWITZERLAND

UK

TRINIDAD

CHILE

= 1 000 US dollars

SECTION 3 Making Comparisons Between Sets of Data

A set of values for a variable is called a *frequency distribution*.
The obvious way to compare frequency distributions is to place them
side by side and to look for differences. This takes a long time and
various methods have been developed to summarise data. The data
can then be compared more easily.

Averages and spreads

When comparing distributions, it is very useful if a single typical
value can be selected to represent the distribution. Such values are
called *averages*. An average gives an impression of the type of values
to be found in a distribution. For example, we are told that the
average test mark of one class is 60% and the *average* test mark for
another class (on the same test) is 85%. We expect a typical student
in the second class to be more able than one in the first class.

Test score averages

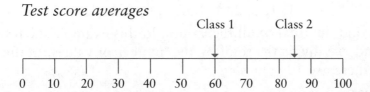

Averages on their own should be treated with care. It is better to make comparisons using an average and *a measure of spread*. Measures of spread tell us of how the distribution is arranged around the average value.

The simplest measure of spread is **the range**. The range is the difference between the greatest and the least values in a distribution.

For example, the greatest mark for a student in Class 1 was 98 and the least mark was 22, the range was $98-22=76$.

The greatest mark for a student in Class 2 was 95 and the least mark was 75, the range was $95-75=20$.

We can now tell that it is not true to say that a typical student in the second class is likely to be more able than a typical student in the first class. Class 1 is probably a mixed ability class and Class 2 is a class that has been set according to ability.

Test score averages

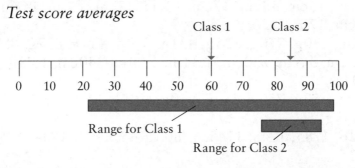

There are three types of average in common use. These are the **mean**, the **median**, and the **mode**.

The mean

The mean, is calculated by adding up all the values in a distribution and then dividing this total by the number of values in the distribution.

Find the mean and range of these values:

1, 1, 2, 2, 3, 4, 4, 5, 6, 6, 6, 8.

First, we find the total of all the values. In this example the total is 48. Second, we divide the total by the number of values. In this example there are 10 values.

So, the mean average is:

$$\frac{48}{10} = 4.8$$

The range is $8-1=7$.

PAUSE

1 Find the mean and the range of each of the following distributions.
   a) 12, 6, 7, 9, 6
   b) 1, 1, 1, 1, 2, 2, 3, 3, 3, 3, 3, 4, 4, 5, 6, 6
   c) £1.50, £1.50, £2.00, £3.00
   d) –2, –1, –2, 0, 0, 0, 3, 4, 1, 2, 6
   e) 2.7, 3.4, 8.9, 5.6, 6.6, 7.3, 5.2, 2.9, 8.0, 7.1
   f) 12 cm, 13 cm, 15 cm, 17 cm, 12 cm, 13 cm, 15 cm, 14 cm, 29 cm, 15 cm, 17 cm, 12 cm
   g) 450 g, 230 g, 770 g, 125 g, 431 g, 874 g, 455 g, 637 g, 888 g, 97 g
   h) 125 cm, 34 cm, 220 cm, 1.34 m, 1.90 m, 340 cm, 1.78 m, 2.55 m, 3.04 m
   i) 550 g, 650 g, 750 g, 850 g, 950 g, 1.05 kg, 1.15 kg, 1.25 kg, 1.35 kg
   j) 1716, 1785, 1745, 1745, 1780, 1765, 1731, 1734, 1754, 1700, 1735

2 The test marks of a group of ten Year 11 students are 56, 72, 35, 47, 89, 98, 13, 45, 34 and 73. The test marks of a group of ten Year 10 students who take the same test are:

   58, 70, 40, 41, 42, 11, 94, 62, 43 and 60.

   a) Calculate the mean and the range of each set of marks.
   b) Comment on your results.

3 Two darts players, Maureen and Eric each throw 9 darts. Maureen's scores are 20, 40, 1, 5, 60, 20, 20, 1 and 60. Eric's scores are 20, 40, 40, 0, 60, 20, 0, 5 and 1.

a) Find the mean and the range of each set of scores.

b) Comment on your results.

4 A group of five trees in a garden have a mean height of 4.5 metres. A sixth tree with a height of 2.1 metres is planted.

a) What is the total height of the five original trees?

b) What is the mean height of all six trees?

5 One group of 5 students have a mean score of 45 on a test. A second group of 11 students have a mean score of 53 on the same test.

a) What was the total score of the group of 5 students?

b) What was the total score of the group of 11 students?

c) Find the mean score for the whole group of 16 students.

■■■■■■■■■■■■■■■■■■■■■■■■■■■■■■■■■■■■

Finding the mean and the range of a discrete distribution presented in a frequency table

Calculate the mean number of children per family and the range for this frequency distribution.

Number of children per family	0	1	2	3	4	5	6
Frequency	13	13	38	17	10	4	5

Remember, to calculate the mean average, we need to know

■ the total number of families,

■ the total number of children in these families.

We can find the number of families by adding all the frequencies (middle column). The third column is used to work out the total number of children.

Number of children per family	Frequency	Number x Frequency
0	13	0
1	13	13
2	38	76
3	17	51
4	10	40
5	4	20
6	5	30
Total	100	230

We now know that 100 families have a total of 230 children. We can calculate the mean:

$$\text{Mean} = \frac{230}{100} = 2.3 \text{ children.}$$

The range is the difference between the greatest value and the least value.

The range = 6 − 0 = 6 children per family.

PAUSE

1 This table shows the results of a survey into the number of children per family on two housing estates.

Number of children per family	0	1	2	3	4	5	6
Frequency (Estate A)	10	9	18	8	5	0	0
Frequency (Estate B)	3	4	20	9	5	4	5

a) Calculate the mean number of children per family and the range for each estate.

b) Comment on your results.

2 The cost of a litre of petrol was checked at a sample of 50 garages in two different cities. The results are shown in the table below.

Cost per litre (pence)	City A	City B
49	2	4
50	5	7
51	12	4
52	21	11
53	7	13
54	3	5
55	0	6

a) Calculate the mean price per litre and the range in each city.
b) Comment on your results.

3 In the GCSE Mathematics examination, grades A,B,C,D,E,F,G and U are awarded. This table shows the results for the students entered in the same year from two different schools.

	A	B	C	D	E	F	G	U
School A	3	14	15	23	13	20	9	3
School B	2	32	18	20	20	0	0	8

a) Calculate the mean grade for each school (Note. To do this you will need to replace grades A to U with the numbers 1 to 8. Calculate the averages and then translate them back into a grade).

b) Calculate the range for each school.

c) Comment on your results.

■ ■

The median

The mean is a commonly used average. Sometimes it is even confusingly refered to as '*the average*', as if no other type of average existed. There are if fact other types of average, one of which is the *median*.

The median of a set of values is simply the *middle value when the values are placed in order*.

Find the median and the range of 1, 4, 7, 5, 6, 3, 3, 2, 1, 5, 1.

First, we arrange the values into order.

$$1, 1, 1, 2, 3, 3, 4, 5, 5, 6, 7$$

Then we pick out the *middle* value.

$$\text{The median} = 3$$
$$\text{The range} = 7 - 1 = 6$$

If there are an even number of values, we select a value which is half way between the two middle values.

Find the median and the range of £4.00, £5.00, £4.50, £6.00, £5.50, £6.00.

First, we arrange the values into order.

$$£4.00, £4.50, £5.00, £5.50, £6.00, £6.00$$

The *middle* position is half way between £5.00 and £5.50.

$$\text{The median} = £5.25$$
$$\text{The range} = £6.00 - £4.00$$
$$= £2.00$$

PAUSE

1 Find the median and the range of each of the following distributions.
   a) 12, 6, 7, 9, 6
   b) 1, 2, 1, 3, 4, 5, 5, 3, 4, 1, 3, 5, 2, 2, 5
   c) £5.00, £1.50, £4.00, £5.50, £4.50, £6.00, £2.00
   d) £5.00, £1.50, £4.00, £5.50, £4.50, £6.00, £2.00, £1.50
   e) –2, 3, 0, –1, 0, 2, 0, 0, 0, –3, 1, 1, 1, 1, 2, –1, –2, 3, 3, 0, –1, –1
   f) 2.7, 3.4, 8.9, 5.6, 6.6, 7.3, 5.2, 2.9, 8.0, 7.1
   g) 12 cm, 13 cm, 15 cm, 17 cm, 12 cm, 13 cm, 15 cm, 14 cm, 29 cm, 15 cm, 17 cm, 12 cm
   h) 450 g, 230 g, 770 g, 125 g, 431 g, 874 g, 455 g, 637 g, 888 g, 97 g
   i) 125 cm, 34 cm, 220 cm, 1.34 m, 1.90 m, 340 cm, 1.78 m, 2.55 m, 3.04 m
   j) 550 g, 650 g, 750 g, 850 g, 950 g, 1.05 kg, 1.15 kg, 1.25 kg, 1.35 kg
   k) 1716, 1785, 1745, 1745, 1780, 1765, 1731, 1734, 1754, 1700, 1735

2 The test marks of a group of ten Year 11 students are 56, 72, 35, 47, 89, 98, 13, 45, 34 and 73. The test marks of a group of ten Year 10 students who take the same test are: 58, 70, 40, 41, 42, 11, 94, 62, 43 and 60.
   a) Find the median and the range of each set of marks.
   b) Comment on your results.

3 Two players, Maureen and Eric both throw 9 darts. Maureen's scores are: 20, 40, 1, 5, 60, 20, 20, 1 and 60. Eric's scores are: 20, 40, 40, 0, 60, 20, 0, 5 and 1.
   a) Find the median and the range of each set of scores.
   b) Comment on your results.

4 The set of 5 values: 1, 2, 5, 7, 20 has a median of 5 and a mean of 7. Find a set of values which meets each of the following conditions.
   a) Number of values = 5, median = 9, mean = 10.
   b) Number of values = 7, median = 5, mean = 4.
   c) Number of values = 10, median = 7.5, mean = 8.
   d) Number of values = 10, median = 10, mean = 10.

Finding the median and the range of a discrete distribution presented in a frequency table

Calculate the median and the range for this frequency distribution:

Number of children per family	0	1	2	3	4	5	6
Frequency	19	21	36	14	7	3	0

Remember, to find the median we need to know the value which represents the mid-point of the distribution.

To discover this value we add an extra line to the table, called the *cumulative frequency* or running total. So for example, in this table:

Number of children per family	Frequency	Cumulative frequency
0	19	19
1	21 ◄ + =	40
2	36 ◄ + =	76 etc
3	14	90
4	7	97
5	3	100
6	0	100

With 100 values, the median is between the 50th and 51st values. We use the cumulative frequencies to pick out the values that are in these positions.

For example, the cumulative frequencies tell us that there are 40 families with 0 or 1 child and 76 families with 0, 1 or 2 children. This means that the 50th and 51st families must both have 2 children. So:

the median = 2 children per family,

the range is 5−0 = 5 children per family.

PAUSE

1 A survey was conducted into the number of eggs in 100 nests of two different bird species. This table shows the results.

Number of eggs	0	1	2	3	4	5	6
Number of nests (species A)	12	13	22	28	18	7	0
Number of nests (species B)	10	31	29	25	5	0	0

a) Find the median number of eggs per nest for species A and the range.

b) Find the median number of eggs per nest for species B and the range.

2 Trading Standards Officers checked the claims of two brands of matches to have '*average contents 40 matches*'. They counted the contents of 200 boxes of each brand. This table shows their results.

Number of matches per box	36	37	38	39	40	41	42	43	44
Number of boxes (Flares Matches)	12	19	23	46	50	30	17	3	0
Number of boxes (Squibs Matches)	0	3	13	24	27	82	31	16	4

a) Find the median number of matches per box for Flares Matches and the range.

b) Find the median number of matches per box for Squibs Matches and the range.

c) Comment on your answers.

3 A television factory has two different production lines. They find that far too many televisions are being produced with faults. They call in a quality control inspector who checks 50 television sets produced by each production line. These are her results.

Number of faults per set	0	1	2	3	4
Number of televisions (Line A)	24	23	2	1	0
Number of televisions (Line B)	11	12	27	0	0

a) Find the median number of faults per television for Line A and the range.

b) Find the median number of faults per television for Line B and the range.

c) Comment on your answers.

4 One of the questions in a survey on school meals asked Year 11 students how many days they had chips with their school meal during the previous week. These are the results.

Number of days	0	1	2	3	4	5
Frequency (girls)	12	20	21	17	6	4
Frequency (boys)	4	13	21	16	12	14

a) Find the median number of days that girls ate chips with their meal and the range.

b) Find the median number of days that boys ate chips with their meal and the range.

c) Comment on your answers.

■ ■

The mode

The third type of average which we will study is called the **mode** (or **modal average**). The mode of a set of values is **the value that occurs most frequently**.

Find the mode and the range of: 1, 4, 7, 5, 6, 3, 3, 2, 1, 5, 1.

First, we sort the values into groups.

$$1, 1, 1, 2, 3, 3, 4, 5, 5, 6, 7$$

Then we pick out the value which occurs most frequently. In this case, 1 occurs most frequently so:

the mode = 1.

In small distributions, where many (or all) values occur the same number of times there is no sensible modal average.

Find the mode of: 11, 11, 12, 12, 13, 13, 14, 14, 15, 16, 16.

There is no value that can be selected as a sensible mode.

If data is organised into a frequency table, we select the value of the variable which has the greatest frequency.

What is the modal number of children per family for the data in this frequency distribution?

Number of children per family	0	1	2	3	4	5	6
Frequency	13	13	38	17	10	4	5

The modal number of children per family is 2, because it occurs with the greatest frequency (38).

In a grouped table, the modal average becomes a **modal group**, and we select the **group of values** which occurs most frequently. In a large distribution, if two or more values of the variable each occur with the

341

same frequency, they may be stated as alternative values for the mode.
Find the modal group and the range for the students' test marks
shown in this table.

Test mark	1-5	6-10	11-15	16-20	21-25	26-30	31-35	36-40	41-45	46-50
Frequency	1	2	11	17	25	18	25	6	3	4

Two groups each occur with a frequency of 25, which is greater than
any other group's frequency.

So, the modal group is either 21–25 or 31–35.

PAUSE

1 Find the mode of each of the following distributions.
   a) 12, 6, 7, 9, 6
   b) 1, 1, 1, 1, 2, 2, 3, 3, 3, 3, 3, 4, 4, 5, 6, 6
   c) £1.50, £1.50, £2.00, £3.00, £3.00, £2.00, £2.50, £1.50, £1.50,
      £1.50
   d) –2, –1, –2, 0, 0, 0, 3, 4, 1, 2, 6
   e) 2.7, 3.4, 8.9, 5.6, 6.6, 7.3, 5.2, 2.9, 8.0, 7.1
   f) 1, 0, 0, 1, 0, 0, 1, –1, –1, –1, 0, 0, 0, –1, 1, 1, 1, 1, 1, 0, 1, –1,
      0, –1
   g) 12 cm, 13 cm, 15 cm, 17 cm, 12 cm, 13 cm, 15 cm, 14 cm, 29 cm,
      15 cm, 17 cm, 12 cm
   h) 10 g, 11 g, 10 g, 12 g, 11 g, 11 g, 12 g, 10 g, 11 g, 12 g, 12 g, 12 g,
      12 g, 13 g, 12 g, 11 g, 11 g
   i) 125 cm, 340 cm, 220 cm, 1.34 m, 1.90 m, 340 cm, 1.78 m, 2.55 m,
      3. 40 m
   j) 550 g, 650 g, 750 g, 850 g, 950 g, 1.05 kg, 1.15 kg, 1.25 kg,
      1.35 kg

2 The cost of a litre of petrol was checked at a sample of 50 garages
   in two different cities. The results are shown in the table below.

Cost per gallon (pence)	City A	City B
49	2	4
50	5	7
51	12	4
52	21	11
53	7	13
54	3	5
55	0	6

Find the modal price in each of the cities.

3 Michelle Jackson, the film star has two woods in her estate, Rooksend and Streamside. She orders a survey to be carried out into the size of the trees in the two woods. The circumferences of 100 selected trees is measured in both woods. The results are shown in this table. Find the modal group for each wood.

Circumference C (cm)	Rooksend	Streamside
$0 \le C < 20$	3	5
$20 \le C < 40$	17	3
$40 \le C < 60$	22	6
$60 \le C < 80$	25	11
$80 \le C < 100$	19	18
$100 \le C < 120$	7	24
$120 \le C < 140$	5	26
$140 \le C < 160$	2	7

■■■■■■■■■■■■■■■■■■■■■■■■■■■■■■■■■■■■■■

A summary of the ways to compare frequency distributions

In order to condense and summarise the data in a frequency distribution, we can find:

■ the mean average,
■ the median average,
■ the quartiles,
■ the modal average,
■ the range,

In two different types of distribution:

■ a simple list of values,

343

- a frequency distribution table.
- We can also state the modal class in a group frequency table.

PAUSE

1 Find the mean, median, mode, and range for each list of values:
   a) 1, 1, 2, 3, 3, 4, 4, 5, 8, 7, 6, 5, 4, 4, 3, 3, 3, 2, 1
   b) 12, 23, 11, 19, 11, 12, 12, 17, 18, 19, 13
   c) 36, 36, 37, 36, 38, 41, 39, 40, 37, 37, 38, 39, 37, 38, 40
   d) 102, 101, 102, 101, 102, 100, 100, 100, 102, 100, 101, 100, 99
   e) 1, 2, 4, 5, 3, 3, 3, 1, 1, 6, 7, 10, 4, 1, 1, 1, 6, 1, 1, 2, 2, 2, 2

2 In order to test the manufacturers' claims of 'average content 40 matches', two samples of 100 match boxes are opened and their contents counted. The first sample are 'Burners' matches and the second sample are 'Flames'. The table below shows the results.

Number of matches per box	Frequency 'Burners'	Frequency 'Flames'
36	2	0
37	5	0
38	7	12
39	13	24
40	24	38
41	26	17
42	13	9
43	8	0
44	2	0

   a) Find the mean for each frequency distribution.
   b) Find the median for each frequency distribution.
   c) Find the mode for each frequency distribution.
   d) Find the range for each frequency distribution.
   e) Comment on your results, comparing and contrasting the two distributions.

3 Each year, a game warden in East Anglia checks on the contents of 60 nests of the Egyptian Goose, a bird introduced from Africa in the eighteenth century. The table below shows her results for two successive years.

344

Number of eggs	0	1	2	3	4	5	6	7	8	9
Number of nests (Year 1)	12	0	0	3	0	12	17	12	4	0
Number of nests (Year 2)	17	0	1	5	0	19	12	6	0	0

a) Find the mean for each frequency distribution.
b) Find the median for each frequency distribution.
c) Find the mode for each frequency distribution.
d) Find the range for each frequency distribution.
e) Comment on your results, comparing and contrasting the two distributions.

4 A games teacher starts a ten week training programme for a health and fitness club. She times the students over a one mile race both before and after they complete the programme. The table below shows her results.

Time (seconds)	Frequency (before)	Frequency (after)
$260 \leq T < 280$	0	6
$280 \leq T < 300$	2	12
$300 \leq T < 320$	4	15
$320 \leq T < 340$	14	16
$340 \leq T < 360$	16	8
$360 \leq T < 380$	11	3
$380 \leq T < 400$	8	0
$400 \leq T < 420$	5	0

a) Find the modal group for each frequency distribution.
b) Comment on your results, comparing and contrasting the two distributions.

■■■■■■■■■■■■■■■■■■■■■■■■■■■■■■■■■■■■■■■

Correlation and scatter diagrams

All the work so far has involved values of a *single* variable. Many of the questions that are asked involve *more than* one variable. For example, we might ask:

■ do people with large incomes tend to live in large houses?
■ do tall parents tend to have tall children?
■ how is the amount that is spent on advertising a new product related to its sales success?
■ do taller than average people tend to be heavier than average?
■ do people who are good at Maths tend to be also good at Geography?

All these questions involve the idea that the values of two variables may be *correlated*. This means that the values are linked in some way. For example, if we say that height and shoe size in children are *correlated*, we mean that taller children tend to have bigger feet.

Scatter diagrams are used to detect correlations.

Jamie and Jessica wonder if there is a correlation between a person's homework marks in Maths and Science. They collect the following data from 20 friends who have just had homeworks from both subjects marked out of 10.

Individual	A	B	C	D	E	F	G	H	I	J	K	L	M	O	N	P	Q	R	S	T
Maths mark	1	9	3	6	5	10	7	4	8	5	5	3	3	4	10	7	7	4	5	6
Science mark	2	3	4	6	3	10	5	1	8	6	5	2	3	3	8	6	5	5	4	5

To construct a *scatter* diagram from this data, each individual plots as a single point on the graph. Their two marks are used as *x* and *y* coordinates.

This is a scatter diagram drawn from Jamie's and Jessica's results. The arrow on the scatter diagram points to individual E, plotted at the point (5,3) because his Maths mark is 5 and his Science mark is 3.

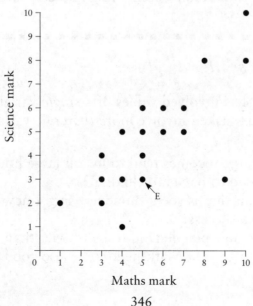

Scatter diagram of homework marks in maths and science for 20 people

The scatter diagram shows that there is a *positive correlation* between the homework marks in Maths and Science. This means that the diagram shows that a student who gets a good mark for Maths tend to also get a good mark for Science. Students who get a poor mark for Maths tend to also get a poor mark for Science.

There are exceptions to this rule, Individual B for example scores 9 for Maths but only 3 for Science.

We can have *negative correlation* as well as *positive correlation*.

For example, this scatter diagram shows the relationship between the engine sizes of 20 cars and their average fuel consumption in miles per gallon. It is clear that as the engine size *increases*, the fuel consumption tends to *decrease*. We say that the two variables in this case are *negatively correlated*.

A scatter diagram to show the relationship between engine size and average fuel consumption for 20 cars

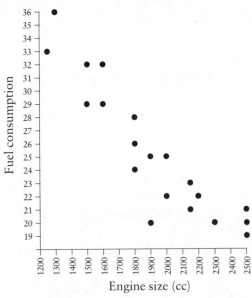

We can of course have instances where two variables are not correlated at all. In this case we would expect to see a random distribution of dots in the scatter diagram.

These diagrams illustrate variables with positive correlation, negative correlation and no correlation.

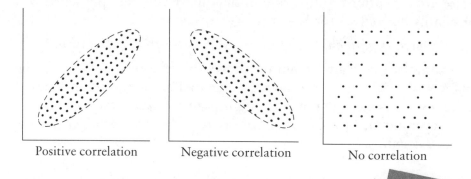

Positive correlation   Negative correlation   No correlation

PAUSE

1 In each of the following cases, say whether you would expect the two variables to have a positive correlation, a negative correlation or no correlation. Explain your answers, saying what likely exceptions there would be to any expected correlation.

a) An adults' height and weight.

b) A person's income and the value of the house they live in.

c) A person's height and the height of their mother.

d) The price of a stereo system and the number sold.

e) The age of a student and the amount of absence they have from school.

f) The age of an adult and the distance they can run without stopping to rest.

g) The length of a person's hair and their shoe size.

h) The age of a child and the distance they can run without stopping to rest.

i) Students' test scores in Maths and English.

j) The age of a used car and its value.

2 The records of 20 pupils are checked and the number of days absence they had in the past year recorded, together with their year group.

Pupil	A	B	C	D	E	F	G	H	I	J
Year group	7	7	7	7	8	8	8	8	9	9
Days absent	0	3	2	4	2	5	3	6	4	7

Pupil	K	L	M	N	O	P	Q	R	S	T
Year group	9	9	10	10	10	10	11	11	11	11
Days absent	5	9	4	7	7	11	6	8	9	15

a) Draw a scatter diagram.

b) Comment on any correlation indicated in the scatter diagram.

3 The length of 20 girls' hair (measured in inches) and their shoe size is recorded in this table.

Girl	A	B	C	D	E	F	G	H	I	J
Hair length	6	7	9	15	11	12	3	7	9	12
Shoe size	3	4	4	3	5	3	6	5	5	4

Girl	K	L	M	N	O	P	Q	R	S	T
Hair length	8	12	15	11	12	2	18	12	11	15
Shoe size	5	3	3	3	6	4	4	5	6	4

a) Draw a scatter diagram.

b) Comment on any correlation indicated in the scatter diagram.

4 A shopkeeper makes a record of the temperature each day for the first two weeks in September. She also records the number of ice-creams she sells. The table below shows her results.

Date	Number sold	Temp (C°)
1	20	21
2	15	16
3	25	24
4	35	27
5	30	27
6	20	18
7	15	18
8	25	24
9	20	24
10	35	29
11	15	16
12	20	18
13	30	21
14	25	18

a) Draw a scatter diagram using axes like this.

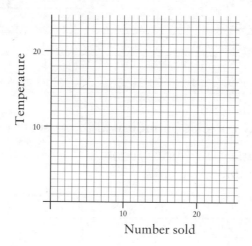

b) Comment on any correlation indicated in the scatter diagram.

5 This table shows the latitude of 15 cities and their average annual temperature.

City	Latitude (nearest degree)	Average temperature (nearest C°)
Algiers	37	58
Amsterdam	52	12
Berlin	53	13
Bombay	19	31
Copenhagen	56	11
Hong Kong	22	25
Karachi	25	31
Leningrad	60	8
London	52	14
Madrid	40	19
Manila	15	32
Paris	49	15
Phnom Penh	12	32
Rangoon	17	32
Saigon	11	32

a) Draw a scatter diagram.
b) Comment on any correlation indicated in the scatter diagram.

■ ■

SECTION 4 Probability

Probability is the name given to the branch of statistics which allows us to predict how *likely* a given result is. This means we can compare our experimental results with theoretical 'perfect' results and draw conclusions about their reliability. For example, probability predicts that when you roll a normal die you have the same chance of scoring a 6 as of scoring a 1,2,3,4 or 5. If, you rolled a die 600 times and recorded 300 sixes, you would suspect that something was wrong with either the die or the experiment.

Simple probability (single events with equally likely outcomes)

An *event* is something which happens, like tossing a coin or rolling a die.

Most events have more than one possible outcome, for example, when a die is rolled, there are six possible outcomes, 1,2,3,4,5 or 6.

If an event is *fair*, all these outcomes will be *equally likely*.

If an event is *biased* all these outcomes will not be *equally likely*.

Several of these outcomes may give the same result. For example, the scores 2,4 and 6 on a die all give the result 'an even number'.

If the die is *fair*, the *probability* that any particular result will be obtained in an event is the fraction:

$$\frac{\text{the number of outcomes that contains the desired result}}{\text{the total number of all possible outcomes}}$$

So, when a fair die is rolled, the probability of obtaining an even score is:

$$\frac{3}{6} = \frac{1}{2}$$

Probabilities can be written as fractions, decimals or percentages.

Remember:

- To turn a fraction into a decimal, divide the top number by the bottom number,

Example

$$\frac{1}{2} = 1 \div 2 = 0.5$$

351

■ To turn a decimal into a percentage, multiply by 100,

Example

$$0.5 = 1 \times 100 = 50\%$$

So, the probability of obtaining an even score when a fair die is rolled can be written as:

$$\frac{1}{2} = 0.5 = 50\%$$

■ You will often need to approximate your answers to a sensible number of decimal places.

The probability of rolling a fair die and obtaining a 6 can be written as:

$$\frac{1}{6} = 0.167 \text{ (to 3 decimal places)} = 16.7\%$$

Remember, these rules can only be applied if an event is *fair* and *all outcomes are equally likely*.

Events may involve a selection, for example taking a bead from a bag or selecting a number for a National Lottery card. It this case, we can only apply the rules if the selection is made *at random*, with no personal preference involved in the selection.

Examples

1. What is the probability of cutting a deck of cards and obtaining an ace? Give your answer as a fraction, decimal and percentage.

   The number of outcomes that includes the result is 4 (ace of hearts, diamonds, clubs and spades).

   The total number of all possible outcomes is 52.

   The probability of obtaining an ace is:

   $$\frac{4}{52} = \frac{1}{13} = 0.077 \text{ (to 3 decimal places)} = 7.7\%.$$

2. What is the probability of selecting a letter at random from the word 'probability' and obtaining a vowel? Give your answer as a fraction, decimal and percentage.

   The number of outcomes that includes the result is 4 (o, a, i, i).

   The total number of all possible outcomes is 11.

The probability of obtaining a vowel is:

$$\frac{4}{11} = 0.364 \text{ (to 3 decimal places)} = 36.4\%.$$

If any result is certain to happen because it is included in all the possible outcomes it has a probability of 1. For example, the probability of cutting a deck of cards and obtaining a red or black card is 1 (52 out of 52).

If any result cannot happen because it is not included in any of the possible outcomes it has a probability of 0. For example, the probability of cutting a deck of cards and obtaining a green card is 0 (0 out of 52).

PAUSE

Give all numerical answers in this exercise as a fraction, decimal and percentage.

1 List three different ways that somebody could select National Lottery numbers 'at random'.

2 A fair die is rolled. What is the probability that the result is:
   a) a 4,
   b) an odd number,
   c) a prime number,
   d) a 1 or a 6?

3 A card is cut from a normal deck of 52 cards. What is the probability that the card is:
   a) a picture card,
   b) not a picture card,
   c) a 5 of spades,
   d) a 5,
   e) a red 5,
   f) a red picture card,
   g) a red card or a king,
   h) a club or a queen,
   i) a diamond or a club,
   j) a card higher than a 7?

4 A bag contains 3 red, 5 yellow and 4 green beads. If one bead is selected at random from the bag, what is the probability that it is:

a) red,

b) yellow,

c) green,

d) red or green,

e) red or yellow,

f) yellow or green,

g) not green,

h) purple,

i) red, yellow or green,

j) not yellow?

5 In a maths class of 30 students, 15 hate the subject, 7 dislike it, 5 like it and 3 love it. If a student is selected at random from the group, what is the probability that they will:

a) hate maths,

b) dislike maths,

c) like maths,

d) love maths,

e) either hate or dislike maths,

f) either like or love maths,

g) either love or hate maths?

6 This table shows the number of children per family in 50 families on each of two housing estates.

Number of children per family	0	1	2	3	4	5	6
Frequency (Estate A)	10	9	18	8	5	0	0
Frequency (Estate B)	3	4	20	9	5	4	5

a) What is the probability of selecting a family at random on Estate A and obtaining one with:

  i) no children,

  ii) 4 children,

  iii) less than the median average number of families for that estate?

b) What is the probability of selecting a family at random on Estate B and obtaining one with:
   i) 2 children,
   ii) 1 child,
   iii) more than the mean average number of families for that estate?

7 Two darts players, Maureen and Eric both throw their three darts 50 times. The 50 total scores for each player are shown in this table.

Score	1–30	31–60	61–90	91–120	121–150	151–180
Frequency (Maureen)	7	8	10	9	8	8
Frequency (Eric)	0	16	18	14	2	0

a) If we assume that these scores are typical of the players' performances, what is the probability that on her next throw Maureen will score:

   i) more than 90,
   ii) less than 61,
   iii) between 31 and 150?

b) If we assume that these scores are typical of the players' performances, what is the probability that on his next throw Eric will score:

   i) more than 90,
   ii) less than 61,
   iii) between 31 and 150?

c) Comment on your answers to this question. Can we be certain that the probabilities are accurate or are they just estimates?

■ ■

The probability scale

A probability of 0 means an outcome cannot happen, it is *impossible*.
A probability of 1 means an outcome must happen, it is *certain*.
All probabilities must be between 0 and 1.
Probabilities can be illustrated on a *probability scale*.
A probability scale is a number line from 0 to 1, divided into either

355

fractions, decimals or percentages. This diagram shows fraction, decimal and percentage probability scales.

If outcomes are *mutually exclusive*, this means that if one happens the other(s) cannot happen.

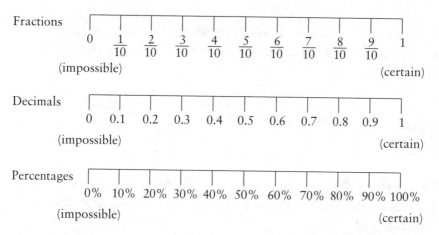

For example, it may rain tomorrow or it may stay dry all day. The two outcomes are *mutually exclusive* because it cannot both rain and stay dry all day.

The probability of all the mutually exclusive outcomes of an event *must add to 1.*

Example

The probability that it will rain on a June day in Hemerton is 0.15.

a) What is the probability that it will stay dry all day on a June day in Hemerton?

b) Show the probabilities that it will rain or stay dry on a decimal probability scale.

c) Estimate on how many days it will stay dry during a typical June in Hemerton.

a) The probability that it will stay dry all day $= 1 - 0.15 = 0.85$.

b)

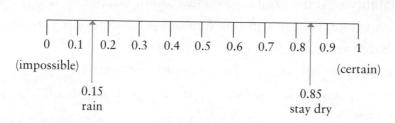

c) Estimate of number of dry days during June

= probability that it will stay dry all day × total number of days in June

= 0.85 × 30

= 25.5 days or 26 days to the nearest day.

PAUSE

1 Experience has shown that the probability that Jane is late for school is 0.1.
   a) What is the probability that Jane is not late for school?
   b) Show the probabilities that Jane is late and not late for school on a decimal probability scale.
   c) In Year 10 Jane attended school for 190 days. Estimate on how many of these days she was late.

2 Experience has shown that the probability that Simon wears white socks to school is 0.6.
   a) What is the probability that Simon does not wear white socks to school?
   b) Show the probabilities that Simon does or does not wear white socks on a decimal probability scale.
   c) In Year 11 Simon attended school for 185 days. Estimate on how many of these days he wore white socks.

3 June always wears either a tracksuit, shorts or a skirt to play netball. Experience has shown that the probability that she wears a tracksuit is 0.25 and the probability that she wears shorts is 0.4.
   a) What is the probability that June wears a skirt to play netball?
   b) Show the probabilities that June wears a tracksuit, shorts or a skirt to play netball on a decimal probability scale.
   c) In one season, June played 60 games of netball. Estimate in how many of these games she wore:
      i) a tracksuit,
      ii) shorts,
      iii) a skirt.

4 A bag contains beads coloured blue, green and orange. If a bead is selected at random, the probability that it is blue is $\frac{1}{12}$ and the probability that it is green is $\frac{7}{12}$.
   a) What is the probability that a bead selected at random from the bag is orange?
   b) Show all three probabilities on a probability scale divided into twelfths.
   c) If there are 36 beads in the bag, estimate how many are:
      i) blue,
      ii) green,
      iii) orange.

5 A bag contains a mixture of mints, toffees and eclairs. If a sweet is selected at random, the probability that it is a mint is $\frac{3}{16}$ and the probability that it is a toffee is $\frac{5}{16}$.
   a) What is the probability that a sweet selected at random from the bag is an eclair?
   b) Show all three probabilities on a probability scale divided into sixteenths.
   c) If there are 64 sweets in the bag, estimate how many are:
      i) mints,
      ii) toffees,
      iii) eclairs.

6 The probability that a milling machine breaks at least one cutter during an 8 hour working shift has been found to be $\frac{7}{20}$.
   a) What is the probability that the machine does not break a cutter during the shift?
   b) Show both probabilities on a probability scale divided into twentieths.
   c) Bill Yates works the machine for 100 shifts. Estimate in how many of these shifts Bill did not need to change the cutter because it had broken.

7 In a Year 11 class, 56% of the students are boys.
   a) What is the probability that a student selected at random from the class will be a girl?
   b) Show the probabilities that a selected student will be a boy or a girl on a percentage probability scale.
   c) One student is selected at random from the class every day to do litter duty. Estimate how many girls will be picked during a school term lasting for 75 school days.

358

8 A bag contains beads coloured grey, green and purple. If a bead is selected at random, the probability that it is grey is 37.5% and the probability that it is green is 12.5%.

a) What is the probability
   that a bead selected at random from the bag is purple?
b) Show all three probabilities on a percentage probability scale.
c) If there are 120 beads in the bag, estimate how many are:
   i) grey,
   ii) green,
   iii) purple.
d) Explain why there cannot be 60 beads in the bag.

9 An ice cream van sells four flavours of ice cream, vanilla, strawberry, mint and chocolate. The owner worked out that the probability a customer chose vanilla was 40%, the probability that a customer chose strawberry was 25%, and the probability that a customer chose mint was 10%.

a) What was the probability that a customer chose chocolate?
b) Show all four probabilities on a percentage probability scale.
c) If the van sold 460 ice creams during the day, estimate how many were:
   i) vanilla,
   ii) strawberry,
   iii) mint,
   iv) chocolate.

■ ■

Research and experimental probability

There are many real life situations where equally likely outcomes cannot be assumed.

For example, when a drawing pin is dropped on a table, it will either land point down or point up. We cannot assume that these two outcomes are equally likely.

The way to find the probability of the drawing pin landing point up or point down is to do an experiment.

Suppose we dropped the drawing pin 100 times and obtained these results.

	Point up	Point down
Frequency	45	55

We estimate the probability of the drawing pin landing point up as $\frac{45}{100}$ or 0.45, and the probability of it landing point down as $\frac{55}{100}$ or 0.55.

The fractions $\frac{45}{100}$ and $\frac{55}{100}$ are called the *relative frequencies* with which the drawing pin landed point up or point down.

Relative frequencies become more accurate measures of probability if an experiment is repeated a large number of times.

Example

James, Carl, Vali and Jodie each toss two coins 100 times and record the number of times they obtain two heads, two tails or one head with one tail. These are their results.

	One head, one tail	Two tails	Two heads
James	45	31	24
Carl	56	17	27
Vali	61	20	19
Jodie	42	33	25

a) Write down the relative frequencies of one head with one tail, two tails and two heads for each student's results.

b) Write down the relative frequencies of one head with one tail, two tails and two heads for the students' combined results.

c) Which relative frequencies are likely to be the most accurate estimates of the probabilities of one head with one tail, two tails or two heads?

d) If the experiment is repeated 2000 times, estimate how many of the outcomes will be two heads.

a) This table shows the relative frequencies.

	One head, one tail	Two tails	Two heads
James	$\frac{45}{100}$	$\frac{31}{100}$	$\frac{24}{100}$
Carl	$\frac{56}{100}$	$\frac{17}{100}$	$\frac{27}{100}$
Vali	$\frac{61}{100}$	$\frac{20}{100}$	$\frac{19}{100}$
Jodie	$\frac{42}{100}$	$\frac{33}{100}$	$\frac{25}{100}$

b) The combined relative frequencies are:

One head, one tail	Two tails	Two heads
$\dfrac{204}{400}$	$\dfrac{101}{400}$	$\dfrac{95}{100}$

c) The combined relative frequencies are likely to be the most accurate estimates of the probabilities of one head with one tail, two tails or two heads.

d) Estimate of number of two heads outcomes = $\dfrac{95}{400} \times 2000 = 475$.

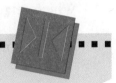

PAUSE

1 A bag contains a very large number of mixed red and green seeds. Stefan, Wayne and Surbajit each select 100 seeds and note the seed's colour, returning each seed to the bag before another is selected. These are their results.

	Green	Red
Stefan	58	42
Wayne	63	37
Surbajit	59	41

a) Write down the relative frequencies of green and red seeds for each student's results.
b) Write down the relative frequencies of green and red seeds for the students' combined results.
c) Which relative frequencies are likely to be the most accurate estimates of the probabilities of selecting a green seed or a red seed?
d) If there are 5000 seeds in the bag, estimate how many of the seeds are red.

2 Four plant researchers each open 30 pods of a new type of broad bean and count the contents. These are their results.

361

Number of beans	4	5	6	7	8	9
Number of pods (Researcher A)	3	4	7	6	5	5
Number of pods (Researcher B)	6	7	6	5	6	0
Number of pods (Researcher C)	0	11	0	12	5	2
Number of pods (Researcher D)	1	4	6	9	8	2

a) Write down the relative frequencies 4, 5, 6, 7, 8 or 9 beans per pod for each researcher's results.
b) Write down the relative frequencies of 4, 5, 6, 7, 8 or 9 beans per pod for the researchers' combined results.
c) Which relative frequencies are likely to be the most accurate estimates of the probabilities of 4, 5, 6, 7, 8 or 9 beans per pod?
d) If 1000 pods were opened, estimate how many would contain 9 beans.

3 A market researcher asks four groups of 50 people to select their favourite ice cream flavour from the list strawberry, vanilla, chocolate and mint. These are his results.

	Strawberry	Vanilla	Chocolate	Mint
Group A	4	16	24	6
Group B	5	25	15	5
Group C	8	27	10	5
Group D	7	23	8	12

a) Write down the relative frequencies of selecting strawberry, vanilla, chocolate or mint for each group.
b) Write down the relative frequencies of selecting strawberry, vanilla, chocolate or mint for the groups' combined results.
c) Which relative frequencies are likely to be the most accurate estimates of the probabilities that a person will select strawberry, vanilla, chocolate or mint?
d) If a group of 2000 people were asked the same question, estimate how many would select vanilla.

■ ■

Deciding when sufficient trials have been made in a probability experiment

It can be very difficult to decided when to stop a probability experiment. We want to be confident that any relative frequencies we have calculated are close to the real probabilities for those outcomes.

One way to judge this is illustrated in the following example.

Example

A student decided to experiment with a single die.

She knew the die should produce exactly one sixth of its outcomes as a score of one but wondered whether it actually would do this.

She threw the die 4200 times and recorded the number of ones scored after every 600 throws.

Number of ones	91	208	292	382	505	605	709
Total throws	600	1200	1800	2400	3000	3600	4200

She then worked out the relative frequencies by dividing the number of ones by the total number of throws (to 2 decimal places).

Number of ones	91	208	292	382	505	605	709
Total throws	600	1200	1800	2400	3000	3600	4200
Relative frequency	0.15	0.17	0.16	0.16	0.17	0.17	0.17

She drew a graph showing the total number of throws and the relative frequency.

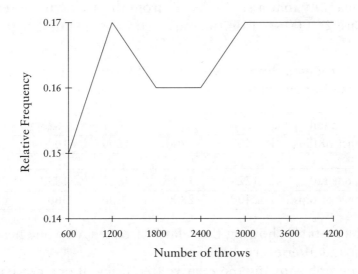

She decided that the relative frequency had settled to a value close to 0.17 and stopped the experiment.

1 A sack contains a large number of mixed red and white seeds. A group of 10 students each select 500 seeds from the bag and count the number which are red. These are their cumulative results.

Red seeds counted	206	412	608	791	1000
Total number counted	500	1000	1500	2000	2500

Red seeds counted	1181	1373	1561	1765	1962
Total number counted	3000	3500	4000	4500	5000

a) Complete a table showing the relative frequency of red seeds after every 500 seeds counted.

b) Draw a graph showing the relative frequency of red seeds after every 500 seeds counted.

c) Do you think the students have produced a reliable estimate of the probability that a seed selected from the sack will be red?

d) There are 26 000 seeds in the sack, estimate the number that are red.

2 A group of students flipped two coins 4000 times. They recorded their results after every 400 flips. These are their results.

One head, one tail	214	407	611	823	1025
Total number of flips	400	800	1200	1600	2000

One head, one tail	1228	1433	1632	1830	2022
Total number of flips	2400	2800	3200	3600	4000

a) Complete a table showing the relative frequency of one head and one tail after every 400 flips.

b) Draw a graph showing the relative frequency of one head and one tail after every 400 flips.

c) Do you think the students have a reliable estimate of the probability that the two coins will land as one head and one tail?

Probability problems with two events

We may be asked to find the probability of obtaining a particular result when two or more events are combined. For example, we may be asked to find the probability of obtaining two heads when two coins are tossed, or of obtaining 5 sixes when five dice are rolled. When *two* events are combined we often draw a small graph or *sample space* to illustrate clearly all the possible outcomes that can be obtained.

Examples
1. Two coins are tossed, find the probability that the result obtained is two heads.

   To illustrate all the outcomes that are possible, we draw this diagram.

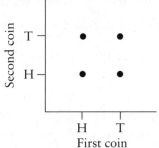

   A diagram like this is called a *sample space*. It is a graph with all the outcomes of one event listed on the *x*-axis and all the outcomes of the other event listed on the *y*-axis. All the possible *combined outcomes are illustrated by the dots on the graph.*

   Our sample space shows that there are four possible combined outcomes, HH, HT, TH and TT.

   Of these, only one gives the required result of two heads.

   So the probability of obtaining two heads = $\frac{1}{4}$ = 0.25 = 25%.

2. Two dice are rolled, find the probability that the score will be greater than 9.

   We can draw this sample space.

365

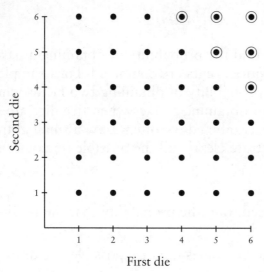

From the sample space we see that there are 36 possible outcomes. Of these, 6 (circled in the diagram) give a score greater than 9.

So, the probability of a score greater than $9 = \frac{6}{36} = \frac{1}{6} = 0.167$ (to 3 decimal places) = 16.7%.

3. An ordinary pack of 52 playing cards is shuffled and a card is chosen. The card is replaced, the pack is shuffled and a second card is chosen. What is the probability that both cards chosen are red?

We can draw this sample space:

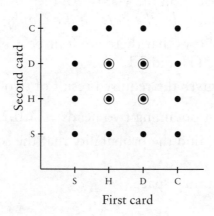

There are 16 possible outcomes of these, 4 give two red cards.

The probability of two red cards is $\frac{4}{16}$.

PAUSE

Give all numerical answers in this exercise as a fraction, decimal and percentage.

1 Find the probability that when two coins are tossed the result will be:
   a) two tails,
   b) a head and a tail.

2 If two coins are tossed 2000 times, how many of the results would you predict will be:
   a) two heads,
   b) two tails,
   c) a head and a tail?
   Would you expect an actual experiment to exactly match your predictions?

3 Two dice are rolled together, and their total score recorded.
   Copy and complete the sample space diagram.

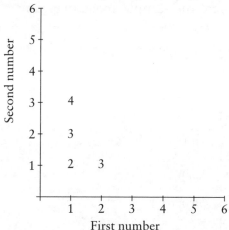

Use the diagram to answer these questions. Find the probability of the result being:
a) an 8,   f) a 12,
b) a 7,   g) an even number,
c) a 4,   h) a prime number,
d) a 5,   i) greater than 1,
e) a 10,   but less than 13.

367

4 If two dice are rolled 1800 times, how many of the total scores would you predict will be:

a) a 9,   d) a 6,
b) a 2,   e) an 11,
c) a 3,   f) a square number?

5 An ordinary pack of 52 playing cards is shuffed and a card is chosen. The card is replaced, the pack is shuffled and a second card is chosen. What is the probability that the cards cut will be:

a) two spades,
b) two black cards,
c) one red and one black card,
d) both of the same suit,
e) one club and one diamond?

6 Two spinners are made, one numbered from 1 to 5 and the other from 6 to 10. Find the probability that when the spinners are spun together the total score will be greater than 12.

7 Two special dice are made, one has the set of numbers 0,1,1,2,2,3 and the other the set of numbers 0,0,1,2,4,5. Bill rolls the first dice and Anthea rolls the second dice.

a) Copy and complete the sample space diagram:

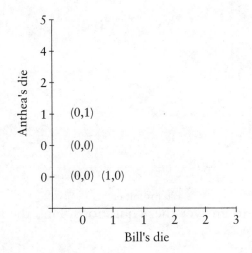

b) What is the probability that Anthea beats Bill?

■ ■

1 Explain the difference between qualitative variables, discrete variables and continuous variables, giving some examples of each type.

2 These are the test scores of 50 students in a maths test. Use a tally chart to organise the results into a table.

2	7	8	9	3	4	1	9	10	2
6	6	5	7	8	9	2	6	4	9
3	4	9	10	6	7	8	4	5	3
2	5	6	7	8	7	6	5	9	10
9	8	7	4	5	6	7	2	8	7

3 Illustrate the 50 test marks in question 2 with a bar chart.

4 This bar chart illustrates a serious problem that existed in British prisons. Estimate from the bar chart the average daily overcrowding for each year from 1977 to 1987.

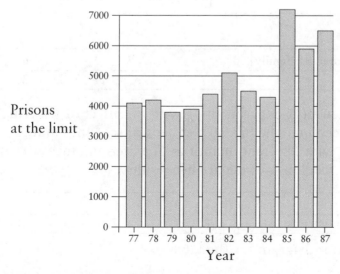

Overcrowding year by year: average daily total of prisoners above recommended level

369

5 Draw a pie chart to illustrate the data in this table:

Activity	Time spent in one day (hours)
Working	9
Travel	1
Leisure	4
Sleeping	8
Meals	2

6 Draw a frequency polygon to illustrate the data in this table.

Height of seedling (mm)	$0 \leq H < 5$	$5 \leq H < 10$	$10 \leq H < 15$	$15 \leq H < 20$	$20 \leq H < 25$	$25 \leq H < 30$
Frequency	5	11	20	26	12	6

7 Find the mean, median, mode and range of each of these sets of numbers.
a) 2,2,4,6,7,4,2,6,1,2,6,8,2,3,1,3,5,7,7
b) 21,22,23,24,22,22,21,23,25,23,22,21,21,24,21
c) –1,0,–1,2,3,–3,2,1,1,1,1
d) 200,300,200,400,500,600,200,300,300,400,500,200,200

8 Find the mean, median, mode and range of the data shown in each of the following tables.
a)

Number of matches per box	36	37	38	39	40	41	42	43
Frequency	3	12	18	27	23	12	5	0

b)

Number of children per family	0	1	2	3	4	5	6
Frequency	45	67	124	33	17	12	2

9 A research scientist is experimenting with the effect of watering on a type of seedling. She has 10 test beds of seedlings and supplies them with different quantities of water and measures the growth of the seedlings. These are her results.

Water (1000 litres)	1	2	3	4	5	6	7	8	9	10
Average growth (centimetres)	3	4	4	5	7	7	8	9	8	10

a) Draw a scatter diagram for the table.

b) Comment on any correlation indicated in the scatter diagram.

10 A survey is made into the time that twenty Year 11 students spend each week watching television or doing homework. These are the results.

Watching TV (hours)	0	2	2	3	4	4	5	5	6	8
Doing homework (hours)	14	12	13	11	12	10	8	12	9	8

Watching TV (hours)	10	10	12	12	12	14	14	16	17	18
Doing homework (hours)	5	7	5	4	6	1	3	2	1	0

a) Draw a scatter diagram for the table.
b) Comment on any correlation indicated in the scatter diagram.

11 If a single die is rolled, what is the probability that the score will be:

a) even,

b) a factor of 12,

c) less than 5,

d) a 3?

12 If a single card is cut from a deck of 52 cards, what is the probability that it will be:

a) a club,

b) a red card,

c) the king of diamonds,

d) a picture card,

e) not a spade,

f) a queen or a red card,

g) a queen and a red card,

h) a five or a black card?

13 Hannah is an animal researcher studying a large colony of bats. She wishes to know the relative frequencies of males and females in the colony. She traps ten groups of twenty bats, determines their gender and then releases them. These are her results:

Males	9	15	24	34	43	51	55	63	73	78
Females	11	25	36	46	57	69	85	97	107	122
Total	20	40	60	80	100	120	140	160	180	200

a) Write down the relative frequencies of females after each of the ten samples has been checked.

b) Which relative frequency is likely to be the most accurate estimate of the probability that a bat selected at random will be female?

c) If there are 1200 bats in the colony, estimate the number of these bats which are female.

14 Two dice are rolled together. Draw a sample space for the results and find the probability that the final score will be:

a) a prime number,   e) a factor of 12,

b) 12,   f) 13,

c) greater than 8,   g) 1,

d) 7,   h) 2 or 12.

FASTFORWARD

1 Nadia wants to find out which computer games people play. She has designed a questionnaire with only boxes to tick.

QUESTIONNAIRE: COMPUTER GAMES

1. Do you have a computer game at home? | YES | NO |

2. Tick the computer you have games for:

☐ ☐ ☐

ZEGA   SAMURI   PC

3. Tick the type of computer game you like best:

☐ ☐ ☐ ☐ ☐

Arcade   Shoot'em   Fantasy   Factual   Educational

4. How many computer games have you bought in the last 12 months?

☐ ☐ ☐ ☐

None   1   2   3

---

a) How could you improve part 4 of the questionnaire?

Nadia also wants to find out how much time people spend playing computer games each week.

b) Design a question that she could use.

Include tick boxes for a response. (ULEAC)

2 In a survey about children, Valerie asks a number of women how many boys and girls they each have.

Her findings are shown in the table below.

Number of girls	0	1	2	3	4	5
5						
4	1	1				
3	3	4				
2	3		1			
1	4	7	1		1	1
0	8	3	1		1	

Number of boys

a) How many of these women have no children?

b) How many women were included in the survey?

c) How many boys did these women have altogether?

3 Lorraine is writing a questionnaire for a survey about her local Superstore.

She thinks that local people visit the store more often than people from further away. She also thinks that local people spend less money per visit.

Write three questions which would help her to test these ideas.

Each question should include at least three responses from which people choose one.

(SEG)

373

4 The bar chart shows the numbers of customers shopping in a department store one week.

   a) On which day of that week did the store have the least number of customers?

   b) How many customers did the store have:

     i) on Wednesday,

     ii) on Thursday?

On Saturday, each customer spent an average of £14.20.

   c) Work out the total amount of money spent in the store on Saturday.   (ULEAC)

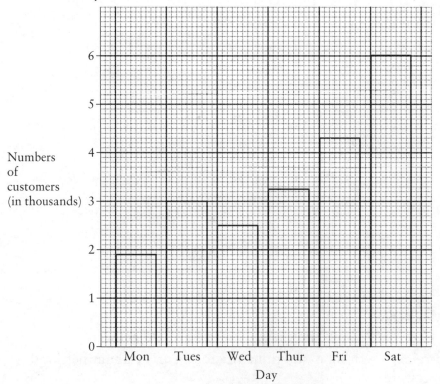

5 Sally did a survey of car colours. The notebook shows all her results.

w	w	r	w	g
r	w	r	b	r
r	r	w	r	r
b	w	r	r	w
r	g	r	w	r
g	w	w	b	r

Key:

w white
b blue
r red
g green

a) Copy and complete her frequency table.

Colour	Tally	Frequency
White		
Blue		
Red		
Green		

b) Show this information as a bar chart.   (SEG)

6   Each morning in September, Liz picked mushrooms from her field.
    The bar chart below shows the number of mushrooms that she
    picked in the 30 days of September last year.

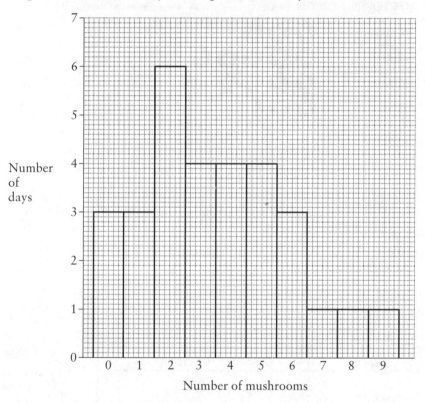

a) Write down the number of days on which Liz picked:
   i) two mushrooms,
   ii) no mushrooms.
b) Find the total number of mushrooms Liz picked in the month.
c) Find the modal number of mushrooms Liz picked in the
   month.

d) Find the median number of mushrooms Liz picked in the month.

e) Calculate the mean number of mushrooms Liz picked in the month.

These days in September are typical.

f) Find the probability that Liz will pick at least four mushrooms on 23rd September next year. (ULEAC)

7 The table below shows the number of records sold by a small record shop in Megtown.

MEGTOWN RECORD SHOP	⊙ represents 20 records	
JANUARY	⊙ ⊙ ⊙	60
FEBRUARY	⊙ ⊙ ⊙ ⊙ ⊙	95
MARCH	⊙ ⊙ ⊙ ⊙	
APRIL	⊙ ⊙ ⊙	
MAY		100
JUNE		45

a) In the table above enter the number of records sold in March and April.

b) Complete the table by drawing the symbols to show the number of records sold in May and June.

c) Complete a bar chart below to illustrate the information in the above table. (MEG)

8

Town	Quantity of ice cream
Torquay	🍦 🍦 🍦 🍦 🍦 🍦 🍦
Brighton	🍦 🍦 🍦 🍦 🍦
Bournemouth	🍦 🍦 🍦 🍦
Folkestone	

Key

🍦 represents 10 tonnes.

The pictogram shows the amount of ice cream sold in Summer 1993 in three English holiday towns.

a) How much ice cream was sold in Summer 1993:

   i) in Bournemouth,

   ii) in Torquay?

The amount sold in Folkestone in Summer 1993 was 60 tonnes.

b) Copy and complete the pictogram.

c) Find the mean amount of ice cream sold in the four towns during Summer 1993. Give your answer to the nearest 5 tonnes.

(ULEAC)

9 Out of every £180 received from the rates a district council spent as follows:

Highways and planning	£13
Sports and recreation	£29
Environmental health	£37
Housing	£24
Administration	£49
Emergency fund	£28

Illustrate this expenditure by means of a pie chart of radius 5 cm.

(SEG)

10 A class in a junior school conducted a survey on how they each travelled to school that morning.

The table shows the results.

Method of travel	Number of pupils
Walk	10
Parents' car	4
Friend's car	2
Bus	8

a) How many pupils took part in the survey?

b) What fraction of the class came to school by bus?

c) i) Find how many pupils came to school by car.

   ii) What fraction of the class is this?

A pie chart is to be drawn to represent the result of the survey.

d) i) Copy and complete the table showing the angle for each sector.

377

Method of travel	Angle
Walk	150°
Parents' car	
Friend's car	
Bus	

ii) Using a circle of radius 6 cm, draw and label this pie chart.

(MEG)

11

Type of crisp	Tally	Frequency	Angle
Plain	ЖІ ІІІІ		
Salt and vinegar	ЖІ ЖІ ЖІ І		
Cheese and onion	ЖІ ЖІ І		
Beef	ЖІ І		
Crispy bacon	ІІІ		
	Total	45	

The table shows the result of a survey taken on the sale of crisps one day in a School Tuckshop.

a) Copy the table and complete the Frequency column.
   The information is to be shown on a pie chart.
b) Calculate the size of the angle of each sector of this pie chart.
   Write your answers in the Angle column in the table.
c) Draw an accurate pie chart to show this information.
   Label the sectors clearly.

(ULEAC)

12 Tracey asked 50 pupils how they travelled to school. Here are the results.

Type of travel	Number	Percentage
Special bus	23	
Public transport	14	
Walked	8	
Car	5	
Total	50	

She wants to draw a pie chart.

378

a) Work out the percentages and fill them in on a copy of the table.

b) Draw the pie chart. (MEG)

13 The table below shows how each £1 of expenditure of Derbyshire County Council was divided up in 1987/8.

How spent	Amount
Day-to-day business	47p
Repaying loans and interest	23p
Investing in assets	30p

Draw a pie chart to illustrate this information, showing clearly how you calculated the angles required. Record them, correct to the nearest degree, on your diagram. (MEG)

14 The three main costs of a factory are shown in the pie chart as wages, overheads and raw materials. Two angles at the centre of the circle are given.

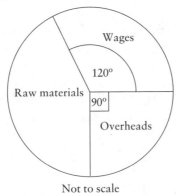

Not to scale

a) Calculate the angle which represents 'raw materials'.

b) What fraction of the total cost is 'wages'? Give your fraction in its lowest terms. (NEAB)

15 The BBC estimated that the money collected from licences was spent in this way:

Capital expense and transmission 25%

BBC1 35%

BBC2 20%

Radio 20%

Draw a fully labelled pie chart to show this information. (ULEAC)

16 Where do local products go?

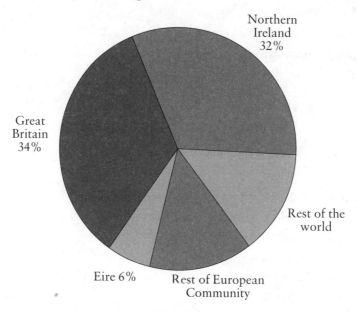

'Rest of the world' and 'Rest of European Community' take equal amounts of local products. What percentage does each take?

(NICCEA)

17 Thirty-five people took part in an ice-skating competition.
The points they scored are shown below.

18 24 19 3   24 11 25 10 25 14 25 9   16 26
21 27 13 23 5   26 22 12 27 20 7   28 21 20
22 16 12 25 7   25 19

a) Work out the range of points scored.
b) Complete the frequency table.

Class Interval	Frequency
1–5	2
6–10	4
11–15	
16–20	
21–25	
26–30	

(ULEAC)

18 This graph shows the number of people, in thousands, attending a holiday camp each month from March 1992 to February 1993.

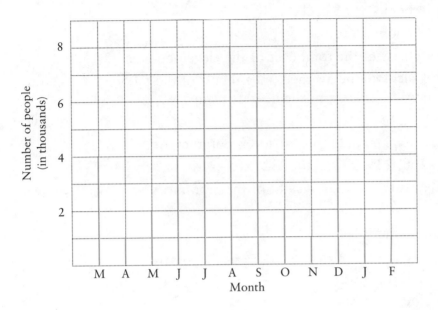

a) How many people attended the holiday camp in April?

b) Which was the modal month?

c) The holiday camp owners call March, April and May 'Spring'; June, July and August 'Summer'; September, October and November 'Autumn'; and December, January and February 'Winter'.

Complete this table to show the number of visitors, in thousands, to the holiday camp each season.

Spring	Summer	Autumn	Winter
7	18	9	

d) Draw and label a pie chart to show the distribution of visitors by seasons.

You must show how you calculate the angles of your pie chart.

(WJEC)

19 At a recent book sale I bought:

   6 books at £5 each,

   4 books at £3 each,

   1 book at £9.

   a) Work out the total cost of the eleven books.

   b) Calculate the average (mean) cost of these books. Give your answer correct to the nearest penny.

(MEG)

20 The weights, in grams, of seven potatoes are:

   260, 225, 205, 240, 232, 205, 214.

   What is the median weight of these potatoes?

(SEG)

21 For the numbers

   −1, 4, 3, −2, 6, 7, −3,

   a) find the median,

   b) find the mean.

(MEG)

22 The number of goals scored in each of the eleven First Division Football League matches one Saturday last season was

   0, 0, 1, 1, 2, 2, 4, 5, 6, 6, 6.

   Find:

   a) the mode,

   b) the median,

   c) the mean,

   d) the range.   (MEG)

23 Samantha and Teresa both did ten Mathematics homeworks. Here are their marks out of ten.

Samantha	10	10	7	4	9	8	5	2	9	8
Teresa	5	7	6	8	6	8	7	8	7	6

   a) Work out the mean mark for each of them.

   b) Work out the range for each of them.

   c) Say who you think was better at maths. Give a reason for your answer.

(MEG)

24 Richard saved some of his pocket money each week to go on holiday. He made a list of how much he saved each week.

£2   £1   £1.50 £1.30 £1.75 £2 £2   £1 £1   £2
£1.30 £1.30 £1.75 £1.50 £1.30 £2 £1.30 £1 £1.30 £1.50

Calculate:

a) the total number of weeks in which he saved money,

b) the total amount of money saved,

c) the mean amount of money saved per week,

d) the median,

e) the mode.   (NICCEA)

25 Eunice measures the lengths of runner beans in a gardening competition. The lengths in centimetres of the longest ten runner beans are given.

$$26, 34, 27, 28, 24, 36, 30, 28, 25, 32$$

a) What is the range in the lengths of these runner beans?

b) What is the mean length of these runner beans?

c) In last year's competition the mean length of the longest ten runner beans was 29 cm and the range was 8 cm. Explain how the lengths of the runner beans differ this year from last year.   (SEG)

26 Class 5E had an English test and a Maths test. Here are the results of 10 of the pupils.

English	20	30	25	26	30	15	20	25	30	29
Maths	25	16	15	28	15	12	15	20	25	29

a) Work out the mean mark for these 10 pupils in the Maths test. The mean mark for these 10 pupils in the English test was 25. This test had a total mark of 40.

b) Write the mean mark for English as a fraction of the total mark.

c) Change your fraction into a percentage.   (ULEAC)

	Jan	Feb	Mar	Apr	May	June	July	Aug	Sept	Oct	Nov	Dec
Great Britain	74	44	40	48	50	29	48	37	61	75	84	70
The Gambia	0	0	0	0	1	2	84	352	185	81	27	0

a) The mean rainfall per month in Great Britain is 55 mm.

Calculate the mean rainfall per month in The Gambia.

b) Find the range of the monthly rainfall:

i) in The Gambia,

ii) in Great Britain.

c) In which of these two countries are water shortages more likely?

d) Explain your answer to part c), using the means *and* the ranges.

(MEG)

28 The following table is taken from a holiday brochure for the Greek island of Kos. It shows the mean midday temperature (in °F) for each of the months from April to October for Kos and for London.

	Apr.	May	Jun.	Jul.	Aug.	Sep.	Oct.
Kos	69	74	80	86	86	80	75
London	55	62	70	71	71	65	59

a) Mary says that the range of the temperatures given for London is greater than the range of the temperatures given for Kos.

Is she correct? Show your working.

b) On the following grid the line graph of the mean midday temperatures in London, from April to October, has been drawn.

Draw a line graph showing the mean midday temperatures in Kos from April to October.

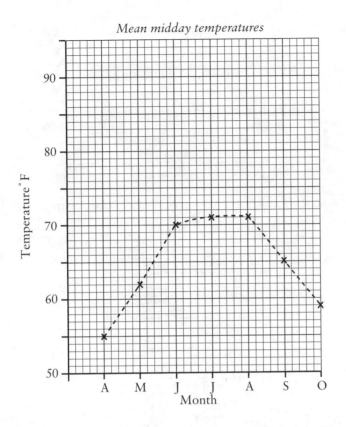

Mean midday temperatures

c) i) The midday temperatures (in °F) recorded in Kos for one week during the month of October are given below.

Sun	Mon	Tues	Wed	Thur	Fri	Sat
82	85	79	85	83	86	88

Calculate the mean midday temperature for this week.

ii) John is surprised at the answer to i) as he thinks that the mean for the week should be the same as the mean for the month of October shown in the table.

Give a reason why this is not so. (WJEC)

29 This table gives the marks scored by pupils in a French and in a German test.

French	15	35	34	23	35	27	36	34	23	24	30	40	25	35	20
German	20	37	35	25	33	30	39	36	27	20	33	35	27	32	28

a) Draw a scatter graph of the marks scored in the French and German tests.

b) Describe the correlation between the marks scored in the two tests.

(ULEAC)

30 Melaine does a survey to find the prices of second hand cars in her town.

Here are her results for Ford Fiestas.

Age (years)	2	4	1	3	5	4½	3	2	5½	3½	5	6
Cost (£)	6000	3500	7500	5000	3000	3500	5250	5800	2700	4600	2800	2200

a) Draw a scatter diagram to show her results, using axes like these.

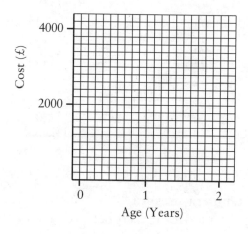

b) About how much would you expect to pay for a Ford Fiesta 2½ years old in Melaine's town?

(WJEC)

31 a) On the line below, mark with an H the probability of getting a head when one coin is tossed.

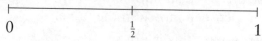

b) On the line below, mark with an S the probability of getting a 5 when a six sided dice is thrown.

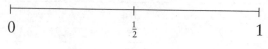

(ULEAC)

32 Here are three possible events.

    A A coin when tossed will come down heads.

    B It will snow in August in London.

    C There will be a baby born tomorrow.

      Which of the three events is

      i) most likely to happen?

      ii) least likely to happen?

(ULEAC)

33 Janine throws an ordinary dice.

  a) What is the probability she gets a 3?

     To win a game she needs a 3 or a 5.

  b) What is the probability that she wins?   (MEG)

34 Chris taped five pop broadcasts, each on a separate tape.

  The broadcasts lasted for 40 minutes, 55 minutes, 30 minutes, 42 minutes and 48 minutes.

  a) Chris picks a tape at random.

     What is the probability that the chosen broadcast will last for more than 3/4 hour?

  b) Find the mean length of time of the five recordings.

35 To play a game you spin the pointer. You win the prize on which the pointer stops.

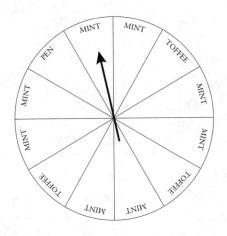

Richard has one spin.

a) Which prize is Richard most likely to win?

b) Explain your answer to part a).

Donna has one spin.

c) On the line below mark with a P the probability that Donna will win a pen.

d) On the line below mark with a W the probability that Donna will win a watch.

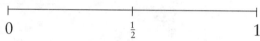

36 A six-faced dice and a coin are thrown at the same time. One possible outcome is a Head and a 1 (H, 1).

List all the other possible outcomes. (ULEAC)

37 In the school dining hall there is a choice for the main course.

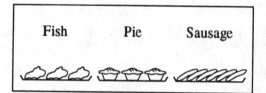

Bill first chooses one from fish, pie or sausage.

Then he chooses either chips or baked potato.

List all the possible meals he could choose. (SEG)

38 A game is played using the two boards shown below.

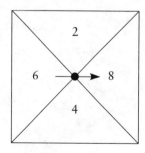
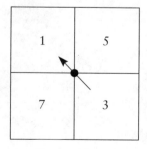

In one 'go' a player spins both arrows.

The sum of the numbers where the two arrows point is the score for the 'go'.

In the diagram the score for the 'go' is 9.

a) Copy and complete the table below showing all possible scores for one 'go'.

+	1	3	5	7
2				
4				
6				
8	9			

b) Write down the most likely score in one 'go'.

c) Write down the probability that a player will score 11 in one 'go'.

d) Calculate the probability that a player will score 13 in each of two 'go's'. (ULEAC)

39 a) A bag contains 2 red marbles, 1 blue marble and 1 yellow marble.

A second bag contains 1 red marble, 2 blue marbles and 1 yellow marble.

A marble is drawn from each bag.

Complete the table showing all the possible pairs of colours.

Marble from
second bag

		R	B	B	Y
Marble from first bag	R	RR	RB	RB	RY
	R	RR			
	B	BR			
	Y	YR			

b) 2 marbles are drawn from a third bag.

The probability that they are both of the same colour is $\frac{5}{9}$.

What is the probability that they are of different colours? (MEG)

40 a) The probability that Jane wins a race is $\frac{1}{4}$. What is the probability that she does not win the race?

b) The probability that Claire wins a race is $\frac{1}{3}$. Which of Jane or Claire is more likely to win a race? Explain your answer.

c) The probability that Andrew wins a race is 1. Explain what this means.

(MEG)

41 A machine makes compact discs.

The probability that a perfect compact disc will be made by this machine is 0.85.

Work out the probability that a compact disc made by this machine will not be perfect.

(ULEAC)

How to do Coursework

This tells you how to do a piece of coursework. It is for students who do a task over a period of time rather than in school like an exam. However most of the suggestions here will help with a timed task.

It is important that you understand the *starting point* for your task. If you are unsure, ask for this to be made clear.

Once you understand what the task is about, think of the *simplest case* and build up from there.

Work *methodically*. This means:

1. looking for a path through the investigation,
2. organising your information,
3. looking for patterns and relationships,
4. finding a conclusion,
5. possibly extending the work,
6. writing a report.

When you are working on the task you may get other ideas you want to explore. Always make sure you complete the part of the problem you are working on first. Some of your ideas may not work out. Do not discard them. All the work you do is important.

1. Looking for a path through the investigation

Once you feel that you know what you are looking for, you need to plan how to find it. Your plan might change as you proceed, but that does not matter. Make a note of the changes that you have made and your reasons. Include these in your write up.

Am I looking for just one answer?

Example
'I have a mug rack with four pegs on it. I have two yellow mugs and two blue ones. How many different ways are there to arrange the mugs on the rack?'

In this case you would look for one answer before going on to investigate other combinations of colours and pegs.

Can I simplify the problem in any way?

Example
'The maximum number of straight lines that connect five dots is ten. How many lines will connect 20 dots?'

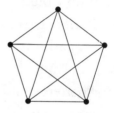

Start by considering how many lines connect two dots, then three, then four.

Can I break the problem up into smaller problems?

Example
'I am 40 and 40 can be written 6 + 7 + 8 + 9 + 10.
6, 7, 8, 9 and 10 are consecutive numbers.
Will I be able to write my age as the sum of consecutive numbers when I am 42?
Are there any ages that cannot be written in this way?'

6 + 7 + 8 + 9 + 10 is the sum of **five** consecutive numbers. Break the problem into smaller problems by looking at the sums of two consecutive numbers, then three consecutive numbers etc.

Can I already see a pattern?

If you see a pattern at any time, then point this out. It may be something very simple like 'the answers are all odd numbers'. Remember there may be several patterns to find.

Do I need to investigate lots of similar situations?

If your answer is yes, you need to give the method careful thought. In the example with the mugs you need to choose a different number of colours or a different number of pegs. Changing yellow and blue to red and green does not change the problem.

2. Organising your information

You need to do this methodically and accurately. You cannot look for patterns if you are missing information or if some of your results are wrong.

The way you record your results is important. You gain marks from well-organised tables and diagrams. They also help you to see patterns.

The problem on joining dots would have sketches showing different numbers of dots connected. It would have its results recorded in a table like this:

No of dots	1	2	3	4	5
No of lines	0	1	3	6	10

Suppose you have designed a questionnaire for a statistical project and have collected responses. You need to put the results in a table (or database) so that you can start to process them. You need to draw statistical diagrams to illustrate your data.

3. Looking for patterns and relationships

It is important to have accurate results. Suppose you got this result to the joining dots problem:

$$0 \quad 1 \quad 3 \quad 5 \quad 10$$
$$+1 \quad +2 \quad +2 \quad +4$$

The second +2 spoils the pattern so the 5 needs to be checked.
The corrected pattern can be used to predict the next term:

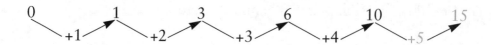

This prediction can be checked by drawing a diagram with 6 dots.
The correct numbers show a pattern so there must be a connection.
The rule is: 'multiply two adjacent numbers and divide by 2'.

No of dots	1	2	3	4	5	6
No of lines		$\frac{1 \times 2 = 1}{2}$	$\frac{2 \times 3 = 3}{2}$	$\frac{3 \times 4 = 6}{2}$	$\frac{4 \times 5 = 10}{2}$	$\frac{5 \times 6 = 15}{2}$

The nth term, where n is the number of dots, is given by: $\frac{n(n+1)}{2}$

You should try to explain the pattern:

There are 4 lines joining one dot to all the
other dots and there are 5 dots.

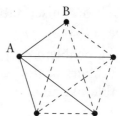

4×5 gives twice the answer, as the line joining
A to B is the same as the line joining
B to A, and so on.

4. Finding a conclusion

You will get to the stage where you feel that you have got an answer.
This may be the rule for a numerical pattern. You may have proved
or disproved a statistical hypothesis or made a model.

Can I see the reasons why my relationships come out the way they do?

Do my conclusions fit the task I started with or the ones I have developed?

If your answer to either of these questions is 'no' then you are not
ready to write a conclusion.
If you finish your work quite quickly, then you could consider

extending it. This should never be done until you have reached a conclusion for the original task.

5. Extending the work

Avoid doing the same type of work again, unless it helps you get a deeper understanding of the task.

It may be that you have been using a square grid for a task. A suitable extension might be to work on other shapes of grid. You might change a space and shape problem from one dimension to two or three dimensions or a numerical problem to sets of more difficult numbers. If the original problem has lots of rules, try breaking the rules one at a time.

6. Writing a report

Remember that you are not just writing about your work for your own teacher. Moderators and teachers from other schools may read your work. Show the reader exactly what you understand from the work that you have been doing. You could do this at different points throughout the work or altogether at the end.

Start with an introduction that states the initial problem. If it is a statistical investigation state your hypothesis clearly.

Describe your path through the investigation. Show your results with clear diagrams and tables and say what you did to get them.

Write about anything you have noticed or any ideas of your own that you have developed. Explain any predictions you have made.

Give a precise conclusion. Include any rough work at the end of your report.

Answers

NUMBER
SECTION 1
WHOLE NUMBERS

Pause – page 3

1 a) The 1 represents 10 arrested.
   The 7 represents 7 arrested.
 b) The first 2 represents 200 jobs.
   The second 2 represents 20 jobs.
   The 6 represents 6 jobs.
 c) The 6 represents £600.
   The 5 represents £50.
   The 0 represents 0.
 d) The 7 represents £7000.
   The 4 represents £400.
   The first 3 represents £30.
   The second 3 represents £3.
 e) The 2 represents 20 000 beer mats.
   The 4 represents 4000 beer mats.
   The first 9 represents 900 beer mats.
   The 7 represents 70 beer mats.
   The 9 represents 9 beer mats.
 f) The 6 represents £60 000.
   The 7 represents £7000.
   The 9 represents £900.

2 a) 708, 780, 807, 870   b) 870
3 a) 299, 929, 992   b) 992
4 a) 2345, 2354, 2435, 2453, 2534, 2543,
   3245, 3254, 3425, 3452, 3524, 3542,
   4235, 4253, 4325, 4352, 4523, 4532,
   5234, 5243, 5324, 5342, 5423, 5432
 b) 5432

Pause – page 4

1 a) Two thousand, two hundred and fifty.
 b) Seventy-five thousand, two hundred and
   ninety-one.
 c) Twenty thousand and forty-nine.
 d) One hundred and twenty-two thousand,
   seven hundred and seventeen.
 e) Eight hundred and five thousand, seven
   hundred.
 f) One million, eight hundred and thirteen
   thousand, four hundred and forty-six.

2 a) 6519   c) 60 000   e) 530 085
 b) 2786   d) 73 496   f) 1 633 153

Pause – page 5

1 a) 10   c) 30   e) 50   g) 60   i) 80
 b) 10   d) 40   f) 50   h) 80   j) 90
2 a) 0   c) 50   e) 70   g) 100
 b) 80   d) 40   f) 20   h) 50

Pause – page 6

1 a) 90   c) 250   e) 480   g) 680   i) 850
 b) 120   d) 330   f) 550   h) 790   j) 970
2 a) 100   c) 300   e) 500   g) 700   i) 800
 b) 100   d) 300   f) 500   h) 800   j) 1000

3 a)

Category of complaint	Number of complaints	Number of advertisements referred to
Misleading	860	480
Offensive	950	240
Harmful	470	200
Other	300	150
Total	2580	1070

 b)

Category of complaint	Number of complaints	Number of advertisements referred to
Misleading	900	500
Offensive	1000	200
Harmful	500	200
Other	300	200
Total	2600	1100

Pause – page 7

1 a) 750   e) 4720   i) 8590
 b) 1570   f) 5480   j) 9600
 c) 2940   g) 6450
 d) 3170   h) 7440
2 a) 700   e) 4700   i) 8600
 b) 1600   f) 5900   j) 9600
 c) 2900   g) 6500
 d) 3200   h) 7400
3 a) 1000   e) 5000   i) 9000
 b) 2000   f) 6000   j) 10 000
 c) 3000   g) 6000
 d) 3000   h) 7000

4

Status before marriage	Number married in 1994		
	a)	b)	c)
Bachelor	256 540	256 500	257 000
Divorced man	83 070	83 100	83 000
Widower	10 130	10 100	10 000
Spinster	259 080	259 100	259 000
Divorced woman	81 220	81 200	81 000
Widow	9 430	9 400	9 000
Total number of people married	699 470	699 400	699 000

Type of marriage	Number of marriages		
	a)	b)	c)
First marriage for both partners	222 370	222 400	222 000
First marriage for one partner	70 880	70 900	71 000
Re-marriage for both partners	56 490	56 500	56 000
Total number of marriages	349 740	349 800	349 000

Pause – page 9

1 Frome

13	Radstock		
18	14	Shepton Mallet	
13	18	31	Trowbridge

2 Cambourne

17	Falmouth			
35	18	Helston		
13	30	31	Hayle	
23	39	21	10	Penzance
6	11	25	19	29	Redruth

3 Ashburton

12	Newton Abbot			
21	13	Paignton		
22	10	18	Teignmouth	
21	9	5	13	Torbay
13	21	8	26	13	Totnes

Pause – page 11

1 a)

6	1	8
7	5	3
2	9	4

c)

15	1	11
5	9	13
7	17	3

b)

9	2	7
4	6	8
5	10	3

d)

17	11	11
7	13	19
15	15	9

2 a)

8	2	11
10	7	4
3	12	6

c)

17	3	19
15	13	11
7	23	9

b)

10	3	11
9	8	7
5	13	6

d)

65	10	75
60	50	40
25	90	35

3 a) 24
 b) 3 × third number = magic square total
4 Pupils' own work.

Pause – page 13

1	804	4	1103	7	1217	9	13 771
2	631	5	7935	8	2179	10	6980
3	893	6	473				

11

Saved this week	Total saved	Saved this week	Total saved
£23	£ 23	£22	£272
£19	£ 42	£38	£310
£35	£ 77	£45	£355
£42	£119	£46	£401
£11	£130	£33	£434
£26	£156	£18	£452
£51	£207	£18	£470
£19	£226	£40	£510
£ 5	£231	£27	£537
£19	£250	£73	£610

11

Score	Total so far
89	89
47	136
67	203
19	222
125	347
68	415
17	432
96	528
9	537
85	622

Pause – page 14

1	30	3	425	5	286	7	229	9	78
2	26	4	176	6	36	8	385	10	246

11 a)

Kirsty		Steven		b) Kirsty won
	501		501	
52	449	78	423	
68	381	13	410	
47	334	49	361	
81	253	53	308	
34	219	39	269	
51	168	72	197	
29	139	29	168	
68	71	59	109	
53	18	9	100	
18	0	68	32	

12 a)

Date	Litres used	Litres in tank
1st	247	2321
2nd	189	2132
3rd	207	1925
4th	175	1750
5th	156	1594
6th	295	1299
7th	188	1111
8th	207	904
9th	268	636
10th	199	437

b) 2321 litres   c) 10

Pause – page 16
1 44   **3** 86   **5** 84   **7** 46
2 78   **4** 86   **6** 76   **8** 13

9

	501
44	457
78	379
86	293
86	207
84	123
76	47
46	1
13	1

Pause – page 17
In this exercise the answers given are examples.
Pupils may find correct alternatives.

1 a) $33 + 4 + 3 =$
   b) $33 + 44 =$
   c) $343 + 444 =$
   d) $33 + 4 =$
   e) $34 + 4 - 3 =$
2 a) $5 + 5 + 7 + 7 =$
   b) $55 + 77-$
   c) $444 + 444 - 333 - 3 - 4 =$
   d) $43 + 33 + 3 =$
   e) $333 + 333 - 3 - 3 - 4 - 4 =$
3 a) $99 - 66 + 9 + 6 =$
   b) $96 - 6 - 6 =$
   c) $96 + 6 =$
   d) $666 + 666 + 666 - 99 - 6 - 6$
   e) $999 + 999 + 999 + 999 - 99 - 99$
       $- 6 - 6 - 6 - 6$

Pause – page 18
1 a) 03·00 h   h) 23·00 h   o) 04·45 h
   b) 15·00 h   i) 08·00 h   p) 16·45 h
   c) 05·00 h   j) 20·00 h   q) 01·55 h
   d) 17·00 h   k) 07·15 h   r) 13.55 h
   e) 06·00 h   l) 19.15 h   s) 10·05 h
   f) 18·00 h   m) 02·25 h   t) 22·05 h
   g) 11·00 h   n) 14.25 h

2 a) 2 am   h) 10 am   o) 10·17 am
   b) 2 pm   i) 4 pm   p) 1·02 pm
   c) 7 am   j) 8·22 am   q) 11·49 am
   d) 7 pm   k) 3·41 pm   r) 8·46 pm
   e) 11 am   l) 9·51 am   s) 4·17 am
   f) 11 pm   m) 12·35 am   t) 5·36 pm
   g) 10 pm   n) 2·15 am

Pause – page 19
1 2 h 3 min   **6** 4 h 23 min
2 2 h 33 min   **7** 6 h 7 min
3 6 h 21 min   **8** 5 h 8 min
4 30 min   **9** 21 h 18 min
5 5 h 24 min   **10** 1 h 49 min
11 a) 2·28 pm
    b) 48 min
12 2247
13 a) 0820
    b) 25 minutes
14 a) i) 2 h 30 min   ii) 80 mph
    b) 1547
15 a) 0930
    b) 1 hr 40 min
    c) 1910
    d) 40 miles per hour
16 a) i) 9·28 am   ii) 33 min
    b) 2 pm
    c) 20 buses
    d) 30 mph

Pause – page 23
1 a) 20   e) 470   i) 1010
   b) 50   f) 800   j) 1440
   c) 120   g) 790
   d) 230   h) 1000
2 a) 400   e) 4200   i) 100 000
   b) 700   f) 9000   j) 27 800
   c) 1500   g) 10 000
   d) 2000   h) 10 100

	1981	1994
3 a) i)   344 000   79 000
        ii) 1 100 000   773 000
        iii) 891 000   1 167 000
    b) 126 000   c) 965 000

Pause – page 26
1 120   **11** 3600   **21** 27 000
2 250   **12** 3500   **22** 27 000
3 80   **13** 3200   **23** 28 000
4 720   **14** 1200   **24** 120 000
5 420   **15** 2400   **25** 200 000
6 490   **16** 1600   **26** 450 000
7 540   **17** 4000   **27** 160 000
8 180   **18** 4800   **28** 210 000
9 6300   **19** 10 000   **29** 300 000
10 6400   **20** 15 000   **30** 1 800 000

SECTION 2
TYPES OF NUMBER

Pause – page 27
1 1, 2, 4, 8   2 1, 5, 25   3 1, 13
4 a) i) 1, 2, 3, 6, 9, 18   iii) 1, 23
      ii) 1, 3, 7, 21   iv) 1, 2, 4, 8, 16
   b) i) a prime number has only two factors
       – itself and 1.
       ii) 23
5 42, 170, 1500
6 2, 3, 5, 7, 11, 13, 17, 19, 23, 29
7 6, 12, 18, 24, 30, 36, 42
8 7, 14, 21, 28, 35, 42
9 a) 12, 15, 18   b) 12, 18
10 a) 7, 21   b) 7, 21   c) 7, 13, 19

Pause – page 28
1 1, 4, 9, 16, 25, 36, 49, 64, 81, 100, 121, 144
2 4, 6, 8, 9, 10, 12, 14, 15, 16, 18, 20, 21,
   22, 24, 25, 26, 27, 28, 30, 32
3 1, 3, 6, 10, 15, 21, 28, 36, 45, 55

Pause – page 29
1 a) $\sqrt{81} = 9$ g) $\sqrt{400} = 20$
   b) $\sqrt{49} = 7$ h) $\sqrt{900} = 30$
   c) $\sqrt{121} = 11$ i) $\sqrt{1600} = 40$
   d) $\sqrt{100} = 10$ j) $\sqrt{2500} = 50$
   e) $\sqrt{144} = 12$ k) $\sqrt{6400} = 80$
   f) $\sqrt{64} = 8$ l) $\sqrt{10000} = 100$

SECTION 3
ESTIMATION AND CALCULATION

Pause – page 30

	Estimate	Accurate answer
1	$20 \times 6 = 120$	108
2	$30 \times 9 = 270$	306
3	$7 \times 60 = 420$	413
4	$2 \times 90 = 180$	184
5	$8 \times 80 = 640$	608
6	$600 \times 9 = 5400$	5157
7	$60 \times 90 = 5400$	5130
8	$5 \times 600 = 3000$	3010
9	$60 \times 50 = 3000$	3150
10	$90 \times 400 = 36000$	34000
11	$80 \times 800 = 64000$	63200
12	$20 \times 300 = 6000$	6900
13	$500 \times 70 = 35000$	31500
14	$700 \times 3 = 2100$	2025
15	$9 \times 600 = 5400$	5004
16	$400 \times 60 = 24000$	22440
17	$1000 \times 90 = 90000$	89100
18	$800 \times 400 = 320000$	332800
19	$400 \times 600 = 240000$	226800
20	$2000 \times 500 = 1000000$	1170500

Pause – page 31

	Estimate	Accurate answer
1	$200 \times 50 = 10000$	10530
2	$600 \times 30 = 18000$	14846
3	$700 \times 40 = 28000$	29568
4	$1000 \times 50 = 50000$	51940
5	$700 \times 30 = 21000$	21663
6	$800 \times 40 = 32000$	31242
7	$200 \times 50 = 10000$	11024
8	$1000 \times 20 = 20000$	24244
9	$700 \times 30 = 21000$	16875
10	$300 \times 90 = 27000$	29993
11	$400 \times 200 = 80000$	84777
12	$300 \times 400 = 120000$	140193
13	$400 \times 200 = 80000$	82418
14	$300 \times 300 = 90000$	91980
15	$900 \times 300 = 270000$	253344
16	$400 \times 200 = 80000$	70034
17	$300 \times 800 = 240000$	233496
18	$300 \times 100 = 30000$	35643
19	$400 \times 800 = 32000$	345978
20	$600 \times 200 = 120000$	145314

Pause – page 32
1 a) 6   b) 23   c) 79   d) 10   e) 14
2 a) 4 francs
   b) 20 francs
   c) 42 francs
   d) 101 francs
   e) 278 francs
3 a) 400
   b) 2484
   c) Financial Times
   d) Daily Mail
   e) i) Independent   ii) 284

Pause – page 35

1	3	11	60	21	30
2	5	12	90	22	9
3	2	13	40	23	7
4	8	14	20	24	20
5	6	15	80	25	40
6	7	16	4	26	50
7	6	17	5	27	200
8	6	18	8	28	3000
9	7	19	8	29	600
10	8	20	50	30	90

Pause – page 36

	Estimate	Accurate answer
1	$700 \div 10 = 70$	55
2	$300 \div 30 = 10$	11
3	$900 \div 40 = 22.5$	22
4	$800 \div 20 = 40$	43

	Estimate	Accurate answer
5	$500 \div 20 = 25$	22
6	$400 \div 40 = 10$	11
7	$400 \div 30 = 13 \cdot 3$	13
8	$400 \div 40 = 10$	9
9	$400 \div 30 = 13 \cdot 3$	16
10	$800 \div 10 = 80$	56
11	$900 \div 30 = 30$	27 rem 5
12	$800 \div 40 = 20$	21 rem 21
13	$700 \div 20 = 35$	32 rem 17
14	$600 \div 30 = 20$	17 rem 33
15	$800 \div 10 = 80$	63 rem 7
16	$100 \div 20 = 5$	4 rem 15
17	$300 \div 20 = 15$	14 rem 8
18	$600 \div 40 = 15$	15 rem 17
19	$1000 \div 50 = 20$	21 rem 32
20	$1000 \div 40 = 25$	26 rem 21

Pause – page 37

1. a) $8 \times 1 = 8$
    b) $4 \times 5 = 20$
    c) $6 \times 6 = 36$
    d) $7 \times 3 = 21$
    e) $7 \times 9 = 63$
    f) $16 \times 5 = 80$
    g) $27 \times 4 = 108$
    h) $23 \times 6 = 138$
    i) $12 \times 12 = 144$
    j) $34 \times 9 = 306$
2. a) $32 \div 8 = 4$
    b) $66 \div 6 = 11$
    c) $54 \div 9 = 6$
    d) $27 \div 9 = 3$
    e) $28 \div 7 = 4$
    f) $98 \div 7 = 14$
    g) $80 \div 10 = 8$
    h) $77 \div 7 = 11$
    i) $51 \div 3 = 17$
    j) $144 \div 12 = 12$
3. a) 25   b) 35   c) 210
4. a) 6 cm, 30 cm
    b) 7 cm, 42 cm
    c) 8 cm, 64 cm
5. a) £4, nothing left over
    b) 4 sweets, 2 left over
    c) 14 roses, 2 left over
    d) 2 mince pies, 4 left over
    e) 250 exercise books, none left over
    f) £25 000, nothing left over
    g) 19 marbles, 1 left over
    h) 9 mice, 30 left over
    i) 8 sandwiches, 2 left over
    j) 11 sandwiches, 16 left over

Pause – page 39

1. 750 French francs
2. 3600 French francs
3. 1162·50 French francs
4. 1395 French francs
5. 1495 US dollars
6. 149·50 US dollars
7. 523·25 US dollars
8. 710·13 US dollars
9. 2040 Canadian dollars
10. 204 Canadian dollars
11. 714 Canadian dollars
12. 969 Canadian dollars
13. 4500 Belgian francs
14. 21 600 Belgian francs
15. 11 250 Belgian francs
16. 11 565 Belgian francs
17. 91 750 Spanish pesetas
18. 36 700 Spanish pesetas
19. 33 030 Spanish pesetas
20. 10 643 Spanish pesetas

SECTION 4
DECIMALS

Pause – page 41

1. a) $2 + \frac{7}{10}$
    b) $3 + \frac{9}{10}$
    c) $70 + 5 + \frac{2}{10}$
    d) $7 + \frac{5}{10} + \frac{2}{100}$
    e) $100 + 30 + 8$
    f) $10 + 3 + \frac{8}{10}$
    g) $1 + \frac{3}{10} + \frac{8}{100}$
    h) $\frac{1}{10} + \frac{3}{100} + \frac{8}{1000}$
    i) $8 + \frac{7}{10} + \frac{5}{100}$
    j) $\frac{8}{10} + \frac{7}{100} + \frac{5}{1000}$
    k) $80 + 7 + \frac{5}{10}$
    l) $30 + 4 + \frac{1}{10} + \frac{5}{100}$
    m) $\frac{1}{1000}$
    n) $1 + \frac{1}{100}$
    o) $100 + 1 + \frac{1}{10} + \frac{1}{100}$
2. a) 4·5   g) 6·15
    b) 13·2   h) 7·37
    c) 348·3   i) 7·653
    d) 1·9   j) 750·01
    e) 17·6   k) 604·5
    f) 33·1   l) 530·371
3. a) 74, 0·47   c) 654, 0·456
    b) 91, 0·19   d) 872, 0·278

401

Pause – page 42

1 a)

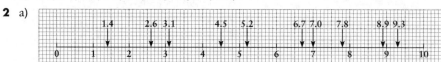

b) 1·3, 1·8, 2·2, 3·5, 4·6, 5·7, 6·1, 7·4, 8·3, 9·9

2 a)

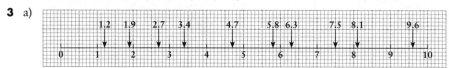

b) 1·4, 2·6, 3·1, 4·5, 5·2, 6·7, 7·0, 7·8, 8·9, 9·3

3 a)

b) 1·2, 1·9, 2·7, 3·4, 4·7, 5·8, 6·3, 7·5, 8·1, 9·6

Pause – page 43

1 a)

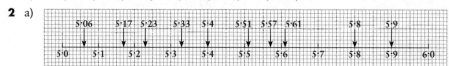

b) 1·08, 1·15, 1·23, 1·32, 1·48, 1·53, 1·63, 1·70, 1·85, 1·97

2 a)

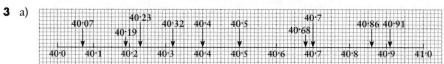

b) 5·06, 5·17, 5·23, 5·33, 5·4, 5·51, 5·57, 5·61, 5·8, 5·9

3 a)

b) 40·07, 40·19, 40·23, 40·32, 40·4, 40·5, 40·68, 40·7, 40·86, 40·91

Pause – page 44

1 a)

b) 1·009, 1·013, 1·02, 1·032, 1·037, 1·041, 1·047, 1·052, 1·068, 1·07

2 a)

b) 4·956, 4·962, 4·972, 4·981, 4·99, 5·007, 5·015, 5·027, 5·048

3 a)

b) 15·308, 15·319, 15·328, 15·339, 15·340, 15·35, 15·363, 15·374, 15·38, 15·392

Pause – page 45

1
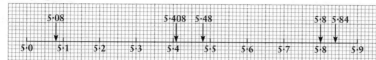

5·08, 5·408, 5·48, 5·8, 5·84

2

2·06, 2·1, 2·106, 2·16, 2·61

3
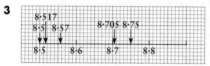

8·5, 8·517, 8·57, 8·705, 8·75

4
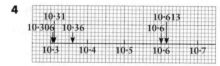

10·306, 10·31, 10·36, 10·6, 10·613

5
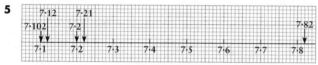

7·102, 7·12, 7·2, 7·21, 7·82

6
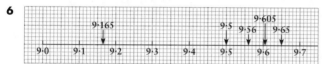

9·165, 9·5, 9·56, 9·605, 9·65

7
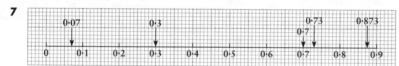

0·07, 0·3, 0·7, 0·73, 0·873

8
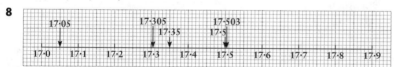

17·05, 17·305, 17·35, 17·5, 17·503

Pause – page 46
1 6, 2, 8, 7, 4, 5, 6, 2, 10, 1
2 3, 5, 9, 1, 5, 3, 7, 8, 7, 9
3 8, 1, 6, 3, 8, 10, 5, 6, 3, 2
4 2, 0, 2, 4, 4, 6, 7, 8, 8, 10
5 2, 2, 1, 4, 5, 6, 7, 9, 5, 10

Pause – page 47
1 1·6, 2·0, 1·2, 1·5, 1·7, 1·5, 1·1, 1·3, 1·9, 1·2
2 5·2, 5·6, 5·5, 5·8, 5·1, 5·3, 5·4, 5·6, 5·9, 5·2
3 5·3, 5·5, 5·6, 5·9, 5·0, 5·4, 5·4, 5·7, 6·0, 5·1
4 8·1, 8·9, 8·7, 8·7, 8·2, 8·2, 8·5, 8·3, 8·5, 8·8
5 8·0, 8·9, 8·8, 8·7, 8·2, 8·3, 8·4, 8·4, 8·5, 8·9

6 15·7, 15·1, 15·4, 15·9, 15·3, 15·2, 15·6, 15·8, 15·4, 15·5
7 15·8, 15·1, 15·5, 16·0, 15·2, 15·1, 15·7, 15·9, 15·3, 15·6

Pause – page 48
1 5·59, 5·51, 5·58, 5·52, 5·57, 5·53, 5·56, 5·54, 5·55, 5·55
2 15·40, 15·30, 15·39, 15·32, 15·38, 15·32, 15·36, 15·33, 15·36, 15·34
3 1·01, 1·07, 1·03, 1·05, 1·05, 1·07, 1·02, 1·01, 1·04, 1·04
4 5·01, 4·96, 4·98, 5·03, 5·05, 4·96, 4·97, 4·99, 5·02, 5·03

5
a) 1·73 e) 6·48 i) 4·24
b) 2·74 f) 12·25 j) 4·37
c) 4·47 g) 1·80 k) 4·76
d) 2·90 h) 9·49 l) 14·14

Pause – page 49

1
a) 12·45 c) 3·138 e) 47·05
b) 27·235 d) 0·6512 f) 45·04

2
a) 1·89 d) 3·465 g) 6·6
b) 3·16 e) 0·398 h) 0·39
c) 4·17 f) 0·014 i) 1·285

Pause – page 50

1
a) 49·6 c) 36·204 e) 112·554
b) 57·68 d) 51·4 f) 1·944

2
a) 7·35 c) 4·7125 e) 2·346
b) 5·8 d) 0·03175 f) 1·501166...

Pause – page 52

1
a) 170 mm f) 78·5 mm
b) 17 mm g) 89·3 mm
c) 1·7 mm h) 12·43 mm
d) 89 mm i) 14·7 mm
e) 93·2 mm j) 10·47 mm

2
a) 245 cm f) 155·7 cm
b) 200 cm g) 120 cm
c) 45 cm h) 570 cm
d) 1237·5 cm i) 730 cm
e) 89·5 cm j) 76·5 cm

3
a) 1237 g f) 7892·3 g
b) 1657 g g) 16 666·6 g
c) 7045 g h) 100 g
d) 8230 g i) 456 g
e) 7600 g j) 7031·4 g

4
a) 6400 ml f) 1 ml
b) 6470 ml g) 0·1 ml
c) 6473 ml h) 1000·1 ml
d) 6473·5 ml i) 2·34 ml
e) 10 ml j) 0·25 ml

Pause – page 53

1
a) 1·7 cm f) 0·785 cm
b) 0·17 cm g) 7·85 cm
c) 0·017 cm h) 78·5 cm
d) 0·89 cm i) 0·0785 cm
e) 9·32 cm j) 0·06 cm

2
a) 2·45 m f) 0·01557 m
b) 2 m g) 0·012 m
c) 0·45 m h) 0·057 m
d) 0·123 m i) 73·55 m
e) 0·0895 m j) 86·52 m

3
a) 1·237 kg f) 78·923 kg
b) 1·657 kg g) 0·0166 kg
c) 7·045 kg h) 0·1 kg
d) 0·823 kg i) 0·01 kg
e) 0·076 kg j) 0·0073 kg

4
a) 0·0064 l f) 0·000 001 l
b) 0·006 47 l g) 0·3 l
c) 0·006 l h) 0·07 l
d) 6·4735 l i) 5 l
e) 0·000 01 l j) 0·65 l

Pause – page 54

1 £116·20 **6** £99
2 £168 **7** £179·20
3 £56 **8** £81
4 £52·20 **9** £158·84
5 £212·40 **10** £114·21

Pause – page 55

1 £201·60 **6** £225·60
2 £220·80 **7** £288
3 £213·60 **8** £283·20
4 £259·20 **9** £290·40
5 £235·20 **10** £259·20

Pause – page 56

1 a) £48 b) 422
2 a) £90·16 b) £3426·08
3 4·73 l
4 a) 313·5 hours b) 765 l

Pause – page 58

1 2·25 lb, 4·5 lb, 11·25 lb, 33·75 lb, 45 lb

2

Pints	1	2	3	4	5	6	7	8	9	10
Litres	0·57	1·14	1·71	2·29	2·86	3·43	4	4·57	5·14	5·71

Pints	10	20	30	40	50	60	70	80	90	100
Litres	5·71	11·43	17·14	22·86	28·57	34·29	40	45·71	51·43	57·14

3
a) 100 miles c) 60 miles e) 92·5 miles
b) 130 miles d) 95 miles f) 128·75 miles

4

Centimetres	5	10	15	20	25	30
Inches	2·0	3·9	5·9	7·9	9·8	11·8

Centimetres	30·5	61·0	91·4	121·9	152·4	182·9
Feet	1	2	3	4	5	6

Pause – page 61

1
a) 292·8 k) 3221·9
b) 1369·9 l) 110·78
c) 705·23 m) 60·366
d) 7991·53 n) 1·76
e) 13·3429 o) 29·55
f) 128·1103 p) 1353·05
g) 590·384 q) 60·017
h) 137·147 r) 9000·68
i) 509·7 s) 67·67
j) 1238·387 t) 79·81

2
a) 0·9 e) 0·08 i) 100
b) 0·25 f) 1·4 j) 0·5
c) 0·16 g) 3·2
d) 5·6 h) 40

3 a) 103·5   e) 169·86   i) 15·875
   b) 1698·6   f) 190·491   j) 114·9
   c) 19049·1   g) 2·46   k) 69·196
   d) 10·35   h) 22·825   l) 0.125
4 a) 797·4   g) 2·3   m) 1·9
   b) 2551·5   h) 0·7   n) 2·1
   c) 127·4   i) 0·1   o) 10·1
   d) 11·5   j) 0·8   p) 138·6
   e) 3·4   k) 1·3
   f) 6·4   l) 65·7
5 a) 1070·96   d) 0·88   g) 4·39
   b) 3·29   e) 3·38   h) 0·91
   c) 0·07   f) 39.30
6 a) £22·16   c) 23 g   e) 117 ml
   b) £13·56   d) 15 p

Pause – page 63

1 6·1111111   **6** 0·5918889
2 12·666667   **7** 9·7053846
3 50·625   **8** 2·2794118
4 1·1522634   **9** 15·241935
5 3·9130435   **10** 0·2743167

Pause – page 65

1 £16·62, £19·06, £17·52, £28·27, £21·30
2 £39·96, £3·64, £27·20, £38·68, £84·31
3 £118·80, £126, £139·50, £160·74, £178·61
4 0·5 kg, 0·6 kg, 0·9 kg, 1·3 kg, 0·83 kg
5

Parts	Parts ÷ 2	Labour	Labour + parts ÷ 2	Call out fee (£25)	VAT (17·5%)	Special reduction (£12)
£32	£16	£80	£96	£121	£142·18	£130·18
£48	£24	£89	£113	£138	£162·15	£150·15
£64	£32	£32	£64	£89	£104·58	£92·58
£12	£6	£50	£56	£81	£95·18	£83·18
£86	£43	£65	£108	£133	£156·28	£144·28
£25	£12·50	£37	£49·50	£74·50	£87·54	£75·54
£59	£29·50	£95	£124·50	£149·50	£175·66	£163·66
£102	£51	£86	£137	£162	£190·35	£178·35
£155	£77·50	£43	£120·50	£145·50	£170·96	£158·96
£99	£49·50	£99	£148·50	£173·50	£203·86	£191·86
£128	£64	£102	£166	£191	£224·43	£212·43

SECTION 5
FRACTIONS

Pause – page 67

1 a) $\frac{1}{4}, \frac{3}{4}$ e) $\frac{2}{3}, \frac{1}{3}$ i) $\frac{1}{6}, \frac{5}{6}$
   b) $\frac{3}{4}, \frac{1}{4}$ f) $\frac{5}{8}, \frac{3}{8}$ j) $\frac{1}{8}, \frac{7}{8}$
   c) $\frac{1}{2}, \frac{1}{2}$ g) $\frac{1}{10}, \frac{9}{10}$
   d) $\frac{1}{3}, \frac{2}{3}$ h) $\frac{7}{16}, \frac{9}{16}$
2 a) $\frac{3}{10}$ c) $\frac{6}{10}\left(\frac{3}{5}\right)$ e) $\frac{4}{10}\left(=\frac{2}{5}\right)$
   b) $\frac{4}{10}\left(=\frac{2}{5}\right)$ d) $\frac{7}{10}$
3 a) $\frac{1}{8}, \frac{7}{8}$ c) $\frac{1}{3}, \frac{2}{3}$
   b) $\frac{1}{5}, \frac{4}{5}$ d) $\frac{3}{4}, \frac{1}{4}$

Pause – page 69

1 $\frac{1}{3}, \frac{2}{6}$ **6** $\frac{1}{4}, \frac{4}{16}$
2 $\frac{1}{2}, \frac{4}{8}$ **7** $\frac{1}{10}, \frac{10}{100}$
3 $\frac{2}{3}, \frac{6}{9}$ **8** $\frac{1}{2}, \frac{50}{100}$
4 $\frac{1}{4}, \frac{2}{8}$ **9** $\frac{75}{100}, \frac{15}{20}, \frac{3}{4}$
5 $\frac{4}{16}, \frac{2}{8}$ **10** $\frac{3}{5}, \frac{6}{10}, \frac{12}{20}, \frac{60}{100}$

Pause – page 70

1 a) $\frac{5}{7}$ e) $\frac{1}{2}$ i) $\frac{1}{2}$ m) $\frac{3}{4}$
   b) $\frac{5}{12}$ f) $\frac{3}{4}$ j) $\frac{2}{3}$ n) $\frac{5}{6}$
   c) $\frac{2}{3}$ g) $\frac{1}{3}$ k) $\frac{1}{2}$ o) $\frac{3}{4}$
   d) $\frac{1}{3}$ h) $\frac{3}{4}$ l) $\frac{1}{4}$

Pause – page 71

1 a) $\frac{8}{24} = \frac{1}{3}$ e) $\frac{4}{24} = \frac{1}{6}$ i) $\frac{15}{24}$
   b) $\frac{6}{24} = \frac{1}{4}$ f) $\frac{18}{24} = \frac{3}{4}$ j) $\frac{6}{24} = \frac{1}{4}$
   c) $\frac{3}{24} = \frac{1}{8}$ g) $\frac{14}{24} = \frac{7}{12}$
   d) $\frac{1}{24}$ h) $\frac{9}{24}$

Pause – page 72

2 a) $\frac{1}{6}$ c) $\frac{1}{5}$ e) $\frac{1}{2}$
   b) $\frac{5}{12}$ d) $\frac{2}{3}$ f) $\frac{1}{4}$
3 a) $\frac{1}{10}$ c) $\frac{7}{10}$ e) $\frac{3}{4}$
   b) $\frac{5}{6}$ d) $\frac{7}{12}$ f) $\frac{1}{3}$
4 a) $\frac{1}{24}$ c) $\frac{1}{4}$ e) $\frac{1}{12}$ g) $\frac{2}{3}$ i) $\frac{5}{6}$
   b) $\frac{1}{6}$ d) $\frac{1}{3}$ f) $\frac{1}{2}$ h) $\frac{3}{4}$ j) $\frac{5}{24}$
5 a) $\frac{1}{4}$ c) $\frac{1}{10}$ e) $\frac{17}{20}$ g) $\frac{12}{25}$ i) $\frac{1}{50}$
   b) $\frac{2}{5}$ d) $\frac{1}{2}$ f) $\frac{3}{4}$ h) $\frac{1}{25}$ j) $\frac{27}{100}$

Pause – page 73

1 a) 45
   b) i) 12   ii) 36
   c) i) 50   ii) 100
   d) i) 13   ii) 39
   e) 80   g) 9   i) 140
   f) 16   h) 63   j) 121·5
2 3125   **3** about 40

Pause – page 74

1 a) $\frac{9}{10}$ c) $\frac{5}{8}$ e) $\frac{9}{10}$ g) $\frac{11}{12}$
   b) $\frac{7}{12}$ d) $\frac{11}{12}$ f) $\frac{29}{35}$ h) $1\frac{17}{24}$
2 a) $\frac{1}{6}$ c) $\frac{1}{12}$ e) $\frac{1}{8}$ g) $\frac{1}{6}$
   b) $\frac{1}{12}$ d) $\frac{1}{2}$ f) $\frac{4}{35}$ h) $1\frac{3}{8}$

Pause – page 75

1 a) $\frac{1}{6}$ c) $\frac{1}{9}$ e) $\frac{1}{2}$ g) $\frac{1}{2}$
   b) $\frac{3}{8}$ d) $\frac{1}{3}$ f) $\frac{5}{8}$ h) $1\frac{1}{6}$
2 a) 2   c) 2   e) $\frac{1}{6}$ g) 6
   b) 2   d) 3   f) 4   h) 28

SECTION 6
PERCENTAGES

Pause – page 76

1 a) $\frac{1}{4}$ b) $\frac{99}{100}$

b) $\frac{3}{5}$ g) $\frac{2}{5}$

c) $\frac{17}{25}$ h) $\frac{3}{20}$

d) $\frac{9}{10}$ i) $\frac{8}{25}$

e) $\frac{16}{25}$ j) $\frac{19}{20}$

3 $\frac{3}{10}$

2 a) 50% b) 10%

b) 85% g) 24%

c) 70% h) 12%

d) 55% i) 50%

e) 48% j) 44%

Pause – page 77

1 a) 39   d) 769·5   g) £22·72

b) 87   e) 40·96   h) £6·75

c) 187   f) 2475   i) 14·4 kg

2 £347·20

3 12 320

4 £10 260

5 £32.20

Pause – page 79

1 a) 32% d) 35% g) 34% j) 40%

b) 40% e) 15% h) 75% k) 12·5%

c) 2·5% f) 75% i) 80% l) 75%

2 36% 47% 65% 74% 78%

80% 85% 93% 54% 88%

70% 18% 14% 57% 60%

98% 73% 59% 49% 50%

3 a) 15%, 16·7%, 17·5%

b) The first one (3 out of 20)

4 The first school (6 out of 10)

5 a) 6·9%   b) 17·9%   c) 18.2%

6 a) $\frac{1}{8}$ b) 12·5%

7 a) 5%   b) 3 extra oranges   c) $\frac{3}{18} = \frac{1}{6}$

8 a) £80   b) 15%

9 12·5%

Pause – page 83

1 a) 0·75   e) 0·5   i) 0·66...

b) 0·8   f) 0·2   j) 0·833...

c) 0·875   g) 0·25

d) 0·9   h) 0·1875

2 a) 75%   e) 50%   i) 66·66...%

b) 80%   f) 20%   j) 83·33...%

c) 87·5%   g) 25%

d) 90%   h) 18·75%

3 a) 10%   e) 64%   i) 50%

b) 80%   f) 8%   j) 37·5%

c) 30%   g) 0·5%

d) 35%   h) 5%

4 a) $\frac{1}{10}$ c) $\frac{3}{10}$ e) $\frac{16}{25}$ g) $\frac{1}{200}$ i) $\frac{1}{2}$

b) $\frac{4}{5}$ d) $\frac{7}{20}$ f) $\frac{2}{25}$ h) $\frac{1}{20}$ j) $\frac{3}{8}$

5 a) $80\% = \frac{4}{5} = 0·8$ f) $55\% = \frac{11}{20} = 0·55$

b) $32\% = \frac{8}{25} = 0·32$ g) $40\% = \frac{2}{5} = 0·4$

c) $25\% = \frac{1}{4} = 0·25$ h) $48\% = \frac{16}{25} = 0·48$

d) $70\% = \frac{7}{10} = 0·7$ i) $65\% = \frac{13}{20} = 0·65$

e) $98\% = \frac{49}{50} = 0·98$ j) $50\% = \frac{1}{2} = 0·5$

6 a) $0·33...$, $0·25$; $\frac{1}{3}$ is bigger

b) $0·75$ and $0·8$; $\frac{4}{5}$ is bigger

c) $0·6$ and $0·833...$; $\frac{5}{6}$ is bigger

d) $0·4286$ and $0·55...$; $\frac{5}{9}$ is bigger

e) $0·666...$, $0·7142$; $\frac{5}{7}$ is bigger

7 37·5%   **8** a) $\frac{54}{1000} = \frac{27}{500}$ b) 0·054

9 a) i) 0·125   ii) 12·5%   b) £3783·81

Pause – page 85

1 £15   **5** £22·50   **9** £78·08

2 £26   **6** £120   **10** £103·95

3 £120   **7** £24

4 £11·20   **8** £25·96

Pause – page 86

1 a) £341   b) £61

2 a) £221.80   b) £31·80

3 a) £371   b) £21

4 a) £427·80   b) £7·80

5 a) £3625   b) £125

6 a) £1373·54   b) £123·54

7 a) £419·90   b) £20·90

8 a) £198   b) £18

9 a) £1355·19   b) £106·19

SECTION 7
RATIO

Pause – page 87

1 a) 2:3   e) 6:7   i) 1:10   m) 5:7

b) 3:4   f) 7:4   j) 1:2   n) 1:5

c) 1:5   g) 2:3   k) 1:100   o) 3:4

d) 5:6   h) 2:3   l) 5:6   p) 1:5

2 1:4   **3** 7:1

Pause – page 88

1 a) 12 kg, 24 kg   g) 3 kg, 33 kg

b) 27 kg, 9 kg   h) 15 kg, 21 kg

c) 30 kg, 6 kg   i) 34 kg, 2 kg

d) 20 kg, 16 kg   j) 10 kg, 26 kg

e) 8 kg, 28 kg   k) 6 kg, 12 kg, 18 kg

f) 32 kg, 34 kg   l) 8 kg, 12 kg, 16 kg

2 a) £75, £25   g) £10, £90

b) £40, £60   h) £70, £30

c) £20, £80   i) £95, £5

d) £62·50, £37·50   j) £15, £85

e) £87·50, £12·50   k) £30, £30, £40

f) £50, £50   l) £10, £25, £65

3 £9375, £15 625

4 £6·20, £9·30. The shares should take account of the amount of time each puts in working on the stall, as well as the amount of money.

Pause – page 89

1 a) 300 ml   b) $\frac{6}{7}$

2 a) $\frac{1}{2}$ b) 600 g   c) 500 g

3

	a)	b)	c)	d)	e)
flour	400 g	600 g	800 g	300 g	500 g
lard	100 g	150 g	200 g	75 g	125 g
butter	100 g	150 g	200 g	75 g	125 g
apples	1000 g	1500 g	2000 g	750 g	1250 g

	f)	g)	h	i)	j)
flour	100 g	150 g	700 g	900 g	50 g
lard	25 g	37·5 g	175 g	225 g	12·5 g
butter	25 g	37·5 g	175 g	225 g	12·5 g
apples	250 g	375 g	1750 g	2250 g	125 g

4 a) 10 cm   b) 15 cm   c) 20 cm
5 a) 6 l c) 12 l e) 1·5 l
  b) 9 l d) 4·5 l

SECTION 8
DIRECTED NUMBERS

Pause – page 90

1 a $= -43°C$ e $= 5°C$ i $= 28°C$
  b $= -27°C$ f $= 12°C$ j $= 36°C$
  c $= -14°C$ g $= 19°C$
  d $= -8°C$ h $= 21°C$

Pause – page 91

1 25°C   **4** −15°C   **7** 25°C
2 35°C   **5** 25°C   **8** 10°C
3 10°C   **6** 5°C
9 a) −30°C, −4°C, −2°C, 14°C, 25°C
  b) −10°C, −1°C, 7°C, 16°C, 18°C
  c) −12°C, −5°C, 0°C, 8°C, 9°C
  d) −14°C, −8°C, −5°C, 4°C, 7°C
  e) −20°C, −13°C, −10°C, −6°C, 0°C
10 a) 12°C   **11** a) 18°C
  b) 8°C   b) 6°C
  c) 12°C   c) −3°C
  d) 14°C   d) −4°C
  e) 25°C   e) −12°C
  f) 12°C   f) −7°C

Pause – page 93

1 $8 + 5 = 13$ $8 - 5 = 3$
  $8 + -5 = 3$ $-8 - 5 = -13$
  $-8 + 5 = -3$ $8 - -5 = 3$
  $-8 + -5 = -13$ $-8 - -5 = -3$
2 $3 + 7 = 10$ $3 - 7 = -4$
  $3 + -7 = -4$ $3 - -7 = 10$
  $-3 + 7 = 4$ $-3 - 7 = -10$
  $-3 + -7 = -10$ $-3 - -7 = 4$

Pause – page 93

1 $13 + 9 = 22$ $13 - 9 = 4$
  $13 + -9 = 4$ $13 - -9 = 22$
  $-13 + 9 = -4$ $-13 - 9 = -22$
  $-13 + -9 = -22$ $-13 - -9 = -4$
2 $5 + 23 = 28$ $5 - 23 = -18$
  $5 + -23 = -18$ $5 - -23 = 28$
  $-5 + 23 = 18$ $-5 - 23 = -28$
  $-5 + -23 = -28$ $-5 - -23 = 18$

Pause – page 94

1 $10 \times 5 = 50$ $10 \times -5 = -50$
  $10 \div 5 = 2$ $10 \div -5 = -2$
  $-10 \times 5 = -50$ $-10 \times -5 = 50$
  $-10 \div 5 = -2$ $-10 \div -5 = 2$
2 $12 \times 8 = 96$ $12 \times -8 = -96$
  $12 \div 8 = 1·5$ $12 \div -8 = -1·5$
  $-12 \times 8 = -96$ $-12 \times -8 = 96$
  $-12 \div 8 = -1·5$ $-12 \div -8 = 1·5$
3 $6·5 \times 5 = 32·5$ $6·5 \times -5 = -32·5$
  $6·5 \div 5 = 1·3$ $6·5 \div -5 = -1·3$
  $-6·5 \times 5 = -32·5$ $-6·5 \times -5 = 32·5$
  $-6·5 \div 5 = -1·3$ $-6·5 \div -5 = 1·3$
4 $1·2 \times 0·4 = 0·48$ $1·2 \times -0·4 = -0·48$
  $1·2 \div 0·4 = 3$ $1·2 \div -0·4 = -3$
  $-1·2 \times 0·4 = -0·48$ $-1·2 \times -0·4 = 0·48$
  $-1·2 \div 0·4 = -3$ $-1·2 \div -0·4 = 3$

SECTION 9
POWERS AND STANDARD FORM

Pause – page 95

1 243   **6** 16 384
2 125   **7** 729
3 64   **8** 15·625
4 256   **9** 0·81
5 2401   **10** 1·61051

Pause – page 96

1 a) 2^5 c) 4^{10} e) 10^5
  b) 3^9 d) 2^{11}

Pause – page 96

1 a) 81   f) 225
  b) 144   g) 56·25
  c) 324   h) 68·89
  d) 121   i) 0·36
  e) 400   j) 0·0625

Pause – page 97

1 a) 400   g) 6 400 000
  b) 700 000   h) 720 000
  c) 8 400 000   i) 190
  d) 900 000 000 000   j) 5600
  e) 12 000   k) 67 000
  f) 30 000 000 000   l) 3 000 000 000 000

Rewind – page 97

1 g) 2, 3, 5, 7, 11, 13, 17, 19, 23, 29, 31, 37, 41, 43, 47, 53, 59, 61, 67, 71, 73, 79, 83, 89, 97

2 a) 1, 2, 3, 4, 6, 8, 12, 24
b) 1, 3, 17, 51
c) 1, 2, 4, 5, 8, 10, 20, 25, 40, 50, 100, 200

3 a) 2, 3, 5   b) 2, 3, 7   c) 3, 5, 7

4 1, 4, 9, 25, 36, 49, 64, 81, 100, 121, 144

5 4, 6, 8, 9, 10, 12, 14, 15, 16, 18, 20, 21

6 1, 3, 6, 10, 15, 21, 28, 36, 45, 55, 66, 78

7 a) 9   b) 7   c) 11

8 a) 80, 130, 270, 350, 480, 590, 610, 770, 840, 950
b) 100, 100, 300, 300, 500, 600, 600, 800, 800, 900

9 a) 900, 1260, 2500, 3790, 4520, 5630, 6170, 7380, 8910, 9170
b) 900, 1300, 2500, 3800, 4500, 5600, 6200, 7400, 8900, 9200
c) 1000, 1000; 3000, 4000, 5000, 6000, 6000, 7000, 9000, 9000

	Estimate	Accurate answer
10 a)	$200 + 300 = 500$	579
b)	$700 + 300 = 1000$	960
c)	$300 - 300 = 0$	77
d)	$500 - 100 = 400$	352
e)	$20 \times 60 = 1200$	1288
f)	$300 \times 90 = 27\,000$	28 449
g)	$1000 \div 30 = 33$	54
h)	$700 \div 10 = 70$	52.2

11 a) 2.6, 2.6, 3.4, 3.7, 4.0, 5.4, 5.5, 6.7, 7.8, 9.1
b) 2.2, 2.28, 3.21, 3.22, 3.25, 3.26, 3.27, 3.29, 3.3
c) 1.5, 1.56, 1.562, 1.563, 1.564, 1.567, 1.567, 1.568, 1.569, 1.57

12 a) 92   c) 9.2   e) 3.3   g) 10.9
b) 11.9   d) 38.9   f) 6.5   h) 2.5

13 a) 118.53   c) 190.63   e) 621.44
b) 620.9   d) 20.49   f) 4954.89

14 a) 807   c) 7287.066
b) 1053.9   d) 51.75

15 a) 2.1   e) 0.1   i) 965.3
b) 3.2   f) 2   j) 9.04
c) 0.36   g) 20   k) 197
d) 1.8   h) 500   l) 99.988

16 a) 166.5   c) 1412.35   e) 9.5
b) 444.6   d) 12.478   f) 4.653

17 a) 797.41   c) 94.6192   e) 16.79
b) 2551.5   d) 31.5   f) 20.08

18 a) 33.1   b) 19.4   c) 3.6   d) 1.8

19 a) 1561.15   c) 1.06
b) 33.14   d) 0.73

20 a) $\frac{5}{6}$ b) $\frac{5}{14}$ c) $\frac{2}{5}$ d) $\frac{2}{3}$ e) $\frac{2}{3}$ f) $\frac{7}{15}$

21 a) $\frac{3}{8}$ b) $\frac{3}{5}$ c) $\frac{5}{60}$

22 Biology

23 a) $\frac{1}{8}$ c) $\frac{1}{4}$ e) $\frac{5}{12}$ g) $\frac{7}{12}$ i) $\frac{1}{48}$
b) $\frac{5}{24}$ d) $\frac{3}{8}$ f) $\frac{1}{2}$ h) $\frac{1}{12}$

24 a) $\frac{1}{4}$ b) $\frac{1}{2}$ c) $\frac{19}{20}$ d) $\frac{3}{4}$ e) $\frac{21}{25}$ f) $\frac{2}{25}$

25 a) 150   c) 108   e) 200   g) 36
b) 35   d) 9   f) 32   h) 84

26 a) $\frac{1}{4}$ b) $\frac{1}{2}$ c) $\frac{14}{25}$ d) $\frac{47}{50}$ e) $\frac{8}{25}$

27 a) 50%   c) 30%   e) 72%
b) 75%   d) 85%

28 a) 36   c) 221   e) 51.84
b) 138   d) 540   f) 9900

29 a) 360   c) £341.55   e) £19 972.44
b) £92   d) £26 250   f) £1950

30 a) 304   c) £248   e) £43 240
b) £80.75   d) £37 050   f) £968

31 a) 64%   e) 7%   i) 40%
b) 60%   f) 93.75%   j) 60%
c) 24.5%   g) 45.2%
d) 30%   h) 25%

32

Fraction	Percentage	Decimal
$\frac{1}{2}$	50%	0.5
$\frac{1}{4}$	25%	0.25
$\frac{3}{4}$	75%	0.75
$\frac{1}{5}$	20%	0.2
$\frac{1}{10}$	10%	0.1
$\frac{3}{20}$	15%	0.15
$\frac{3}{5}$	60%	0.6
$\frac{13}{25}$	52%	0.52
$\frac{1}{25}$	4%	0.04
$\frac{1}{20}$	5%	0.05

33 a) 2:5   c) 1:6   e) 4:7
b) 2:3   d) 5:7

34 a) 10 kg, 30 kg   d) 35 kg, 5 kg
b) 32 kg, 8 kg   e) 28 kg, 12 kg
c) 25 kg, 15 kg

35 a) £90, £30   d) £75, £45
b) £48, £72   e) £75, £30, £15
c) £24, £96

36 a) 75 books   b) 80 cm

37 $8 + 15 = 23$ $8 + -15 = -7$
$-8 + 15 = 7$ $-8 + -15 = -23$
$8 - 15 = -7$ $8 - -15 = 23$
$-8 - 15 = -23$ $-8 - -15 = 7$
$7 + 12 = 19$ $7 + -12 = -5$
$-7 + 12 = 5$ $-7 + -12 = -19$
$7 - 12 = -5$ $7 - -12 = 19$
$-7 - 12 = -19$ $-7 - -12 = 5$

38

$2 \times 5 = 10$	$2 \div 5 = 0\cdot4$
$-2 \times 5 = -10$	$-2 \div 5 = -0\cdot4$
$2 \times -5 = -10$	$2 \div -5 = -0\cdot4$
$-2 \times -5 = 10$	$-2 \div -5 = 0\cdot4$
$2\cdot5 \times 10 = 25$	$2\cdot5 \div 10 = 0\cdot25$
$-2\cdot5 \times 10 = -25$	$-2\cdot5 \div 10 = -0\cdot25$
$2\cdot5 \times -10 = -25$	$2\cdot5 \div -10 = -0\cdot25$
$-2\cdot5 \times -10 = 25$	$-2\cdot5 \div -10 = 0\cdot25$

39 a) 4096   c) 100 000
   b) 32   d) 10 000
40 a) 2^7 b) 3^9 c) 10^9
41 a) 5000   c) 900 000 000
   b) 72 000   d) 160 000 000 000

Fast Forward – page 102
1 a) 9   b) 9   c) 12   d) 11
2 a) 19   c) 21   e) 15
   b) 16   d) 8   f) 18
3 £15 000
4
$$\begin{array}{r} 39 \\ 24\overline{)936} \\ 72\downarrow \\ \hline 216 \\ 216 \\ \hline \end{array}$$
5 490
6 Cost of flour $205 \times 48\,\text{p} \approx 200 \times 50\,\text{p}$
                    $= 10\,000\,\text{p}$
                    $= £100$

14 people pay £0·72
This is less than £14.
Answer is not the right size.
7 a)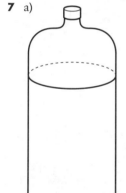
   b) 142 bottles at 39 p
      $\approx 100 \times 40$
      $+ 40 \times 40$
      $= 5600\,\text{p}$
      $= £56$

   c)
$$\begin{array}{r} 142 \\ 39 \\ \hline 4{,}260 \\ 1{_3}2{,}7\,8 \\ \hline 5{,}538 \\ \hline \end{array}$$
      Answer = £55·38

8 a) £55   b) £367   c) £45   d) £360
9 a) 57·803882   b) 57·8
10 a) £15·80   b) i) $6\frac{1}{2}$ hours   ii) £2·92
11 £294·70
12 a) £4·50   b) £6·60   c) £6
13 50 kg
14 a) £3·16   d) £151·50   g) £236·18
   b) 2   e) £49·50
   c) £24·50   f) £201
15 a) 1·75   b) 8·75 pints
16 a) 0·875   b) 12·5%

17 a) 252   b) 25%
18

Basic wage	£184·00
Overtime	£ 41·40
Total wage (gross)	£225·40
Total deductions	£ 76·36
Take-home pay	£149·04

19 a) $\frac{5}{8}$ b) $\frac{3}{8}$ c) 6
20 1 hour 13 minutes 20 seconds
21 35 miles per gallon
22 a) 48 km per hour
   b) 37·5 miles per hour
23 12·5 minutes
24 £27
25 a) $\frac{3}{8}$ b) $\frac{1}{8}, \frac{1}{4}, \frac{3}{8}, \frac{1}{2}$
26 a) £3   b) 50 p
27 a) £76   b) £1036
28 a) $\dfrac{7\cdot2 \times 2\cdot9}{14\cdot4} = \dfrac{20\cdot88}{14\cdot44} = 1\cdot45$
   b) $(8\cdot1)^2 \div 24 = 65\cdot61 \div 24 = 2\cdot73375$
29 a) 73·75   b) £14·24
30 a) $\frac{1}{15}$ b) 90 p
31 £41·13
32 a) £7·99   b) 20%
33 £55 935
34 a) £8640   b) £5240   c) £1414·80
35 a) £286   c) £59   e) £274·94
   b) £26   d) £236   f) £24·99
   g) The Beovision as the Flan works out
      nearly as much because of the interest.
36 a) £16   b) i) £5·60   ii) £17·12
37 a) £60   b) £180   c) £30
38 £23·76
39 a) 1 400 000, 600 000   b) 1 million hectares
40 £66
41 6
42 a) b) Pupils' own work.   c) £4·77
43 a) £276   b) £26   c) £6·91
44 600 g blackcurrants, 240 g sugar,
   210 ml cream, 135 ml water
45 9 g
46 12 cm, 24 cm
47 200
48 80
49 4
50 39 lessons, 26 lessons
51 a) 3 m   b) 4
52 15°C
53 a) at 5 am   b) 7°C
54 a) −2°C   b) 10°C
55 a) −6°C   b) 4°C   c) 2°C
56 a) −7°C   b) 4°C
57 a) −10°C   c) 8°C   e) 3°C
   b) Thurs   d) 1°C

ALGEBRA

SECTION 1
ESTABLISHING RULES

Pause – page 116

1 a) $y - 21$ b) $y + 11$ c) $y - 1$ d) $y - 5$
2 a) $x + 7$ b) $x + 13$ c) $x - 7$ d) $x - 13$

Pause – page 118

1 a) $3c$ c) $\dfrac{c}{3} - 200$

   b) $\dfrac{c}{3}$ d) $3c + 250$

2 a) $3n$ d) $\dfrac{n}{2} - 15$ g) $\dfrac{n}{2} - 8$

   b) $\dfrac{n}{2}$ e) $3n - 30$ h) $3n + 15$

   c) $3n + 25$ f) $\dfrac{n}{2} + 12$

3 a) $3 + e$ e) $\dfrac{5}{w}$ i) $\dfrac{t}{2}$

   b) $v - 18$ f) $18 - v$ j) $\dfrac{2}{t}$

   c) $5w$ g) $12d$ k) $m - 2$

   d) $\dfrac{w}{5}$ h) $y + 13$ l) $2 - m$

Pause – page 120

1 a) i) 3   ii) 4   iii) 5   iv) 6
   b) $b = p + 1$
2 a) i) 48   ii) 120   iii) 240   iv) 576
   b) $r = 24b$
3 a) i) 460   ii) 400   iii) 269   iv) 51
   b) $n = 500 - s$
4 a) i) £12   iii) £738·20
      ii) £500   iv) £10 481·92
   b) $s = \dfrac{w}{12}$
5 a) i) £15   iii) £8·90
      ii) £12·50   iv) £9·95
   b) $c = 5m$
6 a) i) £27   iii) £41·50
      ii) £63   iv) £50·78
   b) $t = m + 3$
7 a) i) £5   iii) £7·50
      ii) £6   iv) £5·45
   b) $C = \dfrac{60}{n}$
8 a) i) £240   iii) £189·50
      ii) £190   iv) £227·86
   b) $l = w - 40$

Pause – page 123

1 a) i) 14 cm   iii) 21 cm
      ii) 36 cm   iv) 62·4 cm
   b) $p = 2l + 2h$

2 a) i) £585   ii) £705   iii) £765
   b) $t = 12n + 225$
3 a) i) £19·50 ii) £17·63 iii) £17
   b) $p = \dfrac{225}{n} + 12$
4 a) i) £150   ii) £125
   b) $a = ns$
5 a) i) 12   ii) 36   iii) 40   iv) 40
   b) $p = rc$
6 a) i) 9   ii) 25   iii) 64   iv) 16
   b) $p = r^2$
7 a) i) 27   ii) 64   iii) 125   iv) 512
   b) $b = r^3$

Pause – page 125

1 a) 33   b) 13   c) 65   d) 25   e) 0
2 a) 13   b) 7   c) 1   d) 5   e) 6
3 a) 30   b) 8   c) 50   d) 12   e) 57
4 a) 5   b) 55   c) 17   d) 43   e) 17
5 a) 14   b) 14   c) 21   d) 21   e) 21

Pause – page 126

1 a) 12   b) 6   c) 2   d) 9   e) 2
2 a) 60   b) 61   c) 3   d) 1   e) 10
3 a) 4   b) 60   c) 10   d) 14   e) 27
4 a) 49   b) 51   c) 2   d) 0·5 e) 12

Pause – page 127

1 a) 27   f) 15   k) 2   p) 81
   b) 28   g) 18   l) 2   q) 150
   c) 42   h) 60   m) 25
   d) 30   i) 45   n) 75
   e) 30   j) 72   o) 216
2 a) 9   e) 0   i) 100 m) 21
   b) 3   f) 20   j) 20   n) 18
   c) 11   g) 40   k) 22
   d) 23   h) 16   l) 28

Pause – page 128

1 a) -17 c) 25   e) 0
   b) -37 d) 25
2 a) 7   c) -5 e) -6
   b) 7   d) -1
3 a) -8 c) 12   e) -57
   b) -30 d) 12
4 a) 0   c) -80 e) -40
   b) -80 d) -10

Pause – page 129

1 a) -12 c) -2 e) -2
   b) -18 d) 5
2 a) -60 c) -3 e) -10
   b) -23 d) -7
3 a) -20 c) -5 e) -2
   b) -29 d) -2
4 a) -200 c) -8 e) -120
   b) 150   d) -5

Pause – page 130

1. a) 3 d) 30 g) −30 j) 25 m) 36
   b) −8 e) −30 h) −45 k) 50 n) 9
   c) 42 f) −15 i) 2 l) 75

2. a) 1 d) 7 g) −10 j) 50 m) 12
   b) 7 e) −20 h) 25 k) 16
   c) −1 f) −20 i) 75 l) 4

Pause – page 130

1.

m	Am	I
1	75	0·5
2	150	1
3	225	1·5

2. a)

Time (t sec)	Depth ($5t^2$ metres)
1	5
2	20
3	45
4	80
5	125

b)

Time (t sec)	Velocity ($10t$ metres per sec)
1	10
2	20
3	30
4	40
5	50

Pause – page 132

1. $3e$
2. $6h$
3. $12y$
4. $2a + 2b$
5. $2m + 10$
6. $2x + 13$
7. $2p + 3q + 8$
8. $2x + 2y + 4$
9. $2a + 2b$

Pause – page 133

1. $7m$
2. $4t$
3. $9e$
4. $2x$
5. $11z$
6. $6r$
7. $6a$
8. $5w$
9. $2x$
10. $6m$
11. $-2d$
12. $-5k$
13. $5x + 5y$
14. $9e + f$
15. $10m + 3n$
16. $4s + 7r$
17. $2r + 4q$
18. $9x + 2y$

Pause – page 134

1. $12v$
2. $14m$
3. $40t$
4. $35u$
5. $16c$
6. $18z^2$
7. $12z^3$
8. $15m^4$
9. $24r^2$
10. $21n^3$

Pause – page 135

1. $6w + 21$
2. $20m + 10$
3. $18 + 12v$
4. $27 + 9s$
5. $12 - 6m$
6. $3p + 21$
7. $15r - 20$
8. $12x - 6$
9. $16 - 8y$
10. $4x^2 + 4$
11. $6w^3 + 30$
12. $15 + 6m^2$
13. $15e + 10f$
14. $21u - 14v$
15. $6s - 9t$

Pause – page 135

1. $5(x + 2)$
2. $3(y + 3)$
3. $2(t + 7)$
4. $7(t + 2)$
5. $3(2x + 5)$
6. $5(x - 3)$
7. $3(g - 7)$
8. $7(2 - x)$
9. $2(8 - z)$
10. $11(w - 2)$
11. $5(2m + 3)$
12. $3(2w + 3)$

13. $2(4y + 5)$
14. $5(3r - 5)$
15. $3(4x - 7)$
16. $10(2x + 1)$
17. $6(2y + 3)$
18. $12(t + 2)$
19. $14(3t + 1)$
20. $12(3x + 1)$

SECTION 2
SOLVING EQUATIONS

Pause – page 137

1. $d = 1$
2. $e = 4$
3. $x = 2$
4. $x = 7$
5. $y = 7$
6. $m = 7$
7. $g = 0$
8. $s = 2$
9. $s = 25$
10. $x = 10$
11. $d = -6$
12. $e = -6$
13. $x = -7$
14. $x = -10$
15. $y = -2$
16. $m = -1$
17. $g = -2$
18. $s = -5$
19. $s = -6$
20. $s = -7$

Pause – page 137

1. $d = 21$
2. $e = 12$
3. $x = 16$
4. $x = 19$
5. $y = 21$
6. $m = 33$
7. $g = 2$
8. $s = 52$
9. $s = 29$
10. $x = 20$
11. $d = 16$
12. $e = 10$
13. $x = 11$
14. $x = 16$
15. $y = 4$
16. $m = 1$
17. $g = 0$
18. $s = 5$
19. $s = -2$
20. $s = 3$

Pause – page 138

1. $x = 6$
2. $m = 4$
3. $t = 5$
4. $u = 7$
5. $e = 2$
6. $x = 2$
7. $m = 4$
8. $x = 10$
9. $r = 8$
10. $z = 2$
11. $s = 11$
12. $c = 4$
13. $m = 10$
14. $m = -10$
15. $z = -11$
16. $x = -2$
17. $u = 5$
18. $t = -10$
19. $x = 14$
20. $x = -50$

Pause – page 139

1. $x = 10$
2. $z = 12$
3. $m = 100$
4. $m = 10$
5. $w = 12$
6. $f = 25$
7. $y = 63$
8. $x = 49$
9. $z = 30$
10. $z = 30$
11. $y = -12$
12. $j = -12$
13. $y = -18$
14. $y = -18$
15. $y = -18$
16. $y = -18$
17. $y = 18$
18. $x = -50$
19. $x = 50$
20. $m = -150$

Pause – page 140

1. $x = 2$
2. $x = 5$
3. $x = 7$
4. $x = 2$
5. $m = 1$
6. $x = 2$
7. $x = 5$
8. $x = 4$
9. $x = -2$
10. $x = -3$
11. $z = 6$
12. $x = 8$
13. $x = 9$
14. $x = 10$
15. $y = 8$
16. $t = 15$
17. $y = 4$
18. $y = -9$
19. $r = 12$
20. $x = 20$

21. a) $2e + 10 = 18$
       $e = 4$
    b) $4h + 20 = 64$
       $h = 11$
    c) $2x + 60 = 84$
       $x = 12$
    d) $4z + 10 = 90$
       $z = 20$
    e) $4a + 12 = 32$
       $a = 5$
    f) $3m + 2 = 32$
       $m = 10$

411

Pause – page 142

1	$w = 4$	5	$r = 2$	9	$r = 1$
2	$m = 2$	6	$x = 5$	10	$f = 4$
3	$v = 3$	7	$y = -2$	11	$t = 2$
4	$s = 1$	8	$m = 4$	12	$s = 2$

Pause – page 142

1	$p = -7$	6	$m = 11$	11	$d = 2$
2	$x = 8$	7	$x = -4$	12	$g = -6$
3	$p = 11$	8	$s = 5$	13	$h = -5$
4	$e = 2$	9	$w = 3$	14	$q = -3$
5	$w = 3$	10	$f = 5$		

SECTION 3
NUMBER PATTERNS AND NUMBER SEQUENCES

Pause – page 143

1 21, 25; +4   3 243, 729; ×3
2 15, 13; −2   4 25, 12.5; ÷2
5 37, 50; add the next odd number
6 16, 22; add the next natural number
7 26, 31; +5
8 23, 30; add the next natural number
9 51, 60; +9   11 42, 50; +8   13 8, 13
10 15, 8; −7   12 64, 128; ×2

Pause – page 144

1 a) 20 b) 100 c) 99 d) 17 e) 25

Pause – page 145

1	$2n - 1$	4	$3n + 1$	7	$8n - 7$
2	$12n - 7$	5	$7n - 3$	8	$2n + 9$
3	$5n + 1$	6	$5n - 2$	9	$m = 2n + 6$

Pause – page 147

1 a)
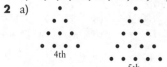
4th
5th

b) 1, 4, 9, 16, 25, 36, 49, 64, 81, 100

2 a)
4th
5th

b) 1, 3, 6, 10, 15, 21, 28, 36, 45, 55

SECTION 4
GRAPHS

Pause – page 148

1 $x \rightarrow x + 4$
$-3 \rightarrow 1$
$-2 \rightarrow 2$
$-1 \rightarrow 3$
$0 \rightarrow 4$
$1 \rightarrow 5$
$2 \rightarrow 6$
$3 \rightarrow 7$

2 $x - 1$
$-3 \rightarrow -4$
$-2 \rightarrow -3$
$-1 \rightarrow -2$
$0 \rightarrow -1$
$1 \rightarrow 0$
$2 \rightarrow 1$
$3 \rightarrow 2$

3 $x \rightarrow x + 3$
$-3 \rightarrow 0$
$-2 \rightarrow 1$
$-1 \rightarrow 2$
$0 \rightarrow 3$
$1 \rightarrow 4$
$2 \rightarrow 5$
$3 \rightarrow 6$

4 $x \rightarrow x + 2$
$-3 \rightarrow -1$
$-2 \rightarrow 0$
$-1 \rightarrow 1$
$0 \rightarrow 2$
$1 \rightarrow 3$
$2 \rightarrow 4$
$3 \rightarrow 5$

5 $x \rightarrow \dfrac{x}{2}$
$-3 \rightarrow -1{\cdot}5$
$-2 \rightarrow -1$
$-1 \rightarrow -0{\cdot}5$
$0 \rightarrow 0$
$1 \rightarrow 0{\cdot}5$
$2 \rightarrow 1$
$3 \rightarrow 1{\cdot}5$

6 $x \rightarrow 2x$
$-3 \rightarrow -6$
$-2 \rightarrow -4$
$-1 \rightarrow -2$
$0 \rightarrow 0$
$1 \rightarrow 2$
$2 \rightarrow 4$
$3 \rightarrow 6$

7 $x \rightarrow 2x + 2$
$-3 \rightarrow -4$
$-2 \rightarrow -2$
$-1 \rightarrow 0$
$0 \rightarrow 2$
$1 \rightarrow 4$
$2 \rightarrow 6$
$3 \rightarrow 8$

8 $x \rightarrow 2x - 1$
$-3 \rightarrow -7$
$-2 \rightarrow -5$
$-1 \rightarrow -3$
$0 \rightarrow -1$
$1 \rightarrow 1$
$2 \rightarrow 3$
$3 \rightarrow 5$

9 $x \rightarrow 2x + 3$
$-3 \rightarrow -3$
$-2 \rightarrow -1$
$-1 \rightarrow 1$
$0 \rightarrow 3$
$1 \rightarrow 5$
$2 \rightarrow 7$
$3 \rightarrow 9$

10 $x \rightarrow x^2$
$-3 \rightarrow 9$
$-2 \rightarrow 4$
$-1 \rightarrow 1$
$0 \rightarrow 0$
$1 \rightarrow 1$
$2 \rightarrow 4$
$3 \rightarrow 9$

Pause – page 149

1 a)
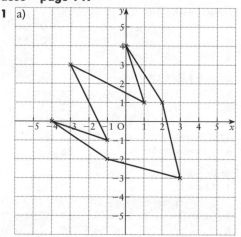

b)

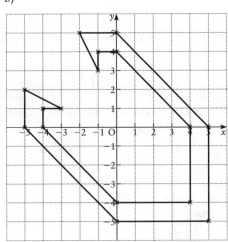

b) $x = -2$ c) $x = 0$ a) $x = 3$
e) $x = -3.5$
d) $x = 4.5$
a) $y = 4$
c) $y = 0$
d) $y = -2.5$
b) $y = -3$
e) $y = -5$

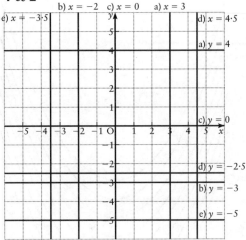

Pause – page 151

1 a)

x	−3	−2	−1	0	1	2	3
$y = x + 4$	1	2	3	4	5	6	7

b)

x	−3	−2	−1	0	1	2	3
$y = x - 4$	−7	−6	−5	−4	−3	−2	−1

c)

x	−3	−2	−1	0	1	2	3
$y = 2x$	−6	−4	−2	0	2	4	6

d)

x	−3	−2	−1	0	1	2	3
$y = \dfrac{x}{2}$	−1.5	−1	−0.5	0	0.5	1	1.5

e)

x	−3	−2	−1	0	1	2	3
$y = 2x + 4$	−2	0	2	4	6	8	10

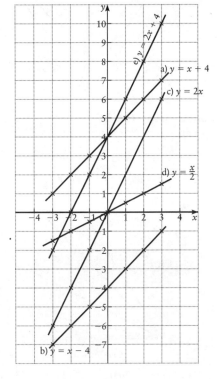

Pause – page 153

1 b)

x	−3	−2	−1	0	1	2	3
y	10	5	2	1	2	5	10

c) i)

x	−3	−2	−1	0	1	2	3
y	11	6	3	2	3	6	11

ii)

x	−3	−2	−1	0	1	2	3
y	12	7	4	3	4	7	12

iii)

x	−3	−2	−1	0	1	2	3
y	13	8	5	4	5	8	13

2 a)

x	−3	−2	−1	0	1	2	3
y	8	3	0	−1	0	3	8

b) i)

x	−3	−2	−1	0	1	2	3
y	7	2	−1	−2	−1	2	7

ii)

x	−3	−2	−1	0	1	2	3
y	6	1	−2	−3	−2	1	6

iii)

x	−3	−2	−1	0	1	2	3
y	5	0	−3	−4	−3	0	5

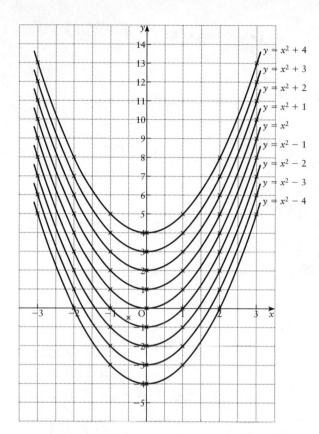

3 a) The curves are all the same shape as x^2.

The number added or subtracted at the end gives the intercept on the y-axis, so $y = x^2 - 2$ cuts the y-axis at -2.

b) i) $y = x^2 + 10$ is the same shape as $y = x^2$. It cuts the y-axis at 10.

ii) $y = x^2 - 15$ is the same shape as $y = x^2$. It cuts the y-axis at -15.

Pause – page 155

1 a)

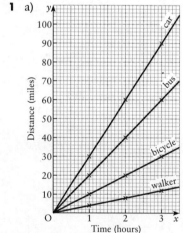

b)
Time (hours)	1	2	3
Distance (miles)	4	8	12

c)
Time (hours)	1	2	3
Distance (miles)	10	20	30

d)
Time (hours)	1	2	3
Distance (miles)	20	40	60

e)
Time (hours)	1	2	3
Distance (miles)	30	60	90

f) The faster the journey, the steeper the time.

2 a) A   b) E

c) A 6 mph,   B 10 mph,   C 15 mph, D 20 mph,   E 30 mph

3 a) 2 km   d) $7\frac{1}{2}$ minutes

b) 5 minutes   e) 5 km

c) 4 km   f) i) 0·4 km per minute

ii) 0·4 km per minute

iii) 0·2 km per minute

Pause – page 159

1 a)
Pounds	1	2	3
Pesetas	175	350	525

b) i) 560 pesetas   ii) £8·60

2 a) i) £43   ii) £33

b) i) 300 units   ii) 480 units

c) The standing charge is £10.

3 a)
Number of kilometres (N)	0	5	10	15
Cost (C millions of pounds)	15	40	65	90

c) i) £75 000 000   ii) £35 000 000

4 a) i)
Days (d)	0	1	2	3	4	5	6	7
Cost (£C)	0	40	80	120	160	200	240	280·

b) i)
Days (d)	0	1	2	3	4	5	6	7
Cost (£C)	80	100	120	140	160	180	200	220

c) Both agencies cost the same (£160) for exactly 4 days. For fewer than 4 days Rick Dastardly is cheaper; for more than 4 days the Purple Panther Agency is cheaper.

5 a) i)

Number of people	10	30	50	70	90
Charge (£)	35	45	55	65	75

b) i)

Number of people	0	20	40	80	100
Charge (£)	50	55	60	70	75

c) Both discos charge the same (£70) for exactly 80 people. For fewer than 80 people the Robin Disco is cheaper; for more than 80 people the Owl Disco is cheaper.

Rewind – page 164

1 a) $y = x + 5$ b) $3t - 4s = r$

2 a) 9   c) 21   e) 18   g) 54   i) 107
   b) -2 d) 19   f) 42   h) 648   j) 48

3 a) -3 c) -7 e) -2
   b) -6 d) 2

4 a) $20x + 6y$ c) $8x - 3y$
   b) $x + 8y$ d) $6x + 7y$

5 a) $12r + 20$ c) $12p - 3$
   b) $28r - 20$ d) $20 - 15q$

6 Amount of oil left $= 12\,000 - 800t$

7 a) $5(4x + 7)$ c) $4(2 - 3p)$
   b) $7(2y + 1)$ d) $b(1 - 6a)$

8 a) $m = 6$ g) $t = -65$
   b) $t = 9$ h) $x = 2$
   c) $x = -2$ i) $m = 5$
   d) $t = 59$ j) $x = 24$
   e) $r = 25$ k) $x = 9$
   f) $r = 10$ l) $x = 1\cdot5$

9 a) $p = -4$ b) $x = 5$ c) $m = -36$

10 a) $+3$; 36, 39   b) $\div2$; 22·5, 11·25
   c) 1 and 2 alternately; 2, 1
   d) Add the previous 2 numbers; 29, 47

11 a) $x \to x + 5$ d) $x \to 3x$
   $-3 \to 2$ $-3 \to -9$
   $-2 \to 3$ $-2 \to -6$
   $-1 \to 4$ $-1 \to -3$
   $0 \to 5$ $0 \to 0$
   $1 \to 6$ $1 \to 3$
   $2 \to 7$ $2 \to 6$
   $3 \to 8$ $3 \to 9$

12

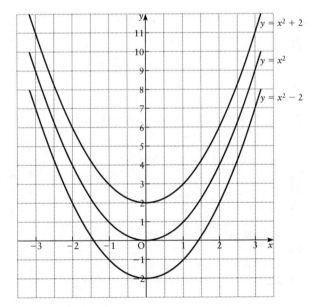

13 a) $(0, 5)$ c) $(0, 0)$
   b) $(0, -6)$ d) $(0, 3)$

14

15 a) 36 miles   c) 20 miles
   b) $\frac{1}{2}$ hr   d) $1\frac{1}{2}$ hours

16 a)

Miles (m)	0	100	200	300	400	500
Cost (£)	20	24	28	32	36	40

c)

Miles (m)	0	100	200	300	400	500
Cost (£)	25	27	29	31	33	35

e) Scheme B   f) Scheme A

Fast Forward – page 167

1 a) $y = 2x + 1$
   b) 19
2 a) Cost $= 7n$
   b) Cost $= 7n - 10$
3 a) 14   b) 7   c) 125
4 a) $S = 1440$
   b) $T = 43.5$
5 $T = 6.1$
6 £2.24
7 a) £140
   b) £3
8 a) $x + 50$
   b) $2(x + 50)$
   c) $2(x + 50) + x + 50 + x = 4x + 150$
   d) $4x + 150 = 670$ $x = £1.30$
9 a) i) $8y$ ii) $6y + 6$
   b) i) $8y = 6y + 6$ ii) $y = 3$
10 a) $3a + 1$
   b) $a = 6$
11 $x = 5$
12 a) $4x + 20$
   b) $9x + 5 = 4x + 20$
   c) 3 kg
13 a) $x = 2$
   b) $x = 1.5$
14 $x = 8.5$
15 $x = 2$
16 a) $x = 11$
   b) $y = 9$
   c) $z = 4$
17 a) 1440
   b) 6
18 $P = 20$
19 a) 86
   b) 5
20 a) 3, 13 and 23 are prime numbers
   b) 4 and 25 are factors of 200
   c) 28 is a multiple of 7
   d) 64 is a cube
   e) $5 \div 15 = \frac{1}{3}$
21 a) 110, 135   b) 1, -6
22 a) 26
   b) The rule is $+6$.
   c) $100 \rightarrow 106$
23 a) 35, 42
   b) Add seven to the previous term.
24 a) 13 15 17 19   Sum $= 64$ $= 4^3$
   b) Line 9 ($9^3 = 729$)
25 a) Shape number (p) 1 2 3 4 5 6
      Number of
      matchsticks (n)   6 11 16 21 26 31
   b) 56
   c) $n = 5p + 1$
26 a) $5^2 - 4^2 = 5 + 4 = 9$

b) i) $7^2 - 6^2 = 6 + 7 = 13$
    ii) $18^2 - 17^2 = 17 + 18 = 35$
27 $4n + 3$
28 a) 323, 971   b) $3x + 2$
29 a) x^9 b) 1
30 a)

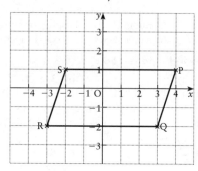

b) parallelogram
31 a) x y
       0   1
       1   3
       3   7
   c) $y = 2x + 1$ d) $x = 4$
32 b) $a = 3$
   c) $1 \rightarrow 3$
       $5 \rightarrow 7$
       $10 \rightarrow 12$
       $x \rightarrow x + 2$
33 a) x -3 -2 -1 0 1 2 3
      y -1 0   1   2 3 4 5
   c) $x = 0.5$
34 a) x 0   20   40   60
      y 0   32   64   96
   c) i) 83 km   ii) 27 miles
   d) 320 km
35 a) x -3 -2.5 -2 -1.5 -1 -0.5 0
      y 9   6.25   4   2.25   1   0.25   0
      x 0.5   1   1.5   2   2.5   3
      y 0.25   1   2.25   4   6.25   9
   d) $(-2.3, 5.3)$, $(1.3, 1.7)$
36 a) b)

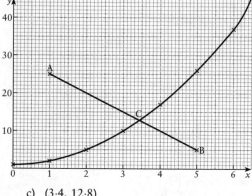

   c) $(3.4, 12.8)$

37 a) 5 does not divide into 36 exactly
b) i) (2, 18), (3, 12), (4, 9), (6, 6),
(9, 4), (12, 3)
iii) One of pairs of lines shown.

ii)

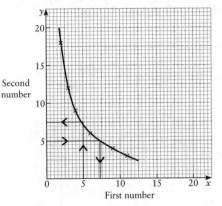

38 a) i) 51 Francs ii) 25 Francs b) i) £6·40 ii) £4·70
39 a) i) 11.40 am ii) 20 minutes b) 12·5 miles
c)

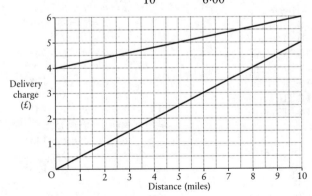

40 a) £4·80 b)

Distance (miles)	Charge (£)
2	4·40
4	4·80
6	5·20
8	5·60
10	6·00

c) £1

d)

e) £1 f) 30 miles g) $c = \frac{1}{2}d$

h) $c = 4 + \frac{1}{5}d$ i) i) £7 ii) 12 miles

417

SHAPE AND SPACE

SECTION 1
GEOMETRY

Pause – page 180

4 a) c, d, a, b

b) $\frac{1}{4}$

Pause – page 182

1 a) $\frac{1}{8}$, acute

b) $\frac{1}{4}$, right angle

c) $\frac{1}{2}$

d) $\frac{3}{8}$, obtuse

e) $\frac{6}{8}$ or $\frac{3}{4}$, reflex

f) $\frac{1}{8}$, acute

g) $\frac{1}{2}$

h) $\frac{6}{8}$ or $\frac{3}{4}$, reflex

i) $\frac{1}{8}$, acute

j) $\frac{3}{8}$, obtuse

Pause – page 184

1 a) acute b) 65°
2 a) acute b) 40°
3 a) obtuse b) 120°
4 a) obtuse b) 130°
5 a) acute b) 77°
6 a) acute b) 83°

Pause – page 191

1 3·5 km **6** 4·5 km
2 2 km **7** 3·1 km
3 6·3 km **8** 7 km
4 6·3 km **9** 8 km
5 7·6 km **10** 6·5 km

Pause – page 193

1 23 km **9** 152 km
2 77 km **10** 102 km
3 65 km **11** 8·9 cm
4 196 km **12** 14.3 cm
5 126 km **13** 1·7 km
6 112 km **14** 2·9 cm
7 28 km **15** 12·1 cm
8 88 km

Pause – page 194

1 100 m **8** 500 m
2 400 m **9** 130 m
3 180 m **10** 5·97 cm
4 220 m **11** 1·47 cm
5 810 m **12** 8·31 cm
6 410 m **13** 10 cm
7 300 m **14** 13 cm

Pause – page 196

1 a) 036° b) 216°
2 a) 315° b) 135°
3 a) 345° b) 165°
4 a) i) 70° ii) 070°
   b) i) 9 cm ii) 180 m
   c) i) 160 m ii) 138°

Pause – page 200

3

Solid	Curved surfaces	Plane faces	Vertices	Edges
Cube	0	6	8	12
Cuboid	0	6	8	12
Triangular prism	0	5	6	9
Hexagonal prism	0	8	12	18
Square pyramid	0	5	5	8
Cylinder	1	2	0	2
Cone	1	1	1	1
Sphere	1	0	0	0

Pause – page 207

1 a) $b = 15°$
b) $q = 62°$
c) $f = 47°$
d) $m = 25°$
e) $g = 30°$
f) $x = 45°$
g) $t = 145°$
h) $k = 67°$
i) $z = 15°$
j) $l = 145°$
k) $x = 40°$
l) $x = 45°$
m) $p = 25\frac{1}{2}°$
n) $y = 60°$
o) $m = 30°$
p) $n = 20°$
q) $r = 279°$
r) $x = 135°$
s) $y = 120°$
t) $m = 130°$

Pause – page 208

1 $a = 140°$ $b = 40°$ $c = 140°$
2 $d = 85°$ $e = 95°$ $f = 85°$
3 $g = 55°$ $h = 125°$ $i = 55°$
4 $j = 162°$ $k = 18°$ $l = 162°$
5 $m = 34°$ $n = 146°$ $p = 34°$
6 $q = 60°$ $t = 30°$ $r = 90°$ $s = 60°$

Pause – page 210

1 a) $b = f = d = 123°$,
   $a = c = e = g = 57°$
b) $a = n = l = 63°$,
   $b = c = p = m = 117°$
c) $c = d = f = 125°$,
   $a = b = e = g = 55°$
d) $b = d = f = 72°$,
   $a = c = e = g = 108°$
e) $a = g = e = 89°$,
   $b = c = d = f = 91°$
f) $b = d = f = 35°$,
   $a = c = e = g = 145°$
g) $b = d = f = 54°$,
   $a = c = e = g = 126°$
h) 160°
i) $a = 70°$ $b = 80°$ $c = 70°$
   $d = 30°$ $e = 80°$
j) 210°

Pause – page 213

1 a) $30°$ c) $61°$ e) $67°$
 b) $45°$ d) $26°$
 f) $a = 80°$ $b = 20°$
 g) $a = 60°$ $b = 57°$
 h) $x = 95°$ $y = 55°$
 i) $q = 59°$ $p = 84°$
 j) $30°$ l) $18°$ n) $42°$
 k) $20°$ m) $20°$
 o) $a = 60°$ $b = 60°$ $c = 60°$
 p) $20°$ q) $100°$ r) $74°$
2 a) i) right angled
  ii) isosceles
  iii) equilateral
 b) i) $50°$ ii) $55°$ iii) $60°$
3 a) $40°$ b) $40°$
4 $x = 79°$ $y = 22°$ $z = 248°$
5 a) $p = 48°$ b) $q = 84°$ c) $r = 84°$

Pause – page 220

1 a) $360°$ b) $90°$ c) $90°$ d) $50°$
2 a) $1440°$ b) $144°$ c) $36°$
3 a) $720°$ b) $120°$ c) $60°$ d) $95°$
4 a) $1080°$ b) $135°$ c) $45°$
5 a) 24 b) 30 c) 12 d) 36
6 20 **7** $x = 79°$
8 a) $ABC = 50°$ b) $CDE = 110°$
9 a) $p + q = 180°$
 b) $q + r + s + t = 360°$
10 a) AC and DB
 b) Angle $BAC = 50°$, as triangle EAC is
  isosceles
11 a) $p = 45°$ b) $135°$

SECTION 2
TRANSFORMATION GEOMETRY

Pause – page 225

1 b) $A \begin{pmatrix} +1 \\ +3 \end{pmatrix}$ $B \begin{pmatrix} +4 \\ +2 \end{pmatrix}$ $C \begin{pmatrix} +4 \\ -1 \end{pmatrix}$ $D \begin{pmatrix} +4 \\ -3 \end{pmatrix}$
 $E \begin{pmatrix} 0 \\ -4 \end{pmatrix}$ $F \begin{pmatrix} -5 \\ -4 \end{pmatrix}$ $G \begin{pmatrix} -5 \\ 0 \end{pmatrix}$ $H \begin{pmatrix} -3 \\ +3 \end{pmatrix}$

Pause – page 240

4

Name	Diagonal	Axes	Order
a) rectangle	no	2	2
b) rhombus	yes	2	2
c) parallelogram	no	0	2
d) kite	yes	1	1
e) square	yes	4	4

SECTION 3
PERIMETER, AREA AND VOLUME

Pause – page 246

1 $8\,cm^2$ **3** $12\,cm^2$ **5** $4\,cm^2$ **7** $12\,cm^2$
2 $16\,cm^2$ **4** $10\,cm^2$ **6** $8\,cm^2$ **8** $7\frac{1}{2}\,cm^2$

Pause – page 248

1 a) $6\,cm^2$ c) $6\,cm^2$
 b) 3 cm by 2 cm
2 a) $4\,cm^2$ c) $4\,cm^2$
 b) 1 cm by 4 cm
3 a) $4\,cm^2$ c) $4\,cm^2$
 b) 2 cm by 2 cm
4 a) $1\,cm^2$ c) $1\,cm^2$
 b) 1 cm by 1 cm
5 a) $10·5$ cm c) $10·5\,cm^2$
 b) 3 cm by $3·5$ cm
6 a) $5·25\,cm^2$ c) $5·25\,cm^2$
 b) $1·5$ cm by $3·5$ cm
7 a) $12.25\,cm^2$ c) $12.25\,cm^2$
 b) $3·5$ cm by $3·5$ cm
8 a) $6\,cm^2$ c) $6\,cm^2$
 b) $1·5$ cm by 4 cm

Pause – page 250

1 a) 24 cm and $26\,cm^2$
 b) 166 m and $1380\,m^2$
 c) 556 mm and $18\,645\,mm^2$
 d) $25·8$ cm and $35·6\,cm^2$
 e) $13·2$ m and $9·45\,m^2$
 f) $21·4$ cm and $24·82\,cm^2$
 g) $7·9$ m and $3·375\,m^2$
 h) 226 cm and $2136\,cm^2$
2 a) 25 cm and $30\,cm^2$
 b) 36 m and $41\,m^2$
 c) 48 cm and $126\,cm^2$
 d) 30 mm and $36\,mm^2$
 e) 16 m and $9·25\,m^2$
 f) $28·2$ m and $28·72\,m^2$
 g) 44 m and $57\,m^2$. This question raises
  interesting points about the minimum
  data needed to solve a problem.
  We cannot, for example be certain from
  the diagram that the two keys are each
  8 m by 3 m. We can however be certain
  that put together they would form a
  rectangle 8 m by 6 m and hence we can
  calculate the area.
3 a) 3 cm by 2 cm, $6\,cm^2$
 b) $3·5$ cm by 2.6 cm, $9·1\,cm^2$
 c) $4·5$ cm by 1 cm, $2·2$ cm by $1·5$ cm,
  $10\,cm^2$
4 a) 6 m d) $4\,m^2$
 b) $24\,m^2$ e) £39·96
 c) £239·76
5 a) $36\,cm^2$ b) i) 6 cm
6 a) $400\,m^2$ b) 104
7 a) $1·8$ m long, $1·2$ m wide
 b) $2·16\,m^2$
 c) £31·32

419

Pause – page 253

1. a) $9\,\text{cm}^2$ c) $6\,\text{cm}^2$ e) $12\,\text{cm}^2$
   b) $9\,\text{cm}^2$ d) $16\,\text{cm}^2$ f) $15\cdot75\,\text{cm}^2$
2. a) $40\,\text{cm}^2$ d) $5\cdot076\,\text{m}^2$
   b) $50\cdot76\,\text{m}^2$ e) $4058\cdot4\,\text{cm}^2$
   c) $32\cdot93\,\text{mm}^2$
3. a) $15\cdot4\,\text{cm}^2$ b) $48\,\text{cm}^2$

Pause – page 256

1. a) $6\,\text{cm}^2$ c) $7\,\text{cm}^2$ e) $3\cdot5\,\text{cm}^2$
   b) $4\,\text{cm}^2$ d) $6\cdot77\,\text{cm}^2$ f) $10\cdot5\,\text{cm}^2$
2. a) $20\,\text{cm}^2$ d) $2\cdot338\,\text{m}^2$
   b) $23\cdot38\,\text{m}^2$ e) $2029\cdot2\,\text{cm}^2$
   c) $16\cdot465\,\text{mm}^2$
3. a) $55\,\text{cm}^2$ b) $14\cdot5\,\text{m}^2$
4. a) $156\,\text{cm}$ b) $432\,\text{cm}^2$ c) $792\,\text{cm}^2$
5. a) $11\,\text{m}$ b) i) $6\cdot72\,\text{m}^2$ c) $1\cdot28\,\text{m}^2$

Pause – page 258

1. $16\,\text{cm}^2$ 3. $75\,\text{cm}^2$
2. $147\,\text{m}^2$ 4. $1950\,\text{mm}^2$
5. $26\,\text{m}^2$
6. a) $2500\,\text{cm}^2$ b) $1500\,\text{cm}^2$ c) $3:5$

Pause – page 260

1. a) $25\cdot1\,\text{cm}$ c) $11\cdot0\,\text{m}$ e) $753\cdot6\,\text{m}$
   b) $50\cdot2\,\text{cm}$ d) $67\cdot8\,\text{mm}$ f) $270\cdot0\,\text{mm}$
2. (using $\pi = 3\cdot14$)
   a) $d = 100\,\text{cm}$ $r = 50\,\text{cm}$
   b) $d = 31\cdot8\,\text{mm}$ $r = 15\cdot9\,\text{mm}$
   c) $d = 18\cdot9\,\text{cm}$ $r = 9\cdot45\,\text{cm}$
   d) $d = 11\cdot8\,\text{mm}$ $r = 5\cdot9\,\text{mm}$
3. a) $204\cdot1\,\text{cm}$ b) $2041\,\text{cm}$
4. $254\cdot96\,\text{cm}$
5. a) $113\cdot04\,\text{cm}$ b) $37\cdot68\,\text{cm}$
6. a) $188\cdot4\,\text{cm}$ b) 3
7. a) 34 square miles
   b) i) 7 miles
      ii) 28 miles per hour
   c) i) 22 miles
      ii) 11 miles
      iii) 11 minutes
   d) 4 minutes
8. a) $18.84\,\text{m}$
   b) $60\cdot6\,\text{m}$
   c) i) $79\cdot44\,\text{m}$
      ii) £54·02

Pause – page 264

1. a) $12\cdot56\,\text{cm}^2$ f) $3\cdot14\,\text{cm}^2$
   b) $38\cdot465\,\text{cm}^2$ g) $7\cdot065\,\text{cm}^2$
   c) $94\cdot985\,\text{cm}^2$ h) $63\cdot585\,\text{cm}^2$
   d) $572\cdot265\,\text{m}^2$ i) $28\cdot26\,\text{m}^2$
   e) $9498\cdot5\,\text{cm}^2$ j) $176\cdot625\,\text{mm}^2$
2. a) $69\cdot08\,\text{cm}$ b) i) $11\,\text{cm}$ ii) $380\,\text{cm}^2$

3. $10\cdot8\,\text{kg}$
4. a) $589\cdot3466\,\text{cm}^2$ b) £206·27
5. a) $24\,\text{m}$ by $13\frac{1}{2}\,\text{m}$ c) $285\cdot535\,\text{m}^2$
   b) $38\cdot465\,\text{m}^2$ d) 12
6. a) $3\cdot82\,\text{m}$ c) $4\cdot5216\,\text{cm}^2$

Pause – page 267

1. $12\,\text{cm}^3$ 3. $27\,\text{cm}^3$
2. $24\,\text{cm}^3$ 4. $48\,\text{cm}^3$

Pause – page 268

1. $112\,\text{cm}^3$ 3. $10\,\text{cm}^3$ 5. $25\,\text{cm}^3$
2. $162\,\text{cm}^3$ 4. $30\,\text{cm}^3$
6. a) $432\,\text{cm}^3$ b) $330\,\text{g}$

Pause – page 270

1. b) $72\,\text{cm}^2$ c) $32\,\text{cm}^3$
2. b) $88\,\text{cm}^2$ c) $48\,\text{cm}^3$
3. b) $42\,\text{cm}^2$ c) $10\,\text{cm}^3$
4. b) $294\,\text{cm}^2$ c) $343\,\text{cm}^3$
5. b) $182\,\text{cm}^2$ c) $147\,\text{cm}^3$
6. a) $36\,\text{cm}^3$ c) $72\,\text{cm}^2$

Rewind – page 359

3. b) $14\cdot5\,\text{m}$
5. cuboid, triangular prism
7. a) $18°$, acute
   b) $55°$, acute; $35°$, acute
   c) $148\cdot5°$ obtuse
   d) $338°$, reflex
   e) $20°$, acute
8. $a = c = d = f = 125°$ $b = e = g = 55°$
   $j = h = k = m = 60°$ $i = n = l = 120°$
   $o = y = v = 63°$ $p = q = 117°$ $s = 109°$
   $r = t = u = x = 71°$ $v = z = 46°$
9. $a = 40°$ $b = 29°$ $c = 70°$ $d = 75°$
   $e = 30°$ $f = 69°$ $g = 69°$ $h = 70°$
   $i = 50°$ $j = 50°$ $k = 80°$ $l = 98°$
10. a) square   d) parallelogram
    b) trapezium   e) rectangle
    c) kite   f) rhombus
11. a) $900°$ c) $128\cdot57°$
    b) $360°$ d) $51\cdot43°$
12. a) $1440°$, $360°$, $144°$, $36°$
    b) $1800°$, $360°$, $150°$, $30°$
13. 18
14. equilateral triangle, square, hexagon
23. $32\cdot5\,\text{cm}^2$
24. $22\,\text{cm}^2$
25. a) $18\,\text{cm}^2$ b) $30\,\text{cm}^2$
26. a) $12\,\text{m}$ b) $48\,\text{m}$
27. a) i) BC and DE
       ii) BC and CD
    b) i) $4\cdot2\,\text{cm}$
       ii) $24\cdot4\,\text{cm}$
    c) $39\,\text{cm}^2$

28 39.75 cm²
29 10.5 cm and 24 cm²
30 30 cm²
31 18 cm and 12 cm²
32 87·08 cm² and 32·86 cm
33 14·18 m² and 13·35 m
34 12 cm and 6 cm
35 64 cm³, 112 cm³

Fast Forward – page 280

4 a) $2\frac{1}{2}$ km   b) 14 cm
7 Only Andrew's is correct.
8 a) 7 cm³   b) ii) 25 cm²
9 $x = 5°$ $y = 57°$
10 70°
11 a) isosceles
   b) i) 51°   ii) 51°   iii) 129°
14 104 cm²
16 a) 5 cm²   b) 20 cm
19 a) 12 m²   b) 24   c) 2 m by 1 m
20 a) i) 7·49 m   ii) 4·9824 m²
   b) i) 7 m   ii) 5 m²
21 a) 0·8 m by 1.5 m   c) 2·88 m²
   b) 1·2 m²
22 a) i) 216 cm²   ii) 432 cm²
   b) 648 cm²   c) 1080 cm²
23 a) i) 9 cm²   ii) 6 cm²   iii) 33 cm²
24 a) i) 65°   ii) 65°
   b) 86 mm
   c) 345 mm²
25 a) 57 cm   b) 19 cm
26 a) 125·6 cm   b) 63 metres
27 a) 410 cm   b) 110 cm   c) 520 cm
28 a) 3 cm   b) 15 cm
29 a) football
   b) cylinder
   c) square based pyramid
30 a) 40 cm³   c) 6 cm
   b) 480 cm³   d) 576

DATA HANDLING

SECTION 1
COLLECTING AND ORGANISING DATA

Pause – page 297

5 a) qualitative   e) continuous
   b) discrete   f) qualitative
   c) discrete   g) discrete
   d) discrete
   h) continuous reduced to discrete
     (when corrected to the nearest metre)
   i) discrete   k) discrete
   j) continuous   l) qualitative

Pause – page 301

1 a) 480,000
   b) 540,000
   c) 319,000
   d) 80,000
   e) **Change in membership**
       +60
       −50
       −3
       −64
       +34
       +396
       −55
       +32
   f) Minus and plus signs could be used as shown above.

2 a) 8016
   b) 7383
   c) 5784
   d) No, far more people travel as passengers in cars or taxis than as passengers on motor bikes. The accident and death figures are therefore higher.
   e) No, very few children aged less than 4 are allowed to use roads unsupervised by adults.
   f) The 20–24 age group has far more accidents than the 40–49 or 50–59 group. The 25–29 group however has fewer accidents than the 30–39 group. But, the 30–39 group covers 10 years and the 20–24 and 25–29 groups only cover 5 years, So, we can conclude that insurers are correct to charge more to insure drivers under 30.

3

Goals scored	Tally	Frequency
0	IIII IIII	10
1	IIII IIII IIII	14
2	IIII	5
3	II	2
4	I	1

5 a)

Mark	Tally	Frequency
0–10		0
11–20		0
21–30	II	2
31–40	IIII	4
41–50	IIII	4
51–60	IIII	4
61–70	IIII IIII II	12
71–80	II	2
81–90	IIII III	8
91–100	IIII	4

b)

Mark	Tally	Frequency
0–10		0
11–20	||	2
21–30	||||| ||||	9
31–40	||||| |||||	10
41–50	||||| |||||		11
51–60	|||	3
61–70	||||	4
71–80			1
81–90		0
91–100		0

c) The first group did much better in the test than the second group.

6 a)

Weight (w grams)	Tally	Frequency
$80 \leqslant w < 90$	|||||	5
$90 \leqslant w < 100$	||||| |||||		11
$100 \leqslant w < 110$	||||| ||	7
$110 \leqslant w < 120$	||||| |||||	10
$120 \leqslant w < 130$	||||| ||||| |||||	15
$130 \leqslant w < 140$	||	2
$140 \leqslant w < 150$		0
$150 \leqslant w < 160$		0

b)

Weight (w grams)	Tally	Frequency
$80 \leqslant w < 90$		0
$90 \leqslant w < 100$	||	2
$100 \leqslant w < 110$	|||	3
$110 \leqslant w < 120$	|||||		6
$120 \leqslant w < 130$	||||| ||	7
$130 \leqslant w < 140$	||||| ||||| ||||| ||||	19
$140 \leqslant w < 150$	||||| |||||	10
$150 \leqslant w < 160$	|||	3

c) The apples in the second sample are, on average, heavier than the apples in the first sample.

Pause – page 306

9 a) Anti-pollution rally, Set C
Factory, Set B
b) Cinema, Set A
The cinema.

SECTION 2
REPRESENTING DATA

Pause – page 308

2 a) i) 34   iii) 24   v) 5
ii) 29   iv) 8   vi) 92

b) Many different comments are possible. The most obvious is that far more single parent families are headed by a woman than by a man.

5 a) i) 9%   iii) 27%   v) 6%
ii) 45%   iv) 13%
b) i) 27%   iii) 16%   v) 4%
ii) 46%   iv) 7%
c) Many comments are possible. The most obvious is that girls are more likely, on average, to consider their health than boys.

7 a) i) 2   iii) 48   v) 123
ii) 9   iv) 104
b) Many comments are possible. The most obvious is the dramatic increase in deaths from solvent abuse during the 1980s.

Pause – page 317

7 a) 26%   b) Plain   c) 50
8 a) 24%   b) 52 p per litre   c) 5
9 a) 60°   b) Football   c) 42
10 a) 112   b) 408

Pause – page 323

3 a)

Weight range (w)	Tally	Frequency
$30 \leqslant w < 40$	||||	4
$40 \leqslant w < 50$	||||| ||	7
$50 \leqslant w < 60$	||||| ||	7
$60 \leqslant w < 70$	||||| |||	8
$70 \leqslant w < 80$			1
$80 \leqslant w < 90$	|||	3

b) $60 \leqslant w < 70$
4 a) Type Y
c) i) Type X
ii) The range of weights for Type X is from 0·5 to 3·0 kg and for Type Y from 1·0 to 3·0 kg.

SECTION 3
MAKING COMPARISONS BETWEEN SETS OF DATA

Pause – page 334

1 a) m = 8   r = 6
b) m = 3   r = 5
c) m = £2   r = £1·50
d) m = 1   r = 8
e) m = 5·77   r = 6·2
f) m = 15·3 cm   r = 17 cm
g) m = 495·7 g   r = 791 g
h) m = 197·8 cm   r = 270 cm
i) m = 950g   r = 800 g
j) m = 1744·5   r = 85

2 a) m = 56·2   r = 85
     m = 51·1   r = 83
   b) The mean of the Year 10 students is lower. The ranges are very similar.
3 a) m = 25·2   *r* = 59
     m = 20·7   r = 60
   b) Maureen's mean score is higher than Eric's. The ranges are very similar.
4 a) 22·5 metres
   b) 4·1 metres
5 a) 225
   b) 583
   c) 50·5

Pause – page 336

1 a) **Estate A**   m = 1·78   r = 6
     Estate B   m = 2·82   r = 6
   b) The mean number of children per family is much higher for Estate B. The range is the same.
2 a) **City A**   m = 51·66   r = 5
     City B   m = 52·22   r = 6
   b) The mean price of petrol in City B is higher than City A. The range in City B is also slightly greater.
3 a) **School A**   m = 4·4   (D–E)
     School B   m = 3·64 (C–D)
   b) **School A**   r = 7 (A–U)
     School B   r = 7 (A–U)
   c) The average grade for School B is higher than the average grade for School A. The ranges are the same. If the grades are taken to the nearest grade, both schools have an average grade of D.

Pause – page 338

1 a) med = 7   r = 6
   b) med = 3   r = 4
   c) med = £4·50   r = £4·50
   d) med = £4·25   r = £4·50
   e) med = 0   r = 6
   f) med = 6·1   r = 6·2
   g) med = 14·5 cm   r = 17 cm
   h) med = 452·5 g   r = 791 g
   i) med = 190 cm   r = 306 cm
   j) med = 950 g   r = 800 g
   k) med = 1745   r = 85
2 a) **Year 11**   med = 51·5   r = 85
     Year 10   med = 50·5   r = 83
   b) The median of the Year 10 students is lower. The ranges are very similar.
3 a) **Maureen**   med = 20   r = 59
     Eric   med = 20   r = 60
   b) The median for both players is the same. The ranges are very similar.

Pause – page 339

1 a) med = 3   r = 5
   b) med = 2   r = 4
2 a) med = 39·5   r = 7
   b) med = 41   r = 7
   c) Flares can only just claim to have 'average contents 40 matches' when the median is corrected to the nearest whole number. Squibs claim is sensible and perhaps even an underestimate. They could claim 'average contents 41 matches' on the basis of this survey.
3 a) med = 1   r = 3   b) med = 2   r = 2
   c) Line B is producing more televisions with faults than Line A. This is shown by the higher median for Line B. The range for Line A is higher but this is caused by a single television with 3 faults.
4 a) med = 2   r = 5   b) med = 3   r = 5
   c) The median for boys is higher and we conclude that boys are more likely than girls to eat chips with their school meal.

Pause – page 342

1 a) 6   f) no sensible mode
   b) 3   g) 12 cm and 15 cm
   c) £1·50   h) 12 g
   d) 0   i) 340 cm
   e) no mode   j) no mode
2 City A = 52   City B = 53
3 Rooksend: $60 \leqslant c < 80$
    Streamside: $120 \leqslant c < 140$

Pause – page 344

		Mean	Median	Mode	Range
1	a)	3·63	3	3	7
	b)	14·09	12	12	18
	c)	37·93	38	37	5
	d)	100·77	101	100	3
	e)	3	2	1	9

		Burners	Flames	
2	a)	40·34	39·87	
	b)	40	40	
	c)	41	40	
	d)	8	6	

   e) Burners have a slightly higher 'average' contents than Flames. Flames have a 'tighter' distribution with less variation in the number of matches per box.

		Mean	Median	Mode	Range
3	a)–d)				
	Year 1	4·783	6	6	8
	Year 2	3·767	5	5	7

   e) The 'average' number of eggs per nest dropped in Year 2. The range was also less in Year 2.

Pause – page 348

1 a) positive   e) positive   h) positive
   b) positive   f) negative   i) positive
   c) positive   g) none   j) negative
   d) negative

2 b) There is a negative correlation.
3 b) There is no correlation.
4 b) There is a positive correlation.
5 b) There is a negative correlation.

SECTION 4
PROBABILITY

Pause – page 353

2 a) $\frac{1}{6} = 0.167 = 16.7\%$
   b) $\frac{3}{6} = \frac{1}{2} = 0.5 = 50\%$
   c) $\frac{3}{6} = \frac{1}{2} = 0.5 = 50\%$
   d) $\frac{2}{6} = \frac{1}{3} = 0.333 = 33.3\%$

3 a) $\frac{3}{13} = 0.231 = 23.1\%$
   b) $\frac{10}{13} = 0.769 = 76.9\%$
   c) $\frac{1}{52} = 0.019 = 1.9\%$
   d) $\frac{1}{13} = 0.077 = 7.7\%$
   e) $\frac{1}{26} = 0.038 = 3.8\%$
   f) $\frac{3}{26} = 0.115 = 11.5\%$
   g) $\frac{7}{13} = 0.538 = 53.8\%$
   h) $\frac{4}{13} = 0.308 = 30.8\%$
   i) $\frac{1}{2} = 0.5 = 50\%$
   j) $\frac{6}{13} = 0.462 = 46.2\%$

4 a) $\frac{1}{4} = 0.25 = 25\%$
   b) $\frac{5}{12} = 0.417 = 41.7\%$
   c) $\frac{1}{3} = 0.333 = 33.3\%$
   d) $\frac{7}{12} = 0.583 = 58.3\%$
   e) $\frac{2}{3} = 0.667 = 66.7\%$
   f) $\frac{3}{4} = 0.75 = 75\%$
   g) $\frac{2}{3} = 0.667 = 66.7\%$
   h) $0 = 0.0 = 0\%$
   i) $1 = 1.0 = 100\%$
   j) $\frac{7}{12} = 0.583 = 58.3\%$

5 a) $\frac{1}{2} = 0.5 = 50\%$
   b) $\frac{7}{30} = 0.233 = 23.3\%$
   c) $\frac{1}{6} = 0.167 = 16.7\%$
   d) $\frac{1}{10} = 0.1 = 10\%$
   e) $\frac{11}{15} = 0.733 = 73.3\%$
   f) $\frac{4}{15} = 0.267 = 26.7\%$
   g) $\frac{3}{5} = 0.6 = 60\%$

6 a) i) $\frac{1}{5} = 0.2 = 20\%$
     ii) $\frac{1}{10} = 0.1 = 10\%$
     iii) $\frac{19}{50} = 0.38 = 38\%$
   b) i) $\frac{9}{25} = 0.36 = 36\%$
     ii) $\frac{2}{25} = 0.08 = 8\%$
     iii) $\frac{23}{50} = 0.46 = 46\%$

7 a) i) $\frac{1}{2} = 0.5 = 50\%$
     ii) $\frac{3}{10} = 0.3 = 30\%$
     iii) $\frac{7}{10} = 0.7 = 70\%$
   b) i) $\frac{8}{25} = 0.32 = 32\%$
     ii) $\frac{8}{25} = 0.32 = 32\%$
     iii) $1 = 1.0 = 100\%$
   c) The answers are estimates based on past performance and we cannot be certain that future scores will exactly reflect this. The final answer clearly demonstrates this because it is obvious that we cannot be certain that Eric will score between 31 and 150.

Pause – page 357

1 a) 0.9   c) 19 days
2 a) 0.4   c) 111 days
3 a) 0.35   c) i) 15   ii) 24   iii) 21
4 a) $\frac{4}{12} = \frac{1}{3}$ c) i) 3   ii) 21   iii) 12
5 a) $\frac{8}{16} = \frac{1}{2}$ c) i) 12   ii) 20   iii) 32
6 a) $\frac{13}{20}$ c) 65
7 a) 44%   c) 33
8 a) 50%   c) i) 45   ii) 15   iii) 60
   d) 37.5% of 60 is 22.5 and 12.5% of 60 is 7.5. This would not be sensible because there can only be *whole* numbers of grey and green beads.
9 a) 25%
   c) i) 184   ii) 115   iii) 46   iv) 115

Pause – page 361

1 a)

	Green	Red
Stefan	$\frac{58}{100}$	$\frac{42}{100}$
Wayne	$\frac{63}{100}$	$\frac{37}{100}$
Surbajit	$\frac{59}{100}$	$\frac{41}{100}$

   b) Green $\frac{180}{300}$ Red $\frac{120}{300}$
   c) The combined results.
   d) 2000

2 a)

Number of beans	4	5	6	7	8	9
Researcher A	$\frac{3}{30}$	$\frac{4}{30}$	$\frac{7}{30}$	$\frac{6}{30}$	$\frac{5}{30}$	$\frac{5}{30}$
Researcher B	$\frac{6}{30}$	$\frac{7}{30}$	$\frac{6}{30}$	$\frac{5}{30}$	$\frac{6}{30}$	$\frac{0}{30}$
Researcher C	$\frac{0}{30}$	$\frac{11}{30}$	$\frac{0}{30}$	$\frac{12}{30}$	$\frac{5}{30}$	$\frac{2}{30}$
Researcher D	$\frac{1}{30}$	$\frac{4}{30}$	$\frac{6}{30}$	$\frac{9}{30}$	$\frac{8}{30}$	$\frac{2}{30}$

b) Number of beans   4   5   6   7   8   9

Combined results $\frac{10}{120}$ $\frac{26}{120}$ $\frac{19}{120}$ $\frac{32}{120}$ $\frac{24}{120}$ $\frac{9}{120}$

c) The combined results.

d) 75 pods

3 a)

	Strawberry	Vanilla	Chocolate	Mint
Group A	$\frac{4}{50}$	$\frac{16}{50}$	$\frac{24}{50}$	$\frac{6}{50}$
Group B	$\frac{5}{50}$	$\frac{25}{50}$	$\frac{15}{50}$	$\frac{5}{50}$
Group C	$\frac{8}{50}$	$\frac{27}{50}$	$\frac{10}{50}$	$\frac{5}{50}$
Group D	$\frac{7}{50}$	$\frac{23}{50}$	$\frac{8}{50}$	$\frac{12}{50}$

b)

	Strawberry	Vanilla	Chocolate	Mint
Combined	$\frac{24}{200}$	$\frac{91}{200}$	$\frac{57}{200}$	$\frac{28}{200}$

c) The combined results.

d) 910

Pause – page 364

1 a)

Red seeds counted	206	412	608	791	1000
Total number counted	500	1000	1500	2000	2500
Relative frequency	0·41	0·41	0·41	0·40	0·40

Red seeds counted	1181	1373	1561	1765	1962
Total number counted	3000	3500	4000	4500	5000
Relative frequency	0·39	0·39	0·39	0·39	0·39

c) Yes, the relative frequency has settled to a value close to 0·39.

d) 10, 140

2 a)

One head, one tail	214	407	611	823	1025
Total number of flips	400	800	1200	1600	2000
Relative frequency	0·535	0·509	0·509	0·514	0·513

One head, one tail	1228	1433	1632	1830	2022
Total number of flips	2400	2800	3200	3600	4000
Relative frequency	0·512	0·512	0·510	0·508	0·506

c) The value is still changing but seems to be settling to a value between 0·5 and 0·51.

Note: These are real results, not invented data. The theoretical probability is 0·5 and this illustrates that a large number of experiments may be needed before a relative frequency settles near a theoretical result.

Pause – page 367

1 a) $\frac{1}{4} = 0·25 = 25\%$ b) $\frac{1}{2} = 0·5 = 50\%$

2 a) 500   b) 500   c) 1000

3 a) $\frac{5}{36} = 0·139 = 13·9\%$

b) $\frac{1}{6} = 0·167 = 16·7\%$

c) $\frac{1}{12} = 0·083 = 8·3\%$

d) $\frac{1}{9} = 0·111 = 11·1\%$

e) $\frac{1}{12} = 0·083 = 8·3\%$

f) $\frac{1}{36} = 0·278 = 27·8\%$

g) $\frac{1}{2} = 0·5 = 50\%$

h) $\frac{7}{18} = 0·389 = 38·9\%$

i) $1 = 1·0 = 100\%$

4 a) 200   c) 100   e) 100
   b) 50   d) 250   f) 350

5 a) $\frac{1}{16} = 0·063 = 6·3\%$

b) $\frac{1}{4} = 0·25 = 25\%$

c) $\frac{1}{2} = 0·5 = 50\%$

d) $\frac{1}{2} = 0·5 = 50\%$

e) $\frac{1}{8} = 0·125 = 12·5\%$

6 $\frac{6}{25} = 0·24 = 24\%$

7 $\frac{4}{9} = 0·444 = 44·4\%$

Rewind – page 477

1 See section at start of Data Handling.

2

Mark	Tally	Frequency
1	|	1
2	卌	5
3	|||	3
4	卌	5
5	卌	5
6	卌 ||	7
7	卌 |||	8
8	卌 |	6
9	卌 ||	7
10	|||	3

4 77, 4100   78, 4150   79, 3700   80, 3800
81, 4450   82, 5050   83, 4500   84, 4250
85, 7200   86, 5800   87, 6500

		Mean	Median	Q1	Q2	Mode	Range
7	a)	4·105	4			2	7
7	b)	22·33	22			21	4
7	c)	0·545	1			1	6
7	d)	330·77	300			200	400
8	a)	39·11	39		40	39	7
8	b)	1·847	2		2	2	6

11 a) $\frac{1}{2} = 0·5 = 50\%$

b) $\frac{5}{6} = 0·833 = 83·3\%$

c) $\frac{2}{3} = 0·667 = 66·7\%$

d) $\frac{1}{6} = 0·167 = 16·7\%$

12 a) $\frac{1}{4} = 0·25 = 25\%$

b) $\frac{1}{2} = 0·5 = 50\%$

c) $\frac{1}{52} = 0·0192 = 1·92\%$

d) $\frac{3}{13} = 0.231 = 23.1\%$

e) $\frac{3}{4} = 0.75 = 75\%$

f) $\frac{7}{13} = 0.538 = 53.8\%$

g) $\frac{1}{26} = 0.0385 = 3.85\%$

h) $\frac{4}{13} = 0.308 = 30.8\%$

13 a)

Females	11	25	36	46	57	69	85	97	107	122
Total	20	40	60	80	100	120	140	160	180	200
Relative frequency	$\frac{11}{20}$	$\frac{25}{40}$	$\frac{36}{60}$	$\frac{46}{80}$	$\frac{57}{100}$	$\frac{69}{120}$	$\frac{85}{140}$	$\frac{97}{160}$	$\frac{107}{180}$	$\frac{122}{200}$

b) $\frac{122}{200}$ c) 732

14 a) $\frac{7}{18} = 0.389 = 38.9\%$

b) $\frac{1}{36} = 0.028 = 2.8\%$

c) $\frac{5}{18} = 0.278 = 27.8\%$

d) $\frac{1}{6} = 0.167 = 16.7\%$

e) $\frac{1}{3} = 0.333 = 33.3\%$

f) 0   g) 0

h) $\frac{1}{18} = 0.0556 = 55.6\%$

Fast Forward – page 372

2 a) 8   b) 40   c) 34

4 a) Monday

b) i) 2500   ii) 3200

c) $6000 \times £14.20 = £85\,200$

5 a)

Colour	Tally	Frequency
White	￦￦￦ ￦￦￦	10
Blue	|||	3
Red	￦￦￦ ￦￦￦ ||||	14
Green	|||	3

6 a) i) 6   ii) 3

b)

Mushrooms	Days	Sub total	Cumulative frequency
0	3	0	3
1	3	3	6
2	6	12	12
3	4	12	16
4	4	16	20
5	4	20	24
6	3	18	27
7	1	7	28
8	1	8	29
9	1	9	30
		Total = 105	

c) 2   d) 4   e) 3.5

f) $\frac{20}{30} = \frac{2}{3} = 0.667 = 66.7\%$

7 a) 80 and 50

8 a) i) 40 tonnes   ii) 65 tonnes

c) 55 tonnes

10 a) 24   b) $\frac{8}{24} = \frac{1}{3}$

c) i) 6   ii) $\frac{6}{24} = \frac{1}{4}$

d)

Walk	150°
Parents' car	60°
Friends' car	30°
Bus	120°

11 a) & b)

Type of crisp	Frequency	Angle
Plain	9	72°
Salt and Vinegar	16	128°
Cheese and Onion	11	88°
Beef	6	48°
Crispy bacon	3	24°

12 a) 46%, 28%, 16%, 10%

13 The required angles are: 169°, 83°, 108°

14 a) 150°   b) $\frac{120}{360} = \frac{1}{3}$

16 14%

17 a) $28 - 3 = 25$

b)

Class interval	Frequency
1–5	2
6–10	4
11–15	5
16–20	7
21–25	13
26–30	4

18 a) 1000   b) August

c)

	Spring	Summer	Autumn	Winter
	7	18	9	6
	63°	162°	81°	54°

19 a) £51   b) £2.73

20 225 grams

21 a) 3   b) 2

22 a) 6   b) 2   c) 3   d) 6

23 a) 7.2 and 6.8

b) 8 and 3

c) Samantha — because she has a higher mean
Teresa — because she is more consistent

24 a) 20

b) £29.80

c) £1.49

d) £1.40

e) £1.30

25 a) 12   b) 29 cm

c) The mean is the same but the range this year is greater. This means there is wider variation in the lengths than in last year's competition.

26 a) 20

b) $\frac{25}{40} = \frac{5}{8}$

c) 62.5%

27 a) 61 mm

b) i) 352   ii) 55

c) The Gambia

d) Although the Gambia has a higher mean rainfall, the range is far higher. This means the variation between months is greater, with no rainfall at all from December to April. This is more likely to lead to shortages.

28 a) Kos: Range $= 86 - 69 = 17$
London: Range $= 71 - 55 = 16$
Mary is not correct

c) i) 84
ii) The mean for the month averages 4 weeks. There is no reason why each week should not have a mean higher or lower than the monthly mean.

29 b) Strong positive correlation.

30 b) £6900

32 i) C   ii) B

33 a) $\frac{1}{6}$ b) $\frac{1}{3}$

34 a) $\frac{2}{5} = 0.4 = 40\%$ b) 43 minutes

35 a) Mint
b) There are 8 mint prizes out of 12.
c) $\frac{1}{12}$ d) 0

36 (H, 1) (T, 1)
(H, 2) (T, 2)
(H, 3) (T, 3)
(H, 4) (T, 4)
(H, 5) (T, 5)
(H, 6) (T, 6)

37 Fish, chips: Fish baked potato
Pie, chips: Pie, baked potato
Sausage, chips: Sausage, baked potato.

38 a)

+	1	3	5	7
2	3	5	7	9
4	5	7	9	11
6	7	9	11	13
8	9	11	13	15

b) 9
c) $\frac{3}{16}$
d) $\frac{1}{64}$

39 a)

	R	B	B	Y
R	RR	RB	RB	RY
R	RR	RB	RB	RY
B	BR	BB	BB	BY
Y	YR	YB	YB	YY

b) $\frac{4}{9}$

40 a) $\frac{3}{4}$
b) Claire because $\frac{1}{3} > \frac{1}{4}$
c) He is absolutely certain to win.

41 0·15

INDEX

translations 224
trapeziums 216, 244
triangles 11, 187, 211–14, 255
triangular numbers 28, 146
twenty-four hour clock 17–19, 21

U
units, Imperial 57–8

V
values, numerical 296
variables
   correlated 345–8
   displaying 307–8, 310, 312–16
   grouping 300
   types of 296–7

vertical 180, 181, 224
vertical line graphs 307–13
volume
   Imperial units 57, 58
   measurement 266, 268, 269
   metric units 51

W
wages 54, 55, 119–20, 122, 159
weight 50–1, 53, 57, 58
whole numbers 2–8, 23, 29–32, 35, 41
writing reports 395

Z
'Z' angles 209, 210